ESSAYS ON THE HISTORY OF SCIENTIFIC THOUGHT IN MODERN JAPAN

JAPAN LIBRARY

Essays on the History of Scientific Thought in Modern Japan

Edited by
Osamu Kanamori

Translated by
Christopher Carr and M.G. Sheftall

Japan Publishing Industry Foundation for Culture

Note to the reader:
In general, Japanese names appearing in this book are given in Western order, with given name first and surname last.

Essays on the History of Scientific Thought in Modern Japan
Edited by Osamu Kanamori
Translated by Christopher Carr and M.G. Sheftall

Published by Japan Publishing Industry Foundation for Culture (JPIC)
3-12-3 Kanda-Jinbocho, Chiyoda-ku, Tokyo 101-0051, Japan

First edition: March 2016

This book is an English translation of excerpts from *Showa zenki no kagaku shisō shi*, published in Japanese by Keiso Shobo Publishing Co., Ltd. in 2011. The English edition comprises Introduction (Osamu Kanamori), Chapter 1 (Takuji Okamoto), Chapter 2 (Masanori Kaji), and Chapter 4 (Shin Chang-Geon) of the Japanese edition.

English publishing rights arranged with Keiso Shobo Publishing Co., Ltd.

Jacket and cover design by Hisanori Niizuma

As this book is published primarily to be donated to overseas universities, research institutions, public libraries and other organizations, commercial publication rights are available. For all enquiries regarding those rights, please contact the publisher of the English edition at the following address: japanlibrary@jpic.or.jp

Printed in Japan
ISBN 978-4-916055-61-3
http://www.jpic.or.jp/japanlibrary/

CONTENTS

Foreword to the English Edition   viii

INTRODUCTION: A PORTRAIT OF THE HISTORY OF
SCIENTIFIC THOUGHT
OSAMU KANAMORI 1

Section 1. Towards a Chronicle of the History of Scientific Thought   3
    1. Prosopography of the Literature   3
    2. Concerning the Title: "The History of Scientific Thought"   5

Section 2. Prewar Trends   13
    1. The Importance of the Materialism Study Group   13
    2. The Kyoto School and Related Work   20
    3. Issues Surrounding World War II   23
    4. "The History of Scientific Thought" from the Perspective of Scientists   28

Section 3. Study of the History of Science Gains Autonomy   33
    1. The Postwar Scientific Spirit   33
    2. A Dissection of "Histoire des Sciences"   38
    3. The Rise of Paradigms   56
    4. Reflections from Scientists   68

Section 4. The Infiltration of "Scientific Politics" and the Disputes
Surrounding It   73
    1. Decline or a Turning Back?   73
    2. "The Political Nature of Science"   76
    3. Science, Technology, and Society   80
    4. Is There a Future for the History of Scientific Thought?   85

CHAPTER 1. NUCLEAR AND ELEMENTARY PARTICLE PHYSICS:
THE EVOLUTION OF A COMPETITIVE VIEW OF SCIENCE

TAKUJI OKAMOTO 101

Section 1. From the Inception of Quantum Mechanics to the
Nobel Prize of Hideki Yukawa   103

Section 2. Establishment of a Competitive Scientific View:
the Agony of Hantarō Nagaoka   106
    1. Challenge to the West   106
    2. Concerning Industrial Application   111
    3. Features of a Competitive View of Science   114
    4. Learning and Competition   115
    5. Academic Expectations of the Nation   117

Section 3. The Development of Competition and the Fate of the
Competitive View of Science: From the Saturnian Model of the
Atom to Anti-Relativity   118
    1. The Saturnian Model of the Atom   118
    2. From Competition to Harmony   122
    3. "Academy Police"   127

Section 4. The Advent of Quantum Mechanics   129
    1. Learning a New Theory   129
    2. From Learning to Research   133
    3. RIKEN's Nishina Laboratory   137
    4. Particles That Mediate the Nuclear Force   138
    5. Japan's Standing in Scientific Research   140

Section 5. Meson Theory, Cyclotron, New Weapons   143
    1. The Breakthrough of Yukawa Theory   143
    2. The Development of Large and Small Cyclotrons   145
    3. The Basic Science of Wartime Japan   149
    4. Military Research   152
    5. Expectations for Nuclear Physics   154
    6. Drop of the Atomic Bomb and Defeat   159

Section 6. Research on the Atomic Nucleus and Elementary Particles
in Defeat   163

  1. Researchers on the Atomic Nucleus Immediately after Defeat   163
  2. Reconstruction of Research on the Atomic Nucleus and Elementary Particles   167
  3. Nagaoka's Catharsis   170

Section 7. Supporters of Basic Science   172

CHAPTER 2. THE FORMATION OF JAPAN'S TRADITION OF
ORGANIC CHEMISTRY RESEARCH WITH RIKŌ MAJIMA
MASANORI KAJI 177

Section 1. In the Beginning: The Promise of the History of Scientific
Thought in Twentieth Century Japanese Chemistry   179

Section 2. The History of Japanese Chemistry up to Majima   181

Section 3. Rikō Majima's Path to Becoming a Chemist   183

  1. Rikō Majima the Student   183
  2. Majima's Research Strategy: The Commencement of Research on Urushiol, the Main
     Component of Japanese Lacquer   188

Section 4. Rikō Majima's Research in Germany   190

Section 5. Rikō Majima's Arrival at Tōhoku Imperial University and
the Completion of His Research on Urushiol   193

Section 6. The Further Development of Organic Chemistry Research
on Natural Products by Majima's Students in Japan: Expansion
and Limitations   195

  1. The Education of Tetsuo Nozoe   196
  2. Tetsuo Nozoe's Trip to Taiwan   197
  3. Encounters with the Taiwan Cypress   198
  4. Taihoku Imperial University   200
  5. The Discovery of Hinokitiol   200
  6. Postwar Days in Taiwan as Retained Japanese and Its Consequences   202

7. The Extent and Limits of Majima's Methods for Natural Products Chemistry   206

Section 7. Rikō Majima's Subsequent Research and Accomplishments, or His Philosophical Pathway as Seen from His Journal   208
1. Rikō Majima the Christian   209
2. Rikō Majima and Family   213
3. The Death of Majima's Family Members   215
4. Rikō Majima the Administrator   217
5. Rikō Majima and the Emperor System   221
6. Conclusion—A "Typical" Exemplar of the Scientific Thought of a Chemist   222

Section 8. In Conclusion—Remaining Challenges Facing a History of Thought in Chemistry   223

CHAPTER 3. THE FORMATION AND DEVELOPMENT OF THE SELF-IMAGE OF KAMPŌ MEDICINE IN JAPAN: THE RELATIONSHIP BETWEEN SHOWA-PERIOD KAMPŌ AND SCIENCE

SHIN CHANG-GEON 235

Section 1. Situating the Issue   237

Section 2. The Historical Foundation of Showa Kampō Medicine   240
1. A Critical Theory of Kampō Medicine   240
2. Kampō as Causal Treatment   243
3. Creating Nihompō (Japanese Medicine): Abandoning the Theory of Yin/Yang and the Five Elements   245
4. Kampō's Theoretical Basis: Symptomatic Theory   248

Section 3. The Origin and Self-Image of the "East Asian Medicine" Movement   250
1. The Development of the 1930s Kampō Medicine Revival Movement   250
2. The Role of Japanese Kampō in Imperial Medicine   251
3. Japanese Kampō Medicine's Self-Image Reaches Completion   252

Section 4. Eliminating Korean Influence from the New
Oriental Medicine   256

    1. Kampō Pharmacology Research at the Keijō Imperial University
      Faculty of Medicine   256

    2. Tokuyuki Sugihara's Idea of Constructing a New Oriental Medicine   258

    3. Under the Spell of Western Medicine and the Expulsion of Korea   261

Section 5. Conclusion   263

Afterword   269

Bibliography   275

Indexes   315

FOREWORD TO THE ENGLISH EDITION

The introduction of Western science into Japanese thought from the end of the Edo period largely took place in line with substantial national policies such as the "promotion of new industry" and "increasing wealth and military power." This is why we believe, for instance, that theoretical, metaphysical discussions on time and space, which had been vigorously developed during the early stage of modern astronomy, were disregarded or understated. Japanese people adopted the utilitarian superficiality of science while discarding the underlying philosophical, theological background—and this commonplace assumption is right on the mark to some extent. However, it also stands to reason that, in introducing specific fields of science such as physics, chemistry and pharmaceutical sciences, scientists reflected on the concepts and theories employed in them as well as their social implications, and this consideration developed into a kind of meta-science. Even if one tries to remain strictly utilitarian, science has to touch on scientific thought at least once in a while due to the nature of science itself. This book is not an abstract assertion of this but its concrete illustration with focuses on several specific fields of science from the early to mid-twentieth century. Also, though my introduction is written in a swift manner, it should prove that the history of scientific thought in Japan has produced more accomplishments than one may have at first imagined. This book aims to seduce academics into further research in this area. As the editor, I believe nothing will give me more pleasure than when this seduction is felt by researchers around the world through this English translation.

The translation may well have been an arduous endeavor. I would like to express my sincere thanks and appreciation to all the people involved who have given me the opportunity to publish a translation of this work, and of course, to the translators who actually rendered each chapter into English.

Osamu Kanamori

INTRODUCTION:
A PORTRAIT OF THE HISTORY OF SCIENTIFIC THOUGHT

OSAMU KANAMORI

Section 1. Towards a Chronicle of the History of Scientific Thought

1. Prosopography of the Literature

(1) This lengthy preface is fundamentally different from the other chapters. Rather than offering an accurate and thorough analysis of individual topics, this chapter seeks to address many different publications, and to arrange them all as a loosely integrated profile within one common discourse space. This will be an imprecise task, like a kind of grand excavation of the past. There is a limit to the extent to which the enormous range of literature excavated for study can be examined comprehensively; thus this profile will be necessarily incomplete. Nevertheless, I have chosen to take this approach because my purpose is not to delve into the details of individual works in themselves: it is to address a large volume of literature and to arrange it as an integrated profile within a common discourse. This space for discourse, while somewhat vague, will take on a certain academic flavor. In the end, it is my intention to create a "literary prosopography."[1]

As I claimed in the first chapter of *Kagaku shisō shi* (History of scientific thought, Kanamori 2010), a work that I edited, the scholarly boundaries of what is considered the history of scientific thought are not clearly delineated. For now let us look at the advantages of this boundlessness and also consider as relevant those works that are only slightly concerned with what is commonly considered the history of scientific thought. Since the distinction between the history of scientific thought and the history of science itself is unclear, it would be advantageous to include items belonging to this latter group as well. While the history of scientific thought is indeed a subfield of the history of science, I would venture to say that in a pure history of scientific thought there is less emphasis on a pure enumeration of facts than there is on a history of ideas, with a focus on exploring the theories, concepts, and theoretical backgrounds of individual scientists. Moreover, history of science is essentially distinct from what we would consider sociology of science, and while history of science may resemble philosophy of science, the two are not the same thing.[2] Therefore, in the following overview, with some exceptions, the literature on sociology of science and philosophy of science will be excluded from discussion.[3]

For a professional scientist to step outside of his own specialty and make judgments for himself is something that can be achieved only through a significant commitment to and knowledge of science; such efforts are not without value even if the writing is impressionistic. We will tentatively refer to such considerations as being "scientific-impressions," and include them in these deliberations.[4]

Bearing in mind these criteria for inclusion and exclusion, I will survey the history of scientific thought in Japan from the early Showa Period up to the present. The overview will be fast-paced. A storm of names will arise, with one mentioned after another in rapid succession, though they soon retreat into the background. It would be fruitless to look for traces of in-depth or precise analysis within such discourse. I am well aware that many of the authors taken up for discussion are persons whose works would, in truth, merit the analyses of many treatises and books. As I am attempting to summarize each author in a few dozen lines, it should be clear that my goal is somewhat different. I even believe that the greatest contribution in this introduction is the quotations themselves, or the act of quoting. This is not an excuse to ward off criticism of insufficient analysis, but a mere assertion that describing the network constituted by this large amount of literature differs qualitatively from analysis. In some instances I have what might seem like "criticism"; however, in light of the underlying fact that these authors created the academic tradition from which I have gotten many of my ideas, this criticism is based on a deep sense of respect and gratitude. I owe what I am to them.

While I call this an overview, it is of course limited by my own background and interests. While I will introduce a large volume of literature in the following pages, this overview notably addresses only a few texts comprising the history of mathematical thought or the history of thought in physics.[5] Blame this on my lack of familiarity with these areas if you must. If any reader should have a special knowledge or familiarity with the material covered in this introductory chapter, if there is anyone who can perform a more comprehensive introductory overview of these particular areas than I can, I would happily like to see that person do so. It would make a productive supplement to this introduction and is something that I would hope to see come to fruition.

(2) In Japan, the introduction of Western science, while emphasizing aspects of technological effectiveness, seems to have taken place in a manner that neglected its metaphysical, religious, and philosophical context. Thus, a recognition that sci-

ence is not only important for its technologies that bring great industrial benefits, but is itself a kind of culture, comparable to literature, religion, art, and philosophy, remains relatively weak throughout society. Indeed, even those scientists directly affected appear not to be concerned by this, and the attitudes of scientists towards the history of scientific thought often reflect this fact. Whether or not scientists themselves are conscious of the important cultural component of their work, their work remains as a legacy of a certain culture. Throughout time and cultures, the science that develops later is indebted to the science that came before; it is colored by the historicity of its temporal relationships. Particular concrete analyses of that historicity is outside the purview of scientists.[6] The history of science and the history of scientific thought are close to science and have their origin in science, but they have achieved their own independence from science. Of course, that independence is not itself something that was intentionally sought after. Establishing the nature and direction of scientific work has its own particularities. From the perspective of scientists who have their own work and their own ideas, it is not surprising that the history of science and the history of scientific thought would come to have their own independence as fields of study. This point is key if we are to gain an understanding of the development of the history of science and the history of scientific thought as arcane scientific fields.

To reiterate, one thing that becomes clear as one studies the history of science and the history of scientific thought is the fact that science itself is a culture and a way of thinking. Furthermore, when we first encounter this field of knowledge called "science," the very question of how and what we should think of it is also a culture, a way of thinking.[7] It is the role of the history of scientific thought in general as a field of knowledge not only to repeat abstract arguments about these things as I am doing here, but also to raise concrete, particular arguments.

With this in mind, I will now describe my own view of the history of science and scientific thought in Japan.

2. Concerning the Title: "The History of Scientific Thought"

(1) I have in front of me a copy of Kenzō Sakamoto's *Kagaku shisō shi* (The history of scientific thought, 1984). Unfortunately, Sakamoto, a man of sophisticated demeanor, died relatively young. As a student I procured by chance a book in which Sakamoto conducted a creative phenomenological analysis of the "mechanism of

the machine." I remember the excitement I felt reading that book as through it were just yesterday. This book was Sakamoto's *Kikai no genshōgaku* (A phenomenology of the machine, 1975). Usually phenomenological analyses marginalize science and technology, seeking to construct a separate world; yet Sakamoto's book targeted the machine as an embodiment of one aspect of science and technology. That Sakamoto felt it necessary at the outset to clarify what it means to philosophize about machines illustrates the novel nature of the subject matter and his treatment of it. To summarize the argument: Sakamoto investigates the dual nature of the machine, looking at the machine both connotatively and denotatively. Within the latter part of the text, specifically in the section on extension theory, in order to understand the machine as a sort of "externalization" of the human experience, there is a broad and comprehensive recapitulation of cultural history. This discussion is rightly regarded as ingenious; nevertheless, I personally think the first part represents the meat and potatoes of the book. There was no one before Sakamoto who explicitly discussed machinery using an alliterative scheme (in Japanese, the *kagyō* syllabary, consisting of ka, ki, ku, ke, and ko), as in poetry. In general, the way an engineer thinks about machines is exact and detailed; whereas the broad contemplation of the essential nature of machines is the province of philosophy. Indeed, there was a kind of tradition of theories and philosophies about technology before the war. Nevertheless, *A phenomenology of the machine* is an achievement of high ingenuity that differs significantly in intellectual origin from those earlier efforts.

Sakamoto's *The history of scientific thought* provides an excellent overview of the development of scientific thought from ancient Egypt and Mesopotamia through the Middle Ages up to the modern age of quantum mechanics and cybernetics. Yet, perhaps because of the sheer breadth of material covered, and the fact that the descriptions are overly compressed, one gets the sense reading through it that Sakamoto had not completely digested his material. If Sakamoto had lived longer, he would have been able to write a history of scientific thought many times the length of this work—indeed, if he had published several more books, the state of the academic world would be very different from what it is now.

Of note, Sakamoto delivers several important judgments in the introductory chapter of *The history of scientific thought*. The conventional approach at the time for histories of scientific thought was to determine which things were scientific and which things were not, as seen through a contemporary lens on modes of thought. Only those things that fell under the current understandings of what was science were included as part of historical description. We now call this perspective "the Enlightenment View of the History of Scientific Thought." However, such were not really histories of scientific thought but simply Enlightenment-style tracts concerning scientific thought. This sort of narrative is useful in providing an opportunity for students of the humanities or for non-scientists to become familiar with science; yet it has absolutely no use for scientists, as it merely rearranges what is already known in chronological order.

For the same reason, Enlightenment histories of scientific thought remain uncritical of modern science. The positive achievements of science are clear. At the same time, the development of weapons of mass destruction, together with the overconsumption of resources, suggests that criticism of science is also essential. Exactly what is science? What meaning does science have for humanity? What is modern science? These are questions that must be answered (Sakamoto 1984, pp. 4–5). There is not much that I can add to Sakamoto's prescription, and his judgment here continues to be important. Although the Enlightenment position has a role to play, it is not the whole story. It is essential to continue to maintain a critical consciousness in the philosophical sense. Additionally, in order for the history of scientific thought to acquire real "historicity," it must grasp the historical context of the period, and bring out into the light various rules, conditions and problems that have not yet been seen. There are countless volumes of literature just waiting to be read that go far beyond mere biographies of individual great scientists. The history of scientific thought is not necessarily driven by a pedagogical goal of leading future generations of young people to science; it is a type of intellectual history that situates science within a deeper philosophical context. That is why Sakamoto wrote in 1984 that "the history of scientific thought now can be regarded as the central theme of research in the history of science" (ibid., p. 12).

In addition to this volume, Sakamoto also produced other interesting works, such as *'Wakeru' koto 'wakaru' koto* ('Separating' and 'understanding,' 1982) and *Sentan gijutsu no yukue* (The future of advanced technology, 1987). The former book describes the essential commonality of analysis and comprehension in a way that is easy to understand; the latter book accepts its contemporary age (the 1980s) as being increasingly centered on technology, and it sounded the alarm that both an ethics for engineers and a philosophy of technology were lacking.

In any case, more than twenty years after the indictments in *The history of scientific thought*, I wondered if the history of scientific thought was still a vibrant field. Additionally, what have we learned from research done prior to Sakamoto's book?

(2) To answer this question, at first I tried a very simplistic method: I tried to find works with the actual Japanese words for "history of scientific thought" in the title. In doing so, I was somewhat surprised to find the following twenty books:

Kagaku shisō shi: Kagaku hen (*A History of Chemistry*, Brown 1913, trans. 1923)

Shizen kagaku shisō shi (*From the Greeks to Darwin*, Osborn 1894, trans. 1932)

Kagaku shisō shi (History of scientific thought, Kunio Oka 1936)

Kodai kagaku shisō shi (*Science in Antiquity*, Farrington 1936, trans. 1942)

Kagaku shisō shi no igi (*La Signification de la pensée scientifique* [The significance of scientific thought], Enriques 1934, trans. 1943)

Kagaku shisō shi (History of scientific thought, Shūichirō Yoshioka 1948)

Kagaku shisō shi (History of scientific thought, Takeo Konno 1948)

Yuibutsu shikan kagaku shisō shi[8] (*The Social Relations of Science*, Crowther 1941, trans. 1952)

Nihon kagaku shisō shi gaisetsu (Outline of the history of scientific thought in Japan, Shūichirō Yoshioka 1952)

Shizen kagaku shisō shi (The history of thought on natural science, Shūrō Honda 1955)

Sobieto kagaku shisō shi (Великиерусские мыслители в ъоръъе против идеализма и религии [History of scientific thought in Soviet Union], Prokof'ev, V. 1952, trans. 1955)

Kagaku shisō shi nyūmon (Introduction to the history of scientific thought, Suketoshi Yajima 1956)

Kagaku shisō shi (History of scientific thought, Yōitsu Kondō and Kaichirō Fujiwara 1959a)

Kagaku shisō shi (History of scientific thought, Nagayasu Shimao 1967)

Kagaku shisō shi gaisetsu (Outline of the history of scientific thought, Shūrō Honda 1975)

Koperunikusu kakumei: Kagaku shisō shi josetsu (*The Copernican Revolution: Planetary Astronomy in the Development of Western Thought*, Kuhn 1957, trans. 1976)

Kagaku shisō shi (History of scientific thought, Hiraku Takebe and Yū Kawai, 1980)

Kagaku shisō shi (The history of scientific thought, Kenzō Sakamoto, 1984)
Risei no kōko gaku: Fūkō to kagaku shisō shi (Michel Foucault's Archaeology of Scientific Reason, Gutting 1989, trans. 1992)
Kagaku shisō shi nyūmon (Introduction to the history of scientific thought, Naomichi Iso, 1993)
Kagaku shisō shi (History of scientific thought, Osamu Kanamori ed., 2010b)[a]

No book published in the twenty-five years after Sakamoto's *The history of scientific thought* had those words in its title, until my own recent book with that title came out. In between Sakamoto's volume and my own, there was only one book on Foucauldian theory, and one introductory-level book by Naomichi Iso. I wondered if the history of scientific thought was on the verge of extinction. If this was all that was written in decades on such an important subject, then maybe it is merely a niche area of scholarship for those of eccentric tastes?

Rather than jumping to a rash conclusion, let's look at two or three books among those listed here. First, there is Kunio Oka who, in the context of the pre-war research on materialism, took up the history of scientific thought in the framework of "the development of the dialectical method" which posited a reciprocal relationship between Nature as a basic condition and active working of technology on Nature (Oka 1936). This was basically just a pamphlet, but Oka presented in it a model for how to conduct a history of scientific thought. However, as will be discussed below, it also reveals the deep relationship between this field and materialism, or with Marxism in general. This was both a strength and weakness for the field overall. Oka's text skillfully digests the prior Western literature in the field and traces the major developments in scientific thought from ancient Greece through the nineteenth century. However, this work presumed the basic dichotomy of "materialism versus idealism," and is based on the value judgment that idealism is an illusionary accouterment of the ruling class, while materialism belongs to the ruled or the rising class. Because of that bias, the book evaluates historical figures in a fashion that is ideological and one-dimensional. While I completely agree that materialism is an interesting philosophy, we must move beyond such an evaluation method that equates materialism with the heroes and idealism with the villains. Human history is not so simple. Such materialism may have been a necessary counter to the strong idealistic trend of that period. Looking back from the present time, however, we can safely conclude that this kind of "value-based history" has become a drag on the entire field.

It should be noted that Oka remained actively engaged in academic and social activities through the postwar years until his death in 1971. Among his various achievements in the history of science, there is also the seven-volume series *Shizen kagaku shi* (History of natural science, 1948–1951). While this series is voluminous, it is not particularly well sourced, as Oka himself states, and it relies primarily on findings from earlier work. However, given the political situation before and during the war, studying abroad or importing books from other countries would of course have been very difficult; this would not have changed very much immediately after the war. Therefore, in adverse circumstances, this work provided a broad survey up to the Industrial Revolution that is still deserving of respect.

Next, I would like to discuss Shūichirō Yoshioka. Yoshioka was a talented scholars who translated Bergson's *L'Évolution créatrice* (*Sōzōteki shinka*; Creative Evolution) in his younger days. Yoshioka's *Sūgaku bunka shi* (Cultural history of mathematics, 1938) was a work that interpreted mathematics in a way that could be readily comprehended by the lay reader as a part of the overarching culture. This work was also consistent with the enlightened intellectual climate after World War II, and played a considerable role in mathematical education. Yoshioka's *Nihon kagaku shisō shi gaisetsu* (Outline of the history of scientific thought in Japan, 1952), consistent with its title, was a broad overview of the history of scientific thought in Japan, encompassing not only the natural sciences but also the social sciences. It specifically concerned the mathematics of Takakazu Seki and Kenkō Takebe, the agricultural theory of Yasusada Miyazaki, the medical science of Tōyō Yamawaki, and works of others of similar repute. Among that lineup, Yoshioka emphasized the work of Gōryū Asada in particular. Because of his tremendous understanding of modern inductive reasoning, Yoshioka praised Asada as the Copernicus of Japan (chapter 5, section 3). What led Yoshioka to write this work in the first place was revealed in the preface to a revised edition: the purpose of the history of scientific thought is not to create a long historical narrative on the nature of various scientific theories; it is to provide historical reflection on the maturation of scientific thought. After Japan was defeated in "that terrible war," Yoshioka believed that scientific thought was necessary in order to rebuild our devastated homeland and way of life. Yoshioka diagnosed that the Japanese, up until that point, had not really engaged in a scientific way of thinking. In reaction to the kind of irrationality that led the nation into a reckless war and in response to the social demands of postwar reconstruction, Yoshioka felt a need to write a history of scientific thought.[9]

Next I will present Shūrō Honda's *Shizen kagaku shisō shi* (The history of thought on natural science, 1955). This is the kind of literature that represents how difficult it is for histories of scientific thought and similar works to clearly establish their own independent discourse space. I find no problem with this text in how it traces the history of science from ancient times up through the modern era. If forced to say something critical about it, I guess one could say that this text puts a bit of emphasis on theories and concepts. For example, the discussion of the struggles between positivism and Kantian Kritizismus in the twelfth chapter brings out the distinctiveness of this work as a history of scientific thought. Still, the way it sets up the debate is similar to Oka's work, insofar as both works have their intellectual basis in Marxism. Honda's analysis is almost completely Marxist: it devotes a considerable amount of effort to an analysis of the natural dialectic method, and along the way he shows a deep knowledge of Hegel.

It should be noted that Honda also has a book called *Kagaku shisō shi gaisetsu* (Outline of the history of scientific thought, 1975). I want to raise just one point about this book: I recall that in discussing modern histories of scientific thought, Honda identifies three important debates ('Introduction,' Honda 1975). First is the conflict between the mathematical method that dominates for the mathematical natural sciences and the narrativity of the narrative natural sciences. Second is the debate over the relationship between science and philosophy. The third debate is between the development of science and the relative strengths of philosophical idealism and materialism. With these three debates in mind, Honda relates the history of scientific thought after the establishment of modern theories of mechanics. In light of his intellectual standpoint it may not seem surprising, but his description of the vulgar materialism advocated by nineteenth-century thinkers such as Moleschott and Vogt is unique.

(3) Only the books mentioned above employ the actual words "history of scientific thought" directly in their titles. Nevertheless, using the approach of looking only at those texts that have these actual words in their titles as a measure of what has contributed to the history of science and scientific thought is, of course, a bit too simplistic. It is necessary to compile a list of works based on their substance.

I noted above my decision to use the early Showa Period as the starting point for my historical narrative. The reason for this decision, as we can see from the above, is that the history of scientific thought has traditionally had a strong connection to Marxism. For example, the activity of the Materialism Study Group (*Yuibutsu ron kenkyūkai*, 1932–1938) was an extremely important source in the early stages of the "history of the history of scientific thought." Thus, it has become a general rule that the history of scientific thought starts in the early Showa period. Even still, there is an important person who must not be overlooked in this matter, namely, Hajime Tanabe.

The important field of the philosophy of science, a field of study related to the history of scientific thought, was authoritatively established by this dignified philosopher. That remains true, even if the philosophy of science in Japan was imported as a rather faithful copy of the prevailing European academic style of the day, which was Neo-Kantianism.[10] From the Taisho Period, Tanabe's *Saikin no shizen kagaku* (Recent trends in natural science, 1915), *Kagaku gairon* (Introduction to science, 1918), and *Sūri tetsugaku kenkyū* (A study of mathematical principles, 1925) provided somewhat unexpected examples of methods of discussion for use in the philosophy of science. *Introduction to Science* especially garnered a large readership, and while adhering to the neo-Kantian style, it considered in detail the theories of Mach, Poincaré, Duhem, Planck, etc. that were prevalent at that time. Furthermore, it highlighted the basic line that seeks an appropriate grounding of science as objective universal knowledge between the forces of intuition and construction.

An intuitive reproduction of empirical facts does not constitute natural science. With this insight, Tanabe carefully unraveled this apparently paradoxical judgment, while never losing sight of the nature of theoretical physics. He finishes with an idealistic and optimistic statement on the potential fulfillment of individual human lives, believing that ultimately a scientific world image is one of the ways through which humanity can realize its desire to live in a civilized world. Through Tanabe's eyes, the Japanese of that time were able to get a bird's eye view of the essence of the philosophical debates that had unfolded over the previous several decades among European scholars. This was very fortunate for Japan, where philosophy itself had been introduced just a few decades earlier. Once again we sense the awesome intellectual gifts of Tanabe and others from the Kyoto school.[11] Although it seems he was "the very picture of integrity," his activities before and during the war were regarded as somehow contributing to the war effort. For that, after the war Tanabe was subjected to condemnation by some, and he himself also reflected on his past activities, immersing himself in considerable soul searching. He spent his last years in lonely seclusion in Kitakaruizawa. It is a shame that Tanabe's efforts were not taken up sufficiently by later generations. The only consolation is that we sometimes see interesting theses published on Tanabe, such as Saburō Ienaga's *Tanabe Hajime no shisō shi teki kenkyū* (A historical study on Hajime Tanabe's thought, 1974) and Shin'ichi Nakazawa's *Firosofia Yaponika* (Philosophy Japonica, 2001). I cannot imagine there is a historian of scientific thought, whether Marxist or not, who had no interest in Tanabe's work, or in the work of others of his group.[12]

Section 2. Prewar Trends

1. The Importance of the Materialism Study Group

Let us begin our sketch of the history of science and scientific thought in Japan from the early Showa Period. For convenience, I will demarcate that period using the end of World War II in 1945. Accordingly, this chapter discusses the period from the early Showa Period up until the end of the war. Of course, since there is some continuity of intellectual themes after the war, the scope of description here may include the postwar period where there is a continuity of the substance of discussion or of members of the various schools of thought described.

(1) An overview of the history of science and scientific thought in Japan during the period of 1926–1945 shows us, above all, the importance of the activities of the Materialism Study Group (Yuiken) and its affiliates. The journal *Yuibutsu ron kenkyū* (Research on theories on materialism, 1932–1938), edited and published by the Materialism Study Group, is an invaluable aid in assessing the level of discussion at that time. Also, as Shingo Shibata notes, *Yuibutsu ron zensho* (A compendium on materialism, 1935), developed mainly by members of the group, could have been an encyclopedia comparable to *Mikasa zensho* (The Mikasa encyclopedia, 1938–1939), had it been completed (Shibata 1991: pp. 3–46). The importance of these studies remains, even in the present when the authority of Marxism has been in relative decline. Now, liberated from the fetters of Marxist ideology, we can see many things that we could not before. One thing we can see is that these works comprise a great intellectual treasure.

As for the journal *Research on theories on materialism*, because space is limited

I will mention only the first two volumes of Aoki Shoten's reprinted edition (Yuiken 1972, 1973[13]). The most eye-catching part of the first issue (Yuiken 1972) is "*Kanō hakase ni kiku*" (Listening to Dr. Kanō, Number 1, pp. 86–110), a round-table discussion centered around Kōkichi Kanō. There are some geniuses who never have to write anything down, and Kanō was probably one such person. I am unsure if he was the "grand darkness,"[b] but the free-spirited narrative somehow reminds me of *Shisō no doramaturugī* (Dramaturgy of thought, 1974), a much more recent dialogue between Tatsuo Hayashi and Osamu Kuno. The flow of the story is divided into two large parts, with the second part devoted to the ethics of Kanō, a kind of materialist ethics that denies free will. To me, the first half is more interesting. There, in response to requests, Kanō gives a basic overview of the natural sciences of the Edo Period. Noted figures such as Takakazu Seki, Gōryū Asada, and Toshiaki Honda are mentioned, and there is a discussion of the even temperament of Genkei Nakane, which is very interesting. Kanō was acquainted with a great deal of superficial knowledge of the Edo period; it's no surprise he rediscovered Shōeki Ando.

The third issue (Yuiken 1972) contained Kunio Oka's interesting article, "The World of Stars" (*Hoshi no sekai*, Number 2, pp. 82–96). It was more or less a contemporary commentary on the nature of the cosmos; there are some differences between its tenets and modern findings, which is only to be expected. The text becomes interesting suddenly in the second half, when it criticizes the theories of Eddington. Oka censures Eddington as being "mired in idealism," almost like a drunken astronomer of the past.[14] He goes on about how Eddington completely ignores "the social basis of knowledge," that his method of dealing with matter descends into a semiotic scientific category, and that he is snared by the trap of "mathematification" (in a pejorative sense). Oka even criticizes Eddington's religious views as deliberately avoiding analytical thinking. Some say that the weapons of physicists are dangerous because they bring about the collapse of the meaning of nonmaterial things; Oka's response is to ask why we can't just utterly destroy such things. Furthermore, he opened his article with a quote from the Russian expressionist playwright Leonid Andreyev. In the play Oka quotes from there is a serene universe that contrasts with a battlefield full of slaughter and chaos; for Oka is all about "deconstruction." His deconstruction is that cosmology has shown that the universe itself is not so serene and that our terrestrial world has more than just chaos and is anchored in scientific law. From a modern perspective, his argument seems nothing more than a typical case of dialectical materialism, but one cannot overlook a certain skill in the force and composition of his writing.

The seventh issue of *Research on theories on materialism* (Yuiken 1973) featured "The Science of Art and Dialectical Materialism ("Geijutsu gaku to benshō hō teki yuibutsu ron") by Hiroshi Kawaguchi (Number 7, pp. 5–21). This work starts by reminding us that art has long been at the center of idealist philosophy because of its "magical charm." The article praises Taine for his interpretation that counters idealism by looking to external causes of artistic creation, such as racial, environmental, and historical determinism, with Plekhanov and Friche positioned as successors to this rich tradition. They believed that art also had to be understood in the context of social development. Nevertheless, art cannot be dealt with so simply. The claim that "artistic value transcends class" keeps coming back. Not to be deterred by that kind of tenacious resistance, Oka insists yet again that art must be seen as a concrete dialectic method of social praxis. Proximity to Leninism is again specified as the norm here. One of its features is a positive evaluation of the work of Korehito Kurahara.[15] As such, this appears from our point of view today to be a mere repetition of the dogmatic theory of art. Interestingly however, Kawaguchi clearly recognizes that a forced application of dialectical materialism to artistic movements entails the risk of simplification and over-schematization. In general, it is not possible any longer to just dismiss things like the proletarian art movement; it is likewise almost impossible to just repeat a theory that dismisses all forms of transcendence that come from subjective ideas or circumstances as a mere cover for idealism. This short essay by Kawaguchi is an interesting testimony that shows, in ways he hadn't intended, the complexities inherent in art.

The next item to discuss is Fundamental Problems in Materialist Jurisprudence by Yasuzō Suzuki (Shin'ichirō Fujinami, pseud.) in the tenth issue (*Yuibutsu ron hōgaku no kompon mondai*, Yuiken, 1973, pp. 5–26). Suzuki was a man with great influence in the various issues surrounding the constitution after World War II. From the perspective of historical materialism, economics serves as the base in the theoretical distinction between base and superstructure, and law is part of the superstructure. As part of the superstructure, law must be maintained by force. The substance of the law reflects the social relations of human interactions as they arise from their basis in relation to the means of production. Suzuki undertook a critical exposition of the conceptual nature of contemporary Japan's legal system and its theoretical justification, taking the Soviet-style understanding of the law as his norm. Moreover, he contributed to a new argumentative structure that once again insisted critically on the scientific nature of "New Legal Studies."

To summarize, even these few examples show that the journal *Research on theories on materialism* is a complex and rich body of work that deserves a separate study of its own. We should not forget that a key part of "the history of the history of scientific thought in Japan" may lie in its pages.

(2) Because Yuiken itself, along with its journal *Research on theories on materialism* and *A compendium of theories on materialism*, was influential in the history of scientific thought, we should explore in more detail some of the people directly or indirectly involved with it.[16] Among these people we must first discuss Jun Tosaka and Hiroto Saigusa.

Jun Tosaka's *Kagaku hōhō ron* (On scientific methodology, 1929), *Gijutsu no tetsugaku* (A philosophy of technology, 1933), and *Kagaku ron* (On Science, 1935) are particularly noteworthy for their sharp critical awareness and clear objectivity. It is worth noting that Tosaka wrote several publications on space, though they were never published in book form. If you look at his maiden work *On Scientific Methodology*, it is clear that he faithfully incorporated the academic tradition of neo-Kantianism, in particular Rickert and other philosophers of the Baden school. This is shown by his discursive structure that opens with arguments on the mutual determination of the object and the methodology, and then proceeds with differentiating the methodological characteristics of the natural sciences and the humanities as nomothetic and idiographic (idiosyncratic causality) respectively. *On Science*, published a few years later, takes a step further. There Tosaka, while keeping a watchful eye on various trends in the philosophical criticism of science by neo-Kantianism and other schools, extols the virtues of materialism as a means to obtain a more accurate grasp of the world. He connects the underlying concepts that drive both the natural sciences and the social sciences as sharing the same norms, and he pursues the basis for this shared normativity in materialism as a global scientific mode of understanding. Tosaka and Kiyoshi Miki, whom we will describe later, understood Marxism as a social movement in a philosophically deepened form, providing a profound ideological weapon for subsequent left-wing thought. Nevertheless, it is undeniable that Tosaka thought too much of the political system of the Soviet Union. This was, however, a general trend not restricted to Tosaka's text, and one that might have to be chalked up to the political climate and information bias of the time. In order to fully and fairly analyze Yuiken and its Marxist thinkers at the present time, it is essential that we adopt a kind of "distanced" stance that treats Marxism and the great twentieth century experiment in establishing a socialist state through revolution in an objective manner and carefully scrutinizes them.

Let us turn next to the famous Hiroto Saigusa. His materialist theory constructed a world quite different from the monotonous lack of nuance which is sometimes associated with the term "materialist." Within his wide variety of achievements, those related to theories of technology are especially noticeable. These include *Gijutsuka hyōden* (A critical biography of engineers, 1940–1943), *Gijutsu no shisō* (Technological thinking, 1941a), and *Gijutsu no tetsugaku* (A philosophy of technology, 1951). Saigusa is similar to Hiroshi Nagata, who appears later in this chapter, in that he devoted himself to the excavation of Japan's rationalist or materialist traditions of thought. Saigusa was the editor of *Nihon kagaku koten zensho* (A compendium of japanese classic works on science, 1942–1949), which made many important contributions; the products of his own thoughts in preparing this compilation were *Nihon no shisō bunka* (The culture of Japanese thought, 1937) and *Miura Baien no tetsugaku* (The philosophy of Baien Miura, 1941b). Unfortunately, Saigusa died in a tragic accident. *Philosophy of technology* is one of his most important works, with many later editions published. This was a broad overview of Western technological thinking dating back to Greece; in addition to the evolution of thought, it looked carefully at revolutionary innovations in the history of technology. Overall, it had a very balanced structure. Furthermore, the third section is a serious discussion of the philosophy of technology. Here, concepts in the philosophy of technology that are interesting even when looking back from the present day, such as the theory of organic projection and the fourth kingdom, are discussed with precision. This work also serves as a guide to other works, and if read thoroughly, it provides a sufficient understanding of the major philosophies of technology that dominated the hundred years or so from roughly the middle of the nineteenth century. I will touch on this later, but in spite of Saigusa work, Japan's subsequent technology theory and philosophy of technology unfortunately has not shown much productive evolution. Given how our everyday lives have been transformed by feats of engineering since the 1990s, it is time to reexamine Saigusa's contributions.

In addition to these two people, many others were active during this period; for example Hiroshi Nagata, who had his life cut short due to tuberculosis. Despite his consequentially short active period, anyone with an interest in materialism in Japan will come across the name Nagata many times. When I was young, I was interested in what kind of person he was. It is possible to catch a glimpse of the general character of his work in *Gendai yuibutsu ron* (Contemporary debates on materialism, 1935) and *Nihon yuibutsu ron shi* (A history of Japanese debates on materialism, 1936). *A history of japanese debates on materials*, discusses materialism in Japan, a theme not mainstream in the history of thought in Japan, exploring its origins in the Edo period's Ando Shoeki and Bantō Yamagata. However, materialism almost assumes the existence of a mature science; the mature development of materialism had to wait until the Meiji Period.

At that point, it is of course appropriate to look at Hiroyuki Katō and Chōmin Nakae; however, Nagata even includes contributions to materialism from such individuals as Mamichi Tsuda and Yukichi Fukuzawa, who were active in the Meiji Six Society and who were thus, so to speak, philosophers of the Enlightenment tradition. Nagata's skill is as evident as one would expect in dissecting their early consciousness of the threshold of the possibility of epistemology, for example in his analyses of the trajectory of reason in the thought of Amane Nishi. And he also offers a few comments on socialism during its generative period. Nagata could be completely contained within the framework of dialectical materialism; yet if he had been blessed with a long life and been able to extend his energetic approach to the history of Japanese thought, one wonders what might have been; his early death is very unfortunate in that sense.[17]

Next, let's take a look at Yoshishige Kozai's *Gendai tetsugaku* (*Contemporary Philosophy*, 1937). This book is included in *A Compendium of Theories on Materialism*; nevertheless, it does not simply extol materialism directly. Rather it takes the unique stance of focusing on raising questions about the grounds for the establishment of idealism. Kozai confirms that philosophy is at best only indirectly linked with the material conditions of the time; and he offers Hegelian philosophy as one example to buttress his claim. This is most evident in Hegel's mode of conceiving of the history of philosophy as the Spirit (Geist)'s self-unfolding over time. Kozai's work is to make us conscious of the historical conditions and meaning of the continued existence of idealism as a way of thinking opposed to materialism. He regards various schools in the early twentieth century, including the neo-Kantian school and the "philosophy of life," as contemporary developments in idealism, and did everything he could to critically expose their particular features. His project was by no means limited to ideas introduced from the West. For example, Kozai criticizes the idea that the spirit of Japan is found in "*mono no aware*" (pathos) and he criticizes the conception of it as timeless, since he sees it as nothing but certain everyday, ordinary feelings that emerged out of specific conditions of history, geography, and class, and were turned into an abstraction in the name of ethnic identity. Kozai was blessed with a long life, and after World War II worked hard in various peace campaigns and other social movements as a hardline leftist thinker.[18]

There were many people involved with Yuiken who had a deeper association with specific sciences than with philosophy. Take, for example, Takeo Konno. Konno's *Sūgaku ron* (On mathematics, 1935) is a small book but contains a great deal of information and keen observation. After abstractly defining mathematics as a science of necessary linkage between things, especially quantitative linkage, he goes into specific areas of mathematics, giving explanations of algebra, analysis, mathematical analysis, and probability. His writing style is so reader-friendly that even someone unfamiliar with the material can gain an understanding of the outline with careful reading. It is also not merely neutral or descriptive; for example, Konno clearly states his own views in describing casualism. Of course, since this volume was included in *A compendium of theories on materialism*, its ideological foundation is clear from start; still, he does not accept Marx unreservedly. For example, Kozai makes some critical comments on Marx's understanding of differential calculus. In any case, I think we can feel pride in such an early achievement in the history of scientific thought in Japan. After the war, Konno was very instrumental in the growth of the Democratic Scientists Association. He was also at one time a member of the House of Representatives of Japan—indeed a very rare thing for a mathematician.

In biology, Tomoyuki Ishii's *Seibutsu gaku to yuibutsu benshō hō* (Biology and dialectical materialism, 1947) and *Atarashii seimei ron no tame ni* (*For a new theory of life*, 1948) catch the eye. Ishii, although famous after the war as a leader of the Michurin movement,[c] emphasized in *Biology and dialectical materialism* the concept of the philosophy of biology from a more theoretical stance. It is clear from the start what his intellectual framework is. Against the two long-entrenched traditions of mechanism and vitalism, he first excludes theories of life, and rejects the holistic theories of his own time as a variation on vitalism. He also dislikes the static character of mechanism, and states that materialist dialectical biology, which intrinsically describes the movement and development of life, is the correct philosophy of biology. Ishii was focused on the recognition of the dynamic nature of life, especially the power of humans to define the environment; for the same reason he also took a negative stance on eugenics. His conceptual relationship between genetics and the environment probably encouraged his involvement in the Michurin movement.[19]

2. The Kyoto School and Related Work

Especially from the early Showa Period through the prewar period, the history of scientific thought in Japan was not monopolized by the Yuiken group. Although there were people like Hajime Tanabe, there were others from the Kyoto school and its affiliates who, not surprisingly, took a somewhat different approach to the history of scientific thought. Many of these also made important contributions.

(1) For example, the work of Kiyoshi Miki comes to mind. It is difficult to provide a consistent picture of Miki, whose career was interrupted by outrageous political suppression, because his work tended to develop different themes at different points in his life. The study of Pascal, the incorporation of philosophy into Marxism, essays on the power of imagination, philosophy of history, and discussion on Shinran—each of these is a part of Miki, but only together do they constitute the true whole. If you look at the context of our history of scientific thought, then we must mention *Gijutsu tetsugaku* (Philosophy of technology, 1942). *Philosophy of technology* can be understood as offering philosophical correction to the Yuiken group's economic determinism of technology (the general theory of the means of labor). Animal-instinct responses to the environment happen unconsciously, without any mediation. On the other hand, the human intellect feels frustrated in its given environment, and its response towards the environment takes the form of a mediated confrontation, which, although performed in some cases by organs such as the hand, is more generally performed by tools specialized to each purpose. Dissatisfaction overcome by such organs and utensils involves a converged pattern of behavior and materialistic identification with the utensils in question. Miki called this "the form of action." I believe his philosophy of technology was an attempt to foster a more general and radical discussion than that of Yuiken and the conscious application theory by Mitsuo Takeya discussed below. It is a pity that Miki's contribution was not fully utilized in later theoretical debates on technology. It should be noted that one of his key works, *Kōsō ryoku no ronri* (The logic of design power, 1939) is filled with ideas related to the history of scientific thought.

We should reexamine what a cruel disservice public authorities did to Tosaka, Miki and other outstanding intellectuals, even if it is often excused as happening under the wartime regime.

Next I wish to take up *Gūzen sei no mondai* (The problem of contingency, 1935) by Shūzō Kuki. Although it is widely believed that Kuki's career centered on aesthetics, his ideas on contingency are based on the discussions of Boutroux, Cournot, and other members of the French neo-Kantian school, and on the fact that contingency is inextricably linked to the causality of the natural world, so in that sense this book could been seen as belonging to the history of science and scientific thought. But does it? This is a rather difficult problem because at the outset of the book Kuki clearly asserts that even if theories of probability and quantum mechanics touch on contingency and uncertainty, by its very nature contingency does not make for a good subject of science; it is best understood as a metaphysical problem. At least part of the apodictic contingency or disjunctive contingency referred to by Kuki is concerned with the contingent state arising from logical analysis, while hypothetical contingency was discussed from a more empirical standpoint. In that sense, contingency does enter the discourse space of empirical science. Conversely, his description of how one of multiple disjunctive possibilities is realized, and then experienced as "fate" at the core of existence (chapter 3, sections 12 and 13), clearly indicates that Kuki's contemplations include some aspects that go beyond the scientific perspective. Thus, *The problem of contingency* is one of those works that belong on the perimeter of the history of science and scientific thought.[20]

(2) Among the thinkers of the Kyoto school, the person who most directly inherited, or more accurately "was supposed to" inherit, the tradition of Hajime Tanabe is Toratarō Shimomura. I used the phrase "as supposed to," because, as is well known, Shimomura expanded his area of study to an almost unprecedented degree, and his achievements went far beyond the history of scientific thought in a narrow sense. The texts with the most straightforward connection to the history of scientific thought are *Shizen tetsugaku* (Natural philosophy, 1939), *Kagaku shi no tetsugaku* (A philosophy of the history of science, 1941), and *Mugen ron no keisei to kōzō* (The formation and structure of the theory of infinity, 1944). Of these three texts, *A philosophy of the history of science* in particular is studded with important judgments across its pages. *A philosophy of the history of science* starts from the premise that the history of science should be taken as a series of challenges to the

history of ideas. Science should not be seen merely as knowledge and technology, but as an objective self-expression of a historical subject. The history of science is the awareness of the spirit with which science is formed, and of contemplation of the form of science itself. Shimomura refers to this academic awareness not as "history of science" but as "history towards science." This served as the basis for the development of a robust contemplation of the literature conflating Western notions of spiritual history and the history of science. This was the quintessential notion of the history of scientific thought. Shimomura was unique in that he regarded the establishment of mathematics beyond mere arithmetic as an epoch-making event in world history, and as a definitive element in the "Western-ness" of the West. Additionally, this book showcased unique knowledge, such as the relationship between modern technology and traditional magic; at the time of publication, Shimomura was clearly regarded as the heir apparent to Tanabe's mantle as a scholar. This work represented a nodal point in the history of science and of scientific thought in Japan.[21]

However, as is well known, Shimomura continued to expand his areas of study, triggered by a postwar trip to Europe in his mid-fifties. This surely expanded Shimomura's personal intellectual interests. However, when seen from the standpoint of the legacy of the history of science and scientific thought, a slightly different evaluation is possible. If we consider his suggestion that Leonardo da Vinci and the Renaissance artists of that time were, in a sense, scientists working in perspective and space, we can see that the general continuity of this line of work would be a good thing. Nevertheless, his discussion on Burckhardt in the last year of his life, and especially the discussion of Saint Francis of Assisi, took Shimomura far beyond an intellectualist, rationalist stance. I have a strong impression that Shimomura has not received due credit for the sheer quality and quantity of his work, but I can't help but feel that it is because there are elements in his work that frustrate an effort to see his work as a coherent whole. Someone should write a book on Shimomura.

Although this is a bit out of our chronology, I would like to mention Hiroshi Nagai here. We could say that Nagai was one of the few scholars to take on the academic tradition of Shimomura directly. His works include *Sūri no sonzai ron teki kiso* (The ontological basis of mathematics, 1961), *Gendai shizen tetsugaku no kenkyū* (A study on contemporary natural philosophy, 1963), and *Seimei ron no tetsugaku teki kiso* (The philosophical basis of the theory on life, 1973). *A study on Contemporary natural philosophy* is a sequel of sorts to *The ontological basis of* mathematics, which was a philosophical reflection on mathematical existence, which then turned to physical existence. There have been studies on the theories of relativity and quantum mechanics, but they are generally based on an assumption that naive empiricism is insufficient even for physics, and that experience does not correspond with physical nature, i. e. the objects of perception and sensation. In short, they have opened a debate about correctly being conscious of the unique structure of the "image of the physical world." This is neither idealism nor metaphysics. If we analyze the way physicists see the physical world, it really comes down to nothing more than "a creation of the human spirit." In that sense, we can say this is merely an elaboration on the project of "science as spiritual history" in Nagai's mode. *The philosophical basis of the theory on life* is a uniquely valuable contribution to the Japanese intellectual world as a philosophical response to theoretical biology. Am I wrong in thinking that there were no later works from the Nagai tradition? If I am right, that is most unfortunate.

3. Issues Surrounding World War II

(1) There are several items from before 1945 that have been analyzed only insufficiently. The first concerns discussions on Japanese science from just before World War II through the war, and the second the numerous theories for promoting science and technology within Japan that were adopted as ways to advance Japanese scientific and technological interests in response to the war, in what was then regarded as scientific warfare.[22] First, let's look at the idea of Japanese science.[23]

As an offshoot of the Kyoto school tradition, Kunihiko Hashida took the initiative to create a unique fusion of modern science and Sōtō Zen. I once tried to produce a simple analysis of his works (Kanamori 2004a, pp. 2–48). Hashida's *Gyō to shite no kagaku* (Science as asceticism, 1939) includes an ingenious insight that cannot be dismissed as merely an aspect of the ideological clamor of the times.[24] It is impossible, however, to look at overall discourse on Japanese science during that time without taking ideology into account. I myself have no cause to wish for a resurgence of cultural nationalism. All the same, the idea of consigning to oblivion, for political reasons, a great deal of the literature written before the war that was based on the rationality and validity of its day, is not what we can call an attitude of learning from history. In the present era, while not being insensitive to the political elements of the literature, historians must make an earnest attempt at extracting the logic in those texts as objectively as possible.

That discourse on "Japanese science," was all about calling into question the usual way of thinking of science as universal and talked a lot about creating instead a science that conformed to the mentality of the Japanese people, their ethnicity and particular historicity.[25] In addition to Hashida's works, books of this motif include, at very least, Shōichi Sakuta's *Kokumin kagaku no seiritsu* (The establishment of national science, 1934[26]), Tadayoshi Kihira's *Nihon seishin to shizen kagaku* (The Japanese spirit and natural science, 1937) and *Chi to gyō* (*Knowledge and action*, 1938), Seizaburō Uramoto's *Seirigaku teki sekai zō* (Physiological world image, 1941), and Takakazu Maeda's *Nihon kagaku ron josetsu* (Introduction to debates on a Japanese science, 1944). A more detailed investigation of this topic would doubtlessly produce a great deal of similar literature.[27] Reading through secondary sources such as these that blindly follow others may be of value as a study in social psychology, but it will not deepen one's level of thought much. It would be better to perform a close reading of a few relatively "good texts" than to read many texts of lesser quality. In any event, it is certain that we should try to find some sort of meaning at the ideological level instead of dismissing them as particular deviations of the wartime regime.

Uramoto's *Physiological world image* is strongly influenced by Kunihiko Hashida, and attempts to develop a concept of "physiological anthropology." In order to fully develop the vitality of life as a "phase of activity" (p. 83), scientific civilization must be brought from a mechanistic conception centered on physics to something more in touch with "the human sciences." That will then make culture a more ethnic phenomenon. Only with "an ethnic people brimming with vitality" (p. 52) do we see the true value of science and technology. The particular Japanese ethnic life force has suffered in many ways from the materialistic civilization of the late Meiji Period. Uramoto suggests that only now (in his day), Japan should turn back to a more life-centered focus. He believes that Western science is merely a body of knowledge, and when he claims that, in accordance with the Eastern view that knowledge and practice are one and the same thing, science must incorporate this aspect of practice (p. 241), it seems he is merely rehashing Hashida's arguments on "science as practice."[28]

During World War II, Maeda, who had been active in the Japanese navy for a period of time, wrote *Introduction to debates on a Japanese science*. This book stressed that it was necessary to refine the separation between basic science and applied science, that is, the separation between science and technology, within the context of social conditions of the time, when the war was being regarded as a "science war." He argued that important creative ingenuity will not arise unless both basic and applied science are successfully reconciled. Science, Maeda believes, originated as a debate about how the state should govern, and he declares that it must be fostered as an important part of what the state does. If the connection that science has with state policy is lost, and science is liberated from state activity, it will decay and die. It is interesting that this value judgment is the opposite of the classical view that "science is autonomous." Furthermore, Maeda offers a typical worry that science education of that age stressed students' voluntary study and creativity, consequently producing people of little worth who merely gave crafty, ingratiating opinions and remarks, or experimented with overly-subtle whimsy. Also, we occasionally encounter unique theories of the time related to the total war regime, though they do not necessarily have a direct connection to Japanese science. They are the so-called "sciences of daily life," in which scientific spirit is expanded into the general social space and specialized knowledge is connected with that of daily life. When compared with the debates on "Japanese science," these included ideas that were not simply the extreme thought engendered by the harsh wartime regime. I also feel that the established idea of "reducing learning to everyday life," which held sway within postwar science education for a time, took a great deal from this earlier tradition. The following is example from Shūji Murakami.

Murakami's *Mizu no seikatsu kagaku* (Daily life science of water, 1943) is a collection of essays that attempts to provide the broadest possible approach to water, an essential substance for human beings. Its mythical properties, physical properties, industrial uses, literary uses, etc. are comprehensively discussed. Even reading it now, far removed from the context of the war, I believe it is a good example of high-quality instructional writing on science. Of course, there is no doubt that the war regime's footprint can be seen in its pages. The opening lines of praise for the book from military doctors who noted that, in contrast to the Japanese climate where we enjoy plentiful water, in foreign lands like Manchuria, there was a constant struggle to provide water, reveals in a way certainly not intended the connection this text had with the events of its time. There is also a chapter in the text explicitly called "War and Water" (pp. 16–27), where Murakami explains the significance of ensuring that high-quality drinking water be delivered to front lines, and offers some brief technical advice regarding the conveyance and filtering of water. Of note, he quotes the almost poetic depiction of water in *The Ten Thousand*

Leaves, and his lyrical descriptions of water springs, fog, and mist are quite fascinating. This literature was indeed very thought-provoking.

Uramoto's *Physiological world image* (1941) contains a segment on "the concept of a science of daily life" (pp. 99–126).[29] This is a sort of an opinion paper on establishing a national research institute of a science of daily life in response to the Sino-Japanese Incident and the onset of World War II, modeled after the establishment of the Institute of Physical and Chemical Research in the wake of World War I and the establishment of the National Spiritual Cultural Research Institute after the Manchurian Incident. The idea was to establish a national policy for the development of science that is underpinned by the basic sciences of daily life and composed of two branches, namely environmental sciences of daily life and the cultural sciences of daily life. The idea of a science for daily life plainly seemed to be converging towards a common center from the directions of both science and daily life. To understand this as only a special discussion of wartime and the wartime regime leaves a disappointing sense.[30]

(2) The second subject is the debate over the promotion of science under total war. Were I to make a thorough search for relevant texts, a considerable amount of materials would emerge.[31] Before analyzing the literature, however, I would like to reflect a bit on the institutional structure of that era. For example, in 1939 there was the establishment of a Department of Science in the Cabinet Planning Board. Also, the cabinet approved the "Guidelines for Science and Technology under the New Structure" in 1941. Around then, the Agency of Science and Technology and the Science and Technology Council were established under the cabinet. From there on, the science and technology of Japan was placed more explicitly within the confines of the total war system. If one looks at the literature that coexisted within that institutional context, it will include: Takenosuke Miyamoto's *Kagaku no dōin* (Mobilization of science, 1941), Masatoshi Ōkōchi's *Seisan daiichi shugi* (A production-first policy, 1941) and *Kokubō keizai to kagaku* (Science and the national defense economy, 1942), Shigeyoshi Matsumae's *Tōa gijutsu taisei ron* (On an East Asian technology system, 1941) and *Senji seisan ron* (A theory of production during wartime, 1943), Nobuyuki Ōkuma's *Kokka kagaku e no michi* (The path to state science, 1941), and Tamotsu Aoki's *Sensō to seimitsu kōgyō* (War and the precision machinery industry, 1942). This topic requires a treatment similar to that of the first topic.

Ōkōchi's *A production-first policy* critiques the inadequacy of the capitalist economy, suggesting that it prioritizes the pursuit of profit and assumes that enhancing productivity is of secondary concern. Furthermore, he states that the scientific industry as opposed to the capitalist industry should be encouraged. The idea of putting productivity first was a broad criticism of the capitalist system in that sense. Ōkōchi served as a professor at the University of Tokyo and RIKEN director from the late Meiji period through the Taisho Period, and was a prominent figure at the heart of the prewar government science community. Additionally, it was when Rikagaku Kōgyō was established as an institution for connecting the scientific aspect of RIKEN to technological and industrial developments that Ōkōchi was appointed its first chairman. Thereafter, the so-called RIKEN conglomerate became an important contributor to industry. *A production-first policy* was written in Ōkōchi's later years. However, he concretely suggests possible measures at that time to bolster technical strength under tense world conditions. It is interesting reading now—in particular the discussions of machines as tools. All in all, if we were to remove such works as these from the context of wartime attitudes towards technology as national goals, many of them could be seen as having significant commonality with postwar technology promotion in Japan. This is why I believe this theme could sufficiently withstand its political implications.[32]

Matsumae's *On an East Asian technology system* is an analysis of the technologies of the major Western powers and China; he evaluates the present state of Japanese technology in comparison with them, pointing out its backwardness. The book recommends developing policies to decrease the enormous patent royalties coming from a reliance on Western technology, to eradicate the leakage of industrial secrets, and to strengthen the Japanese technological position by developing more self-reliant uses of resources. It advocates state control of technology. Also, it challenges the state of research institutions such as universities, calling for improved support for researchers, increased research funding, and improvement and expansion of facilities. This text is a typical example advocating to enhance national power in a tense global situation through reforming science and technology.[33] Matsumae's activities after the war are well known: he consistently embarked on a board range of social activities, serving as a member of Japan's Lower House of Representatives, and was the founder of Tokai University.

It should be noted that the Japanese History of Science Society was founded through the efforts of Ayao Kuwaki and Jun'ichi Sugai, among others, nearly at the same time as these writings—April 1941.[34] Rather than being driven by pure interest in the history of science, its founding was most likely due to the widely-held view that there was a specific need for the advancement of science; this is probably more consistent with the actual conditions of the time. The promotion of science and technology was an urgent challenge for the nation, and both faced the necessity of directing a great deal of energy to the historical examination of science along with dissemination of scientific knowledge and renewal of scientific education.

Around the same time, virtually the first comprehensive collection on the history of science, a twelve-volume work that covers a wide range of specific areas such as physics, chemistry, biology, and technology, was published[35] (Yoshioka, et al. 1940–1943). This period was still taking a largely adaptive, translation-based approach to the history of science literature, reliant on relevant literature from overseas.[36] In any case, with compilations of this kind, it could be said that history of science in Japan was taking its first steps. To summarize, regarding the publication of these works as viewed within the context of the time and together with the establishment of the History of Science Society, there is no doubt they were considered as part of the wartime strategy of science and technology promotion.

Considering their functional value in the history of science in general, they may have been intended to reinforce the wartime regime during World War II, along with a scientific worldview immediately after the war, and to indirectly reinforce postwar industrial and infrastructure development to recover from postwar devastation. In this sense, we should presume that the history of science had a foundation forcefully supported by social intentions rather than being the hobby-like study we normally assume it is.

4. "The History of Scientific Thought" from the Perspective of Scientists

There were many individuals who actively commentated on the history of scientific thought as professional scientists or mathematicians, with or without being connected to Yuiken. The important mathematician Teiji Takagi published *Kinsei sūgaku shidan* (Discourse on the history of early modern mathematics, 1942) and *Sūgaku no jiyū sei* (Freedom of mathematics, 1949), which are accessible even to a general readership. There are other mathematicians who made contributions, such as Jōichi Suetsuna, who had a deep knowledge of the Kyoto school of philosophy.[37]

Kinnosuke Ogura's series of writings—for example *Sūgaku kyōiku shi* (History of mathematics education, 1932b) and *Kagaku teki seishin to sūgaku kyōiku* (The scientific mind and mathematics education, 1937)—deserve to be mentioned. They are the results of a great deal of mathematical education. There are limits to learning mathematics from a natural accumulation of personal knowledge based on day-to-day experience; it is a field that is conscious of the uniquely human culture of math, and it contains a large amount of individual component parts that must be taught deliberately and systematically from a young age. Mathematics is very much "mathema" (from the Greek for "knowledge"), and it is a subject that should be learned. In that sense, math education can be compared to math itself. There are numerous guides offering assistance for entrance examinations or providing introductions to elementary mathematics students, and there are a great many breezy ruminations written by mathematicians describing daily occurrences. However, a perspective focused on math education as culture while retaining mathematical content does not have such a great presence in the literature, though such work has value in its own right. Taking that idea into consideration, we should be proud of producing people like Ogura at a relatively early stage. Here let us discuss, among his many works, *Sūgaku kyōiku no kompon mondai* (Fundamental problems in mathematics education, 1924).[38] The argument of this book is structured in three levels. In the first part, the contemporary state of math education is discussed. This part exposes the various problems associated with the many instances of adults having indifferent attitudes towards or unpleasant memories of mathematics, and exposes various other problems, including the tendency to favor difficult challenges, or the rigid separation between geometry and algebra (such as flunking a student who solves a geometry problem with algebra). Ogura's response was that logical rigor is certainly necessary, but it is not the only necessary component. He argued that it is better to adopt a more flexible focus on the development of the more practical aspects of math, such as geometric intuition. He also made slightly simplistic comparisons of the British and French traditional modes of mathematical education. In the second part, Ogura compared what are now referred to as the theory of formal discipline and the theory of material discipline.

If one leans towards formal discipline, it should be possible to learn a dense, logical mode of thinking by immersing oneself in mathematics. Nevertheless, it is doubtful whether such a thing exists at all. On the contrary, the phenomena described by the highly logical and simplified conditions of mathematics seem to have little resemblance to the complexities of the real world. Therefore, some ar-

gue that assumption of formal discipline is harmful. Nevertheless, while it would
not be problematic to progress in this direction while faithfully representing reality, there would need to be a massive expansion of topics to be covered by the
teaching materials, because they would need to cover new phenomena using different thinking. This leads to the conclusion that teaching materials should be focused on what happens most frequently in human life. Ogura takes a fairly neutral
stand in describing this ongoing dispute. In the third section, he presents his own
theory of math education more directly. Math is a tool for cultivation of the scientific spirit, and because of this, training in the functional mode of mathematics is
essential. Furthermore, rather than simply teaching a strict set of logic with a
steep learning curve, math education should focus on the presentation of practical, everyday sorts of problems, afterwards allowing students to gain a gradual
familiarity with the more analytical methods. We can find a number of cases of
problem awareness concerning math education that are still valid today. This suggests the profundity of Ogura's work.

Among physicists, Ayao Kuwaki's *Butsuri gaku to ninshiki* (Physics and epistemology, 1922) and *Kagaku shi kō* (Reflections on the history of science, 1944)
stand out. *Reflections on the history of science* is an anthology of topics not included in his previous books, drawing from both Eastern and Western traditions, from
Banri Hoashi, a philosopher in the Edo period, to Poincaré. "Research on the history of science" in the beginning (pp. 1–13) states that the history of science was
established around 1830, citing Comte's work as an early example. Drawing a distinction between *histoire des sciences* (history of particular sciences) and a kind of
histoire de la science (a history of science as a whole), Kuwaki, cautioning himself
against cursory inclination to the latter, consciously sought out the possibility of
establishing a discourse space other than *histoire des sciences*. Kuwaki's expectation is that the discourse space will include the correlation or mutual relationship
between science of a certain period and the contemporary society. Both the sociology of science and the history of scientific thought seem to have been conceived in
a comprehensive and inclusive way. However, while discussing the subsequent
development of the discipline of the history of science, he confirms that that kind
of comprehensive science history is extremely difficult to develop. Finally, he de-
termines that the deepening of subject matter for *histoire des sciences* is important.
Even while praising the achievement of first-rate individual scholars such as Sarton, Kuwaki hopes for the creation of specialized laboratories and research institutions that transcend individual thinkers.[39]

When it comes to science essays on physics, Torahiko Terada's series of essays have their own unique position in the field. Among modern physicists, Terada's physics for everyday life are widely criticized for being merely focused on particulars; yet his ad hoc attempt at physics essays was essentially different from a mere physics for everyday life in that they glimpsed the possibility of an authentic Japanese science. Let's explore Terada's works in his latest complete works of 30 volumes (1996–1999), especially volumes 2, 5, 6, and 10.

To reiterate what I claimed in "Nichijō sekai to keiken kagaku" (Everyday world and empirical science, Kanamori 2009), a short article in a monthly bulletin for the latest complete works of Toshihiko Terada, experience in empirical science is generally not a loose trace or a clever replication of everyday life. Rather, the scientific nature of science lies in a sort of stepping back from experience, where we are removed from a direct recapitulation of everyday experience, purify conditions and construct experience in accordance with the subject matter. If the stepping back from experience is regarded as a general prerequisite, the intermediate nature of Terada's physics, which almost dwells in a boundary between the discourse space of physics and the everyday world, seems all the more paradoxical. The crack of a glass, paper marbling, the sound of the *shakuhachi*, the angles of *kompeitō* candy—these are physics-based approaches to our everyday world, and Terada's constitution lies between the constitutive world of modern science and the view of the amateur. For example, the essays "Densha no konzatsu ni tsuite" (On crowded trains, Volume 2), "Butsuri gaku no ōyō ni tsuite" (On the application of physics, Volume 5), "Butsuri gaku kengai no butsuri teki genshō" (Physical phenomena outside the sphere of physics, Volume 5), and "Shizen kai no shima moyō" (Stripped patterns in the natural world, Volume 6) show these features at their maximum. Keeping in mind the development of physics thereafter, I believe that to simply state that Terada was a pioneer in the areas of non-linear, non-equilibrium physics is to conceal his true nature.[40] Unfortunately, subsequent developments in Japanese physics did not proceed in the direction that would best conserve Terada's legacy. To repeat, Terada's unique physics, which cast light on completely different value judgments from those before, were considered insufficiently separated from daily life, yet they appear to have been well received by teachers. The reactions of professional physicists are easily understood. Nevertheless, if we become more sensitive to the special autonomy of the discourse space of physics, we should be able to gain a firmer understanding of some of Terada's physics as part of everyday life.

The tradition of Terada's physics was not completely discontinued.[41] Ukichirō Nakaya's *Yuki* (Snow, 1938a) and *Fuyu no hana* (Winter flowers, 1938b), Ryū-zaburō Taguchi's *Oto to ongaku* (Sound and music, 1943) and *Iro to oto* (Color and sound, 1952), Morizo Hirata's *Kirin no madara* (The spots on giraffes, 1975), Shin'ichi Kawakami's *Shima shima gaku* (A study of stripes, 1995) more or less sound like echoes of Terada.[42] Although the time sequence here departs a bit from our chronology, we can digress a little to investigate these works.

In the ten years following the 1938 publication of Nakaya's *Snow*, it was reprinted thirty-seven times and became well-known in the world as his representative work (Since I myself grew up in Hokkaidō and experienced a great deal of snow in my youth, I found it hard to concentrate when reading this work—I instead spent my time gazing at the nostalgic snowy scenes in the pages). While there is also reference to the problems of heavy snowfall, at the core of this book is a cultural history of snowflakes and the classification of crystal forms. Toshitsura Doi's *Sekka zusetsu* (Illustrations of snow flakes, 1832) became famous by virtue of being introduced to the public through Nakaya. Snow disappears in an instant if placed in the hand; it has a crystal form that is unique to each flake. With literary sensibilities implicitly nestled within the scientific gaze, the understated plain style drifts sublimely. What a wonderful work![43]

Hirata's *The spots on giraffes* (1975) is a collection of essays compiled by his pupils. Among them, the minor works "Kirin no madara moyō" (The spot patterns on giraffes), "Busshitsu no hyōjō" (Expressions of material substances), and "Wata gashi" (Cotton candy) in particular capture the atmosphere of Terada's physics. His claim that we should regard the patterns of stripes and spots that decorate the body surface of various plants and animals as fissures where the surface could not keep up with interior growth reportedly became a subject of fierce debate among biologists. Whether this phenomenon should be considered more a fissure or more a wave, it is impossible to cast away the fascinating, boundary-crossing perspective of viewing organisms physically. Also, Hirata brilliantly explained the mysterious fluffiness of festival cotton candy with physical mechanisms such as the supercooling of melted sugar; this short work is exactly the model of a physics for everyday life.[44] Among other works where one can find Terada's spirit are: *Bi no kikagaku* (Geometry of beauty, 1979) written, partly for fun, by the prominent nuclear researcher Kōji Fushimi and his friends, and in *Katachi no butsuri gaku* (The physics of shape, 1983) and *Katachi tanken tai* (An expedition of shape, 2002) by Tōru Ogawa, who contemplated the mesoscopic world that is neither macro-scale, like outer space, nor microscopic, like elementary particles, and re-captured shape as a physical problem.

Section 3. Study of the History of Science Gains Autonomy

1. The Postwar Scientific Spirit

The major currents in the history of Japanese scientific thought in the prewar period, along with their derivatives, were presented briefly above. Let's now explore the academic trajectory that the history of scientific thought took after World War II. Here again a rough sketch will have to suffice.

The first thing one must note is the fact that many scientific education books and scientific theories were published by scientists and philosophers of science for several years in the immediate aftermath of the war. These responded to the increasing social demand for rational and enlightened thinking as a reaction to the irrational and unreasonable ethos of the military organization and thought control of the prewar and wartime years. Immediately after the imperial decree announcing defeat, on August 15, 1945, Prime Minister Kantarō Suzuki said that Japan had lost the war of science. His words reflected the thoughts of many people. The article "Nihon no kagaku/gijutsu no kekkan to kyōsan shugi sha no nimmu" (Defects in Japan's science and technology and the mission of the Communists) which the Communist Party of Japan put out in late 1945, concluded that the ruling regime including the totalitarian emperor system and the feudal system of land ownership had led to defects in Japan's science and technology. This piece connected the spiritual climate before World War II with its "non-scientific nature" and condemned it severely. Furthermore, in spite of the damage caused by the destruction of RIKEN's cyclotron or stopping of aerospace research in accordance with GHQ's policies for demilitarization of scientific research, scientists weathered the storm and launched new research suitable to the new social climate. Marxism had been harshly censored from before the war, but Marxist intellectuals after the war were able to finally participate freely in public opinion activities. The Democratic Scientists Association (Minka), which was established in early 1946, was especially active during the first decade or so immediately following the war.[45] Yoshishige Kozai, who had been active with Yuiken from before the war, took a leadership role in the philosophical section of the Association. Minka advocated for what they called "democratic science," which they argued was an important concept for the healthy development of science. Also, the Science Council of Japan was established in early 1949. In this way it is possible to describe the history of scientific theory taking socio-historical context into account and to look at some extremely interesting phenomena; nevertheless, I will not go into detail concerning these matters, since they distract us from the general purpose of this chapter.

(1) The results of a roundtable discussion on science were published as a single volume in 1950. Jōichi Suetsuna, Yoshio Fujioka, Hiroshi Tamiya, Teiji Takagi, and Toratarō Shimomura had held the discussion in 1949. Leading figures of the time in mathematics, physics, biology, psychology, and philosophy had come together and thoroughly engaged in a discussion of the sciences. This interesting project resulted in the publication of *Kagaku to wa nanika* (What is science?, Suetsuna, et al. 1950). This was not from an extrinsic stance à la Tanabe; this roundtable discussion had the express purpose of approaching the various topics from within science, and general principles, outlooks, and limitations were discussed from the perspectives of each sub-discipline, though topics concerning general principles and outlooks accounted for the majority of the volume. Each person naturally had a mastery over his particular professional field, and a gathering of many such men with a broad knowledge of related fields invited a very vigorous debate. Looking back from the present, one cannot help but be amazed at the very notion of scientists and epistemologists (i.e., Shimomura) getting together to discuss methods and principles of each sub-discipline of science.

Takashi Hayashi's *Kagaku gairon* (Introduction to science, 1951), published nearly at the same time, states that most scientists considered an interest in epistemology heretical, and he wanted to oppose that tendency. It appears that there was a relatively strong awareness of this issue at that time. That is also probably why a roundtable discussion such as the above was even possible. *Introduction to science* is itself a powerful, voluminous work. Hayashi, as a neurophysiologist, established his unique philosophy of science by reflecting on his regular scientific research and learning from epistemological traditions. The reason that these kinds of results gradually became more difficult to achieve can be put down to changes in scientists, and to changes in philosophy itself. When viewed from the perspective of the entire culture, I think this this very unfortunate.[46]

There are two Nobel Prize winning physicists who should be singled out for vividly embodying elements of human culture both within the narrow confines of specialization and also within the broad range of liberal arts. Hideki Yukawa was awarded the Nobel Prize in 1949, and Sin-Itiro Tomonaga in 1965. Yukawa wrote *Sonzai no rihō* (The law of existence, 1943), *Me ni mienai mono* (The invisible, 1946), *Kagaku to ningen sei* (Science and humanity, 1948a), *Gendai kagaku to ningen* (Modern science and human beings, 1961), and *Sōzō teki ningen* (The imaginative human, 1966). Tomonaga completed *Ryōshi rikigaku teki sekai zō* (Quantum-mechanical world image, 1949b), *Butsuri gaku to wa nan darō ka* (What is physics?, 1979). These works are essentially the history of science and scientific thought. More than anything else, the personal dignity and presence of these two men, as well as their discrete works, created the impression that science is culture. Both laureates were able to converse freely about a range of intellectual topics of general cultural interest, rather than simply their own chosen specialty. Yukawa's *The law of existence*, published in the 1940s, tried to present the implications of quantum mechanics for physics and for thought in general in as plain and clear a manner as possible. It also included implications for how to think about contemporary reports on the development of particle physics. The main discussions take the form of a dialogue, whereas the appendices take the form of an ordinary thesis. Yet, especially when it comes to the appendix, this work of literature demonstrates a very sophisticated epistemology by a renowned physicist. I remember the surprise I felt when I found that such a book had been published during the war. Yukawa was selected to receive the Nobel Prize in the postwar period, and it gave tremendous confidence and courage to Japanese people. Although this seems rather silly now, that is the way people felt about it. Tomonaga's *What is physics?* is a concise journey through the history of physics up to the early twentieth century; especially interesting as a history of scientific thought is his narrative of the development of the kinetic theory of gases. Unfortunately, Tomonaga wrote this while terminally ill and was unable to complete it. That being said, together with more specialist works like *Ryōshi rikigaku* (Quantum mechanics, 1949a), *What is physics?* maintains its standing as a standard introduction to the history of scientific thought in physics. Towards the end of this work, he has a piece called "Kagaku to bunmei" (Science and civilization) which plainly states his magnificent view of civilization and is still worth reading carefully. Since Yukawa and Tomonaga are both very famous people, I do not believe we need to discuss them in greater detail.

(2) As stated above, the early years after the end of World War II saw increased publishing of books on science education and theory, as well as science magazines. It is impossible to exhaustively examine all of these; I would prefer to focus on the work of Mitsuo Taketani and Mitsuo Hara. Taketani is well known for, more than anything else, his writings on the three categories of phenomenology, substantialism, and essentialism. He advocated the scientific recognition and development of these three categories. His assertive and sharp criticism and aggressive social activism concerning nuclear development showed the range of the new, postwar scientist's image. Taketani authored many books, including *Benshōhō no shomondai* (Various problems in the dialectic method, 1946) and *Sensō to kagaku* (War and science, 1953a). *Various problems in the dialectic method* is a collection of theses including his unique theory on technology. From this collection, it is especially worth mentioning "Tetsugaku wa ika ni shite yūkō sa o torimodoshi uru ka" (How can philosophy regain its validity?, pp. 1–17[47]). This lecture was given at the History of Science Society of Japan in 1942. In summary, when speaking from the perspective of a scientist, Taketani argues that neo-Kantian epistemology is not useful, and an analysis of modern science is essential for epistemology itself to grow. From the stance of a physicist, this may be plausible. Nevertheless, looking back with an awareness of the history that follows, his discussion shows that science could still be found within the domain of philosophy at that time. Regardless of whether or not this directly benefited any scientist, this was very important for the development of philosophy. Furthermore, discussions like Taketani's led to a loss of interest, resignation, and even outright antipathy from philosophers. When viewed from the perspective of respecting the interaction and sensitivity of the whole culture, the value of Taketani's argument has both merits and demerits.

Incidentally, *War and science* and *Minagoroshi sensō to shite no gendai sen* (Modern warfare as total annihilation, 1953b) were published in the same year and constituted a pair. With the Korean War and the remilitarization of Japan in the background, these books transcend a simple commentary on current affairs, revealing Taketani's outstanding capabilities. By projecting the prominently inhuman nature of these new weapons, modern warfare threatens to eliminate the meaning of any distinction between winners and losers in a war, bringing serious destruction to all of humanity. Taketani portrays this aspect assertively, with specific examples, for instance the March 1945 firebombing of Tokyo. In his rational and technical analysis of war damage itself, Taketani's ability shines.

Additionally, Taketani's theory of conscious application of technology was highly appreciated as an oppositional stance to the theory regarding technology as a systematic means of labor, revitalizing theory and philosophy of technology from the prewar era for a short period of time. Although this was inherited by Yoshirō Hoshino, Sakaji Yamada and others, subsequent controversies in technological theory unfortunately did little to deepen discussion. Subsequent thinkers merely took the concepts and controversies explored by their predecessors and repeated them in a kind of war of attrition. Different perspectives and conceptual equipment, leading to new theories of technology and new philosophies, are now much in demand.[48]

Next we will discuss Mitsuo Hara. While elaborating on the research tradition of Yuiken after the war, Hara created an extremely uncompromising philosophy of chemistry. Although his publications include *Shizen benshō hō no kenkyū* (Study on the natural dialectic method, 1946) and *Kagaku to minshū shugi* (Science and democracy, 1948), etc., I want to focus in particular on *Kagaku nyūmon* (Introduction to chemistry, 1953). While it is a small book, it is quite dense and makes many original and valuable contributions. In the introduction, the author makes readers aware that "this is an introduction to chemistry almost unprecedented in the world." As Hara himself insists, the entire discussion was shot through with the Marxist concept that the natural dialectic method is the basis of everything. Thus he reveals his own historical perspective that even in science there are steps towards the formation of an initial hypothesis that are based on magical ingredients or immature concepts, and that those steps are overcome by the verification process. this degree of objective reflection is heightened at a later stage of history. The hypothesis of gradual passage from a relative truth to the absolute truth may be too straightforward and simplistic, but it will give chemists peace of mind when they engage in their research. The book has fairly abundant descriptions of historical events, including a description of the phlogiston hypothesis. The historical development during the formation of modern chemical laws which underpin the discipline, such as the conservation of mass, definite proportions, and multiple proportions, is described simply and in a way that might enlighten and encourage young people who aspire to chemistry.

In that sense, it is an excellent primer, and what I find interesting is the fact that this kind of historical and epistemological reflection was active in areas most deeply connected to industry, such as metallurgy, the ceramics industry, and man-ufacture of new materials. The text does not merely enumerate and describe, say, "the nature of the halogens," but it explores the issues surrounding how chemical knowledge was built up in a way that chemists themselves would appreciate. Whether or not one agrees with the tenets of the natural dialectic method, the fact that a book of this quality was published very inexpensively is also something that should be appreciated. Thexts such as Hara's *Introduction to chemistry*, and Ha-jime Kashiwagi's *Yuibutsu ron keisei no kagaku shi teki haikei* (Chemical historical background to the formation of the materialist thesis, 1949), for example, add a certain philosophical profundity to Japan's history of chemistry.

2. A Dissection of "Histoire des Sciences"

Research on the history of science in Japan presumably freed itself from the ex-trinsically-derived teleology typical of wartime science and technology promotion and enjoyed steady growth in the 1950s and 1960s.[49] As mentioned in the begin-ning, this chapter treats didactic materials only marginally. Nevertheless, *Nihon kagaku gijutsu shi taikei* (Series on the history of science and technology in Japan, 1963–1972), which the History of Science Society in Japan compiled from 1963 to 1972, is quite important and noteworthy. This compilation consists of a spectacu-lar lineup of related materials. The sixth volume is entitled *Shisō* (Thought), and it contains many relevant issues to be discussed in this introductory chapter. Even though this volume is quite dense, it comes across in a fragmented way, perhaps because the corpus of data it addresses is too broad, which gives it the character of an introductory anthology. We will use this exhaustive work as a guide to our own in-depth investigation. In all the literature in the history of science, there has nev-er been, nor will there ever be, such a collection of materials concerning the histo-ry of scientific thought—this is the first and the last of its kind.[50]

There is one more thing I should note: already in this period, it was becoming difficult for one person to craft a cogent view that completely covered the history of science. To that extent, *histoire des sciences* had come of age. Nevertheless, one book that we should discuss is *Kagaku shi* (The history of science, 1961a) by Mi-tsutomo Yuasa; this work presents a unified historical image while adhering to general historical narrative conventions. Although Yuasa's focus does not go back in time beyond the Meiji Period in terms of geography and historical timeframe, he grasps and presents the flow of the development of the sciences in Japan concisely and accurately. Yuasa also offers a retrospective on Japanese policies on science and technology since the Meiji Period; at the same time, he carefully chronicles the historical process of the important cultural decision to abandon the mathematics of the Japanese feudal period and traditional Chinese medicine. Regarding the Meiji Period as a heroic age of science, Yuasa describes a litany of individually talented scientists, such as Shibasaburō Kitasato, Jirō Kitao, Aikitu Tanakadate, Jōji Sakurai, Rikitarō Fujisawa, and Bunjirō Kotō—all individuals worthy of their own biography. Yuasa characterizes science after the Russo-Japanese War as having moved from a transplant phase to a self-growth phrase, with RIKEN and Tōhoku University as good examples of this. Additionally, this work deserves special mention in that it justifiably treated the discussions of scientific advancement and Japanese science immediately before and during World War II despite postwar political criticism. Yuasa also mentioned the general flow with which Japanese science recovered from the postwar chaos as early as 1961. Yuasa's *The history of science*, despite the inherent limitations of being a single authored work, is an excellent illustration of a modern Japanese history of science.

I mentioned earlier that the era when one person working alone could write a complete history had come to an end, and that time was followed by the era of *histoire des sciences*. The description below is obviously not exhaustive, but I would like to give a minimum, though somewhat scholastic, list of representative accomplishments within the *histoire des sciences* approach, giving preference to those works concerned with the history of scientific thought. Needless to say, this is just a preliminary endeavor.

(1) First, we will cover the history of mathematics via the work of Yōitsu Kondō and Chikara Sasaki. I must admit I am up against the limits of my knowledge when it comes to mathematics, so I will not offer an in-depth analysis. I would appreciate it if any interested commentators who are more knowledgeable than I am would delve into this topic—likewise for physics history below. There are many others who have worked in this field, and I will touch on some of them briefly.[51]

Yōitsu Kondō's works include *Kikagaku shisō shi* (The history of geometric thought, 1946), *Sūgaku shisō shi josetsu* (An introduction to the history of mathematical thought, 1947), *Kindai sūgaku shi ron* (On the modern history of mathematics, 1948), *Shotō sūgaku no rekishi* (History of elemental mathematics, 1952), and *Dekaruto no shizen zō* (Descartes's image of nature, 1959b). It is no exaggeration to say that Kondō's works are among the crowning glories in the history of scientific thought in Japan. Because his major works were republished in anthology form in the 1990s, his work will see renewed academic interest in the near future. He was Hajime Tanabe's disciple. The original version of Kondō's *The history of geometric thought*, published in 1946 (not the reprint), features a highly refined introduction, as the editor of his collected works, Chikara Sasaki, notes. While acknowledging a certain independence of mathematics from politics, Kondō suggests that mathematics is—at least at a fundamental level—associated with the material conditions of human society, sort of an assertion of a Marxist view of the history of mathematics. The second half of *The history of geometric thought* especially contains a detailed analysis of the development of non-Euclidean geometry. Euclidean geometry had long been regarded as the infallible fundamental geometry describing the world, not as one of many possible geometries. It was nevertheless discovered that different geometries could also be logically consistent and discretely constructed, giving rise to extremely profound philosophical implications. Kondō begins his explanation from Gauss, who, after struggling for some time against the dominant influence of Kant's theory of space, began the journey towards a non-Euclidean geometry. Kondō carefully follows this developmental process, from Lobachevsky to the Bolyais (father and son) on to Riemann. Indeed, these several decades in the nineteenth century constituted a significant revolution in terms of spatial concepts. This had ramifications for philosophy, and as the nineteenth century drew to a close, philosophers finally began to realize its importance. Kondō argues that Ernst Cassirer's understanding was particularly outstanding. He also discussed Rudolf Lotze and Johann Erdmann separately. Erdmann's remarks on the ontological link between experience and geometric phenomena are especially interesting.

Examples of Chikara Sasaki's work include: *Kagaku kakumei no rekishi kōzō* (Historical structure of the scientific revolution, 1985), *Kindai gakumon rinen no tanjō* (The birth of modern academic ideals, 1992), *Marukusu shugi kagaku ron* (On Marxist science, 1997b), *Kagaku gijutsu to gendai seiji* (Science, technology and modern politics, 2000), *Nijusseiki sūgaku shisō* (Mathematical thought in the twentieth century, 2001), and *Dekaruto no sūgaku shisō* (Descartes's thought on mathematics, 2003). Sasaki's work represents a sort of expert treatise on the theory of the scientific revolution. It is unrivaled as a work exposing the historicity of Cartesian mathematics. Adhering firmly to a Marxist political stance, Sasaki does not try to hide his thorough antipathy to neo-liberalism. When postmodernism was influential, his works such as *Gakumon ron* (On Scholarship, 1997a) attempted a rebuttal of it from a more classical, rationalist position. Because Sasaki's work is ongoing, a final evaluation should be left to the future. Though he is somewhat artless and aloof, there is a large community of people captivated by his grand academic world. The voluminous *The birth of modern scientific ideals* is a relatively early installment among Sasaki's works. It is, in a nutshell, a history of scientific thought in Europe during the seventeenth and eighteenth centuries. Descartes, Hobbes, Newton, etc. are duly lined up and discussed; a noteworthy feature is the many pages devoted to Giambattista Vico as an anti-Cartesian figure. While flatly rejecting obscurantism, Sasaki argues that the unique attention Vigo devoted to Aristotle's *Topics* and the historical world was evidence of his unique approach that escaped from Cartesian rationalism.

Mathematical thought in the twentieth century has three main subjects. First is the history of the foundation of mathematics during the 1930s, when there was an active debate among logicism, intuitionism, and formalism. To this the mathematical philosophy of Wittgenstein was also added; Sasaki summarized this as a mathematical view akin to a language game. The next subject is an analysis of Weyl's mathematical theories, which were influenced by Edmund Husserl. Basically, Weyl was empathetic to the intuitionism of Brouwer but held an eclectic attitude towards formalism. Through his later years, he focused on a constructivist perspective; he did not agree with a strong formalism that eliminated meaning. Sasaki also touched on the outstanding handbook Weyl left on relativity, in addition to his basic theoretical work. The final subject is the work of John von Neumann. His analysis of mathematics is from a social perspective, which is natural when von Neumann's relationships with computer and military science are taken into consideration. A history of twentieth-century mathematical thought that provides an overview of the entire subject might be a nearly impossible challenge even for a mathematician, as Sasaki admits himself. However, in drawing a portrait of various people who symbolize intrinsically mathematical foundations and those related to social history, this book is the first step for subsequent works that may achieve a more comprehensive overview in the future.[52] It should be noted that Sasaki later published *Sūgaku shi* (History of mathematics, 2010) as a nodal point in his career.

Incidentally, and somewhat removed from the confines of a history of mathematical thought, one person who is recently successful in the field of mathematics education is Fumiharu Katō. Katō's *Sūgaku suru seishin* (The spirit to do mathematics, 2007) and *Monogatari: Sūgaku no rekishi* (A narrative account: the history of mathematics, 2009) are both published by Chuko Shinsho and can be purchased at relatively low prices. *The spirit to do* mathematics is an excellent introductory work: sprinkled with interesting anecdotes, this text utilizes rich imagery to explore concepts such as continuity and infinity that are foundational to mathematical thought. The text tries to communicate, in a way that can be understood by the lay reader, the dynamism of both the active involvement of humans in a mathematical world and the idea that formulas speak to humans. As Katō is still quite young, we will continue to watch his future activities.

Regarding mathematics, there is generally a wide gap between the professional world and the world of ordinary people, and mathematicians deal with subject matters beyond the imagination of lay people. While everyone uses the four basic arithmetic operands in their everyday life, few individuals venture very far into mathematics from there. However, even just at the edge of that divide, we can taste the true charm of the culture called mathematics that humans have created; thus I believe mathematics is an area that requires more educational efforts toward the general public than other scientific fields.

I occasionally hear that professional mathematicians do not necessarily think highly of educational activities, but it is sufficiently enjoyable for most people just to touch a small part of the mathematical culture. Perhaps the profession should more actively try to take advantage of such interest. In that sense, the efforts of Fumiharu Katō, Takeshi Yoshida, and Kōji Shiga are quite praiseworthy.

(2) Next comes the history of physics.[53] The history of theories at the beginning of the twentieth century—such as the establishment of modern mechanics, the theory of relativity, and quantum physics—is so fundamentally important to the entire history of science and the history of scientific thought that it is discussed in nearly every text.

That makes it quite difficult to do justice in this context to even a small number of people (And also there are limits to my own abilities). Until recently, it was difficult to get a hold of primary source materials on the dawn of modern physics; plus, the number of works written by Japanese authors is few relative to the importance of the topic. Suketoshi Yajima's *Makkusuueru* (Maxwell, 1950), Hideo Hirose's *Koperunikusu* (Copernicus, 1965), Kanji Fujimune's *Denki ni kaketa shōgai* (A life's devotion to electricity, 1977), Nagayasu Shimao's *Nyūton* (Newton, 1979), and Seizō Aoki's *Garirei no michi* (*The way of Galileo*, 1980) are some notable works.[54] One interesting aspect of this discussion is that often enough the historical background of the development of twentieth century physics is so important that it is incorporated into textbooks. Of course, those textbooks are not history books, but a general description has made its way into whole texts. An accurate survey of this would be nearly impossible, and it would be difficult for even a serious history book to completely cover it all. Based on this limitation and with the caveat that this list will be extremely incomplete, we should at least consider Kiyoshi Amano's *Ryōshi rikigaku shi* (History of quantum mechanics, 1948), Suketoshi Yajima's *Butsurigaku shi* (History of physics, 1949), Takeshi Sugawara's *Rikigaku shi* (History of mechanics, 1957), Hitoshi Takeuchi's *Butsurigaku no rekishi* (History of physics, 1969), Takehiko Takabayashi's *Netsugaku shi* (History of thermology, 1948) and *Ryōshi ron no hatten shi* (History of quantum theory, 1977), and Shigeko Nishio's *Gendai butsurigaku no chichi: Nīrusu Bōa* (The father of modern physics: Niels Bohr, 1993), among many others. I believe it is worth particularly mentioning two other scholars: Tetsu Hiroshige and Yoshitaka Yamamoto.

Amano died towards the end of World War II in a bombing raid at the age of 38. His *History of quantum mechanics* is a logical chronology from old quantum theory (including black-body radiation) to the establishment of quantum theory and the proposition of the reciprocity (reversion) principle. If Amano had survived the war, the description of twentieth-century physics history in Japan would have been phenomenally rich. It is impressive that as early as the 1940s he produced an epistemological study of quantum theory that is comparable to similar books in the West.

Tetsu Hiroshige was an excellent historian of physics who was active throughout the 1960s and early 1970s. In contrast to the inherent historical focus of this introductory chapter, his focus was to approach history from a socio-historical, extrinsic perspective that was influenced by the Minka group. Not unlike Amano, Hiroshige also died too soon, but from disease. He wrote *Sengo nihon no kagaku undō* (Scientific trends in postwar Japan, 1960), *Kagaku to rekishi* (Science and history, 1965), *Kagaku no shakai shi* (A social history of science, 1973), and *Kindai kagaku saikō* (Rethinking modern science, 1979). Let's look specifically at *Scientific trends in postwar Japan*. Hiroshige's writing was motivated by a sense of crisis that postwar scientific trends were essentially the same as during the much criticized wartime state system, when science was involved in state power, and that these trends were not responding to the incorporation of science into the monopoly capitalist system that had been apparent since the mid-1950s. Scientists must have a different sense of purpose and values than merely to extol the virtues of rationalism: for example, the welfare of the people. Given this mindset, Hiroshige described the general trends of the postwar Japan in four parts: (i) the trial period of recovery efforts in the midst of the chaos immediately following the war, (ii) the deflationary period following the Dodge Line, (iii) the reconstruction period after 1952, and (iv) the popularity of science and engineering. As discussed above, he believes institutional problems facing science in Japan emerged from the mid-1950s. He emphasized the Association of Democratic Scientists (Minka) as a concrete organization, as well as theories of elementary particles and nuclear issues as fields of research, attempting individual analyses of them. The central idea of this discussion is physics, but this is not only due to Hiroshige's particular area of expertise, but also because of the enormous presence that physics had in the academic world at that time. Hiroshige's ideal regarding the autonomy of science from politics, as well as his awareness of its compromise when that autonomy collapses, are still relevant topics today. Moreover, it should be noted that such a discursive space could be most apparent in physics at that time, while a similar dynamic had occurred since the 1970s in biology and medicine. In this sense, it is no exaggeration to say that the work of Hiroshige, far from being obsolete, is even increasing in relevance today.

The fourth chapter of Hiroshige's *Science and history* is entitled "An Overview of Science during the Showa Period: The Modernization of the System of Scientific Research." Although offered as an introduction to science history in the Showa Period, it treats the prewar and postwar periods not separately but as one continuous historical process. Hiroshige's attempt to see the "history of science as a social phenomenon" (p. 141) is worth mentioning as one of his great accomplishments, though it is not necessarily related to the history of scientific thought. As I just described, Hiroshige's important approach was to show the fact that modernization (in this context, a strengthening of mutual cooperation between science and technology) had virtually started in the 1930s; thus he refused to jump on the postwar bandwagon that held that pre-modernism dominated science before the end of World War II. As one example, Hiroshige emphasized the founding of the Japan Society for the Promotion of Science in 1932. The back and forth of ideas surrounding the establishment of the framework for research a few years after the war—for example, the establishment of the Science Council of Japan—was also discussed. Hiroshige discovered an array of important facts when he decided to emphasize the institutional basis for producing knowledge rather than merely knowledge itself. In that sense, this is a supreme socio-scientific analysis. I can't help but feel we lost this promising young genius too early.

Yoshitaka Yamamoto has had an interesting career—though a proponent of academism, he has elected not to pursue an academic position. This has been considered a disadvantage in the history of science research field, specifically because success in the field relies on the very laborious collection of literature and access to primary documents. Yamamoto's work includes *Jūryoku to rikigaku teki sekai* (Gravity and the mechanical world, 1981), *Netsugaku shisō no shiteki tenkai* (The historical development of thermological thought, 1987), *Koten rikigaku no keisei* (The Formation of classical mechanics, 1997), *Jiryoku to jūryoku no hakken* (The discovery of magnetic force and gravity, 2003), and *Jūrokuseiki bunka kakumei* (The sixteenth-century cultural revolution, 2007). All of these works are epic, and recently *The discovery of magnetic force and gravity* became a bestseller, something uncommon in this field. It is good to see the success of a man of unyielding spirit like Yamamoto. He causes you to reflect on your position as an academic. The three-volume *The discovery of magnetic force and gravity* especially explores the shifting Western concepts of force, especially magnetic force. Yamamoto clearly states that he wrote this work because conventional narratives of the history of physics focused on successful, orthodox theories, while ignoring other elements such as the quasi-magical worldview which also affected modern mechanics. He therefore intended to supply the missing parts. This idea is what I referred to as "a scientific history of alterity" in my *Kagaku shisō shi* (History of scientific thought, Kanamori 2010b), and actually it is not so rare an attitude in the study of scientific history. Yamamoto traced this process from antiquity to the end of the scientific revolution with a focus on the development of magnetism. If one feels that the closer he gets to the present, the more dull his arguments become, perhaps this can be chalked up to the fact that he used to be a scientist himself.[55]

(3) In terms of the history of chemistry, we should mention Mitsuo Hara, whom we discussed earlier, Masaji Kubo's *Kagaku shi* (A history of chemistry, 1949–50), Minoru Tanaka's *Kindai kagaku shi* (A history of modern chemistry, 1954), Nozomu Yamaoka's *Kagaku shi den* (A tale of the history of chemistry, 1968) and *Kagaku shi sō* (A window on the history of chemistry, 1971), Yoshito Takeuchi's

Kagaku no rekishi (A history of chemistry, 1973), *Kagaku no oitachi* (The rise of chemistry, 1992) and *Kagaku shi* (History of chemistry, 1993), Chikayoshi Kamatani's *Nihon kindai kagaku kōgyō no seiritsu* (*The establishment of Japanese modern chemical industry*, 1989), and Nagayasu Shimao's *Jimbutsu kagaku shi* (A biographical history of scientists, 2002). Given the fact that chemistry essentially has strong ties to industry, its historical exploration could be a secondary concern. On the contrary, however, the history of chemistry has been a thriving academic discipline for quite a long time. This may be because alchemy—which existed just before the rise of modern science and outlined a particular kind of knowledge that lay in the interstices between science and non-science—naturally draws interest. Yamaoka was actively engaged in education as a high school teacher, and in his long career which started back in the Taisho Period he wrote *Kagaku shi hitsu* (Scribblings on the history of chemistry, 1976) and *Kagaku shi jin* (Dust from the history of chemistry, 1978), among others, in addition to the above-mentioned two books. In this normally sober field, Yamaoka's contribution in the spread of culture merits praise. At one time, I studied chemical history extensively and I fondly remember being accurately guided by and enthralled with Yamaoka's texts. Yamaoka highlighted not only the scientific contributions of Cavendish, Bunsen, etc. but also the human qualities of each of these thinkers.

Kamatani's *The establishment of Japanese modern chemical industry*, more than just a history of scientific thought, should perhaps be considered strictly in the context of industrial history; I mention it because in some sense it represents the ideals of the history of chemistry. Its chronology traces the development of Japan's inorganic chemical industry from the close of the Edo Period through the Meiji Period. The major players are discussed, such as government-run factories involved in the development of mass production of chemical industrial products, along with the processes employed in the lead chamber process for the production of sulfuric acid or the Leblanc process for producing sodium carbonate. This book offers an empirically-based recollection of how, by as early as the second decade of the Meiji Period, the production of these substances had created a foundation sufficient to carry the burden of Japan's domestic industrial activities. If we can consider "history of chemistry as a history of scientific thought," it would be based on Kamatani's kind of work like this one, and that is also why it is an important contribution.[56]

(4) Akira Yuasa's *Seibutsugaku shi* (A history of biology, 1952), Yōjirō Kimura's

Shīboruto to Nihon no shokubutsu (Siebold and Japanese plants, 1981), *Nachurari-suto no keifu* (The genealogy of naturalists, 1983), and *Seibutsugaku shi ronshū* (A collection of theses on the history of biology, 1987), Teiri Nakamura's *Seibutsuga-ku to shakai* (Biology and society, 1970) and *Seibutsugaku no rekishi* (A history of biology, 1983), Kei Nagano's *Hen'yō suru seibutsugaku* (Transforming biology, 1993), and Yoshimi Kawade's *Seibutsu kigō ron* (Biosemiotics, 2006) are key works in the literature on the history of biology.

Nakamura was long active in the history of the biology research group in the biology section of the Democratic Scientists Association (Minka). He focused on the seventeenth century biology research of William Harvey; at the same time, he was deeply involved with the problems of Trofim Denisovich Lysenko from his early days, exhibiting a sharp political awareness.[d] Nakamura's *Biology and society* is a collection of papers, all augmented with keen political sensibilities, that is of a different nature from normal historical research. In particular, Nakamura already made the insightful prediction in the 1960s that modern biology would be increasingly integrated into the profit motive of the capitalist system, and that this profit motive would affect the direction of research. For instance, in "Four impressive meetings held in the summer of 1964" (pp. 246–260), Nakamura succinctly describes that atmosphere. This text was particularly prophetic, given the explosion in biotechnology that marked the opening years of the 1970s. It is debatable whether subsequent histories of biology have inherited the same concerns as Nakamura, something that must surely cause him chagrin.

I feel a quiet joy that a work like Kawade's *Biosemiotics* was made in Japan. Normally, such a work might be more appropriate as a discussion of biological philosophy rather than a history of biology. While Kawade's background is in molecular biology, a field distinguished by its mechanistic and analytical perspective on life, he takes the view that living things are entities that embrace independence. Instead of characterizing the interaction of the organism and the environment as a purely physical relationship, Kawade recognizes the imposition of a certain kind of meaning for the organism. In that context, he envisions a kind of biological semiotics as a science that recognizes certain meanings behind phenomena. More specifically, he interprets the transmission of information within an organism—for example that in the nervous system and the immune system—in a semantic fashion. At the end of the argument, Kawade looks to an original biological philosophy that connects biological and symbolic realms. Paradoxical though it may be, this theory of biological semiotics sought to sublimate the concept of life at a molecular biology level, which was only possible by an accomplished scholar of molecular biology. This work can be viewed as a laborious undertaking offering the beginnings of another kind of theory of life.

I have one more additional remark concerning biological history in general. As is well known, biology is a field that has seen a great deal of academic progress since the latter half of the twentieth century. In particular, the biotechnology that has been progressively developing since the 1970s has created technologies we have never seen before, causing us to rethink a host of new problems. It appears that the history of biology in Japan has yet to accurately reflect these changes. It seems obvious that biotechnology is not merely a subject for historical description but an extremely complex subject containing a variety of intellectual, philosophical and social problems. In the future, it will be necessary to write philosophies of biotechnology and histories of scientific thought centered on biotechnology.

(5) There are also many individuals who work primarily in the history of medicine. For instance, the following authors and works serve as representative samples of the various historical eras:[57] Yū Fujikawa's *Nihon igaku shi* (A history of Japanese medicine, 1904[58]), Seishū Ogawa's *Seiyō igaku shi* (A history of western medicine, 1943), Kiyotsune Inoue's *Igaku shi gaisetsu* (An introduction to the history of medicine, 1968), Toshirō Hattori's *Edo jidai igaku shi no kenkyū* (A study on the history of medicine in the Edo Period, 1978), Shizu Sakai's *Nihon no iryō shi* (Japanese history of medicine, 1982), Shun'ichi Yamamoto's *Nihon korera shi* (A history of cholera in Japan, 1982), Takeshi Kawakami's *Gendai nihon byōnin shi* (A modern history of Illness in Japan, 1982), Hajime Sōda's *Zusetsu Nihon iryō bunka shi* (An illustrated history of Japanese medical culture, 1989), and Shōji Tatsukawa's *Yamai no ningen shi* (A human history of disease, 1989).[59]

Hattori covered Japan before the Meiji period, giving us vast quantities of material on the Nara, Heian, Kamakura, Muromachi, and Edo Periods. Here, let us look at *Muromachi Azuchi Momoyama jidai igaku shi no kenkyū* (Studies on medical history from the Muromachi to the Azuchi-Momoyama Period, 1971); although voluminous, it is enjoyable because it is multi-layered and multi-faceted. The book contains discussion of contemporary diets, excerpts of medical descriptions in diaries, summaries of representative medical books of the various eras, and the introduction of Christian medicine to Japan. Towards the end, it discusses the personalities and causes of death of Ashikaga shoguns and the personality of Oda Nobunaga. This era served as a bridge between Japan's feudal era and modern times, an era that saw contact with the West through Christianity, and an age in which there was little respite from war. For this reason, the Sengoku Period was particularly noteworthy for its battlefield surgeons. One impression is that the diet of that time is surprisingly like that of the present. I actually smiled when I found that people at that time seemed to drink a lot of alcohol. Overall, despite the fact that it is professional literature, the concrete nature of the examples and animated description make it a lively history book. We should look forward with anticipation to the arrival of younger researchers who will produce something comparable to these five books, from the Nara Period through the Edo Period.

Kawakami's *A modern history of Illness in Japan* is a massive complement to his own *Gendai Nihon iryō shi* (Modern history of medicine in Japan, 1965). This text treats disease as a social problem from the perspective of those who are sick; social context, treatment and discrimination related to disease, and the reactions of healthy people are discussed. It deals with both the social context of medicine as well as the history of medicine. Cholera, tuberculosis, Hansen's disease (leprosy), and psychosis are picked as particularly important diseases, and even relatively rare ones such as trachoma make an appearance. This book is indeed voluminous with high documentary value. While engaging in clinical activities with a strong sense of social justice, Kawakami also put together enormous books. He went far beyond the frame of a history of scientific thought.[60]

Here I would like to separately describe the work of four other scholars: Hisayuki Omodaka, Yonezō Nakagawa, Bin Kimura, and Yoshio Kawakita.

First, we should describe the work of Hisayuki Omodaka as philosophy of medicine rather than as history of medicine. Against the backdrop of the French school of philosophy on the theory of life, as can be seen in the work of Bergson, Omodaka tried to articulate an Eastern tradition of medical thought in his three-volume *Igaku gairon* (An introduction to medical science, 1959); it represents a unique contribution to the literature in Japan. Each volume corresponds to one aspect of analysis: the first volume concerns science, the second volume is about the life sciences in particular, and the third volume concerns medicine. Here we will specifically focus on the second part. Omodaka had a firm Cartesian base, but he did not merely reiterate Cartesian dualism. He looks at both spirit and body as actually existing together, and offers his own approach to the issue. If the spiritual world is represented by A, and the material world by B, then the product of the two is C, C being equal to alpha times beta. In this case alpha is not the same as A, since alpha and beta are inseparable. Likewise, beta is not the same as B. Omodaka calls

alpha energy (*ki*) and beta the form (*tai*). The human body is a monad composed
of the dualism of energy (*ki*) and form (*tai*). Omodaka devotes a large part of the
second volume to elucidating C. First he analyses the mind and body as something
neither identical nor different. With this elucidated, the story turns towards the
organism and the environment. The energy (*ki*) arises when organisms depart
from the environment and become more internally mature. Because it does not
happen all at once, the entire process can be looked at over time. The process of
extrapolation of alpha is philosophically called individuation, and Omodaka reflects that it is a kind of "uncomfortable gratitude" (*arigatasa*) of being thrown
into solitary existence. Such a conceptual argument is constructed in the second
part on which the entire remaining argument is built. The medical discussions of
the third volume, even when discussing health and disease theory, harken back to
this original Cartesian framework and the concept of individuation. It is more
accurate to say that this unique ontology of the body represents more a philosophy
of medicine than a general medical history. Omodaka was a sort of Japanese
Georges Canguilhem; it is unfortunate that there is not more work like his.

An important person in this intellectual tradition during the next generation is
Yonezō Nakagawa. His works include *Igaku no bemmei* (a justification of medicine, 1964) and *Iryō teki ninshiki no tankyū* (An Exploration into medical epistemology, 1975). In *An Exploration into medical epistemology*, Nakagawa discusses
the harmful effects of blindly regarding the growing medical sciences as a branch
of science from a variety of perspectives. It emphasizes that seeing the sick patient
as opposed to just the disease is the ultimate goal. In the practice of medicine, the
physician may seem to have the authority to decide things, but this is but a pre-
tense arising from the nature of the practice; the person who requests the practice
is the ultimate actor. Nakagawa's perspective here is far from any sort of anti-sci-
entific stance that denies the scientific validity of medicine, but he coherently attempts to warn us about the current overly scientific nature of medical education.
However, when he took up specific statements within a plethora of individual citations, the central drift of his argument appears to have lost its focus. Rather
taking this book as a whole, it makes more sense to delve into its individual parts.
And even though we are more than thirty years out from the book's original publication, the medical community seems not to have taken Nakagawa's assertions to
heart. Indeed, the field of bioethics has taken on increasing importance around
the world and, belatedly in Japan as well, beginning during the latter half of the
1980s. Nevertheless, that was in response to a kind of external pressure; how much

the medical community considered the tradition of a sincere self-critique as Na-kagawa had engaged in is hard to see from outside the medical community. Not only in the case of Nakagawa, but also in the case of Omodaka discussed previous-ly, I have a strong impression that no scholar has yet completed a sufficient analy-sis. The history of medicine, the philosophy of medicine, and bioethics are separate and distinct from one another. The types of conceptual challenges that each field faces are segmented within each separate subject area; the task of fol-lowing it all is indeed formidable, yet indispensable for the future. Given such excellent predecessors as Omodaka and Nakagawa, it is very unfortunate that there is not more attention paid to the philosophy of medicine in Japan.

Bin Kimura is a psychiatrist, but, early in his career he committed himself to the analysis of Being (*Daseinsanalysis*) of Ludwig Binswanger, and wrote a great deal at the intersection of philosophy and psychiatry. Psychiatry (in Japanese, *seishin igaku*, or the medical study of the "spirit," *seishin*), is a branch of medicine that studies the mind, and to that extent it has a strong relationship with philoso-phy. There are many psychiatrists in Japan who, like Kimura, have a deep knowl-edge of philosophy. Anyway, there is no doubt that Kimura can speak in general terms for the profession. Although his collected works (2001) exist, I would like to mention specifically *Jikan to jiko* (Time and the self, 1982). Drawing attention to the ontological difference between objects and ideas, Kimura considers that time is a phenomenon that has certain idea-like characteristics. After confirming this, he tries to model the abnormal experience of time in psychiatric patients: patients with schizophrenia are reported to have a conception of time as *ante festum* (the night before a festival), or a constant impulse to anticipate the future; patients with depression tend to have a conception of time as *post festum* (after the festi-val), or a tendency to dwell on the past. Patients with epilepsy or manias, whose experience of time was characterized by the dominance of the present are de-scribed as imbued with a time structure of *intra festum* (during the festival). Kimura's performance is a model of the philosophy of psychiatry that will contin-ue to tower over Japan's academic history for a long time into the future. This situation remains essentially unchanged even now, as we see the ascendency of biology within psychiatry.

The final individual to discuss is Yoshio Kawakita. Because we are in the same field, I had the opportunity to meet him several times, and being in the presence of such rigorous scholarship humbled me. I remember him freely lending me valuable texts in European languages. While having an air of purity, Kawakita's attitude toward work had a rigorous academic flavor. Twenty years ago, I confessed, "I just started studying the history of medicine." With a wry smile, he offered me warm support. I feel too embarrassed to face him now, given my lack of serious work thereafter. Examples of Kawakita's work include *Kansen ron* (On infection, 1964), *Pasutūru* (Pasteur, 1967), *Kindai igaku no shieki kiban* (The historical basis of modern medicine, 1977), and *Igaku gairon* (An introduction to medicine, 1982). In particular, *The historical basis of modern medicine* is a tome worthy of a life's work, providing an ideal model of describing histories of medicine. This book is a monumental work, to be sure, but perhaps because it overflows with Kawakita's scientific knowledge, one gets the sense that explanation is often incomplete, which is frustrating at times. In any case, this corpus provides a solid foundation for the discipline even now.[61]

(6) With all the authors and titles I have mentioned, readers must be exhausted, but I would like you to stay with me a bit longer. To repeat, this chapter aims to single out texts and authors in a field-specific way. Below I want to mention briefly the history of science in the Far Eastern cultural zone, including Japan.

The first Japanese historian of science to discuss is Mitsukuni Yoshida. His works include *Nihon kagaku shi* (A history of science in Japan, 1955) and *Nihon gijutsu shi kenkyū* (a study on the history of technology in Japan, 1961). A history of science in Japan is a history of soft science which explores the ancient understanding of nature in Japan through the analysis of poetry and literary works. It has been more than fifty years since it was published, and this text still remains a classic. Particularly in the first chapter, the exploration of ancient Japanese works, such as *The Kojiki: Records of Ancient Matters*, *Nihongi: Chronicles of Japan from the Earliest Times to AD 697*, and *The Ten Thousand Leaves* reveals a view of nature, the attitude of clear natural contemplation, and the nature-centered lyricism that the ancient Japanese held. This is an especially noteworthy aspect of this entire text. Although it continues up until the Meiji period, the strength of this book is the sheer volume of descriptions from ancient to early modern times. The example of characterizing matters in a Japanese understanding of nature is a motif repeated throughout the text many times. For better or worse, this book is an exemplary performance in the history of science and the cultural history of Japan. It has become a classic that must be passed on to subsequent generations.[62]

Among histories of Chinese science are massive works of Kiyoshi Yabuuchi, which include *Kinsei tenmongaku shi* (The early-modern history of astronomy,

1947), *Chūgoku no tenmongaku* (Astronomy in China, 1949), *Chūgoku kodai no kagaku* (Science in ancient China, 1964), *Chūgoku no tenmon rekihō* (Astronomical ephemeris in China, 1969), and *Chūgoku no kagaku bunmei* (Scientific civilization in China, 1970). Keiji Yamada has a deep knowledge of both Japan and China. Among his works dealing with China, are *Shushi no shizengaku* (Zhu Xi's study of nature, 1978) and *Chūgoku igaku no kigen* (The origin of Chinese medicine, 1999); works such as *Kuroi kotoba no kūkan* (The space of black words, 1988) concern the history of Japanese thought. Michio Yano is a real heavyweight in Indian histories of science, with works that include *Mikkyō sensei jutsu* (Astrology of esoteric Buddhism, 1986), *Indo sūgaku kenkyū* (A study on Indian mathematics, 1997), and *Hoshi uranai no bunka kōryū shi* (The history of cultural relations in astrology, 2004).

Yabuuchi was for many years an important member of the National Institute for the Humanities at Kyoto University. In addition to his central area of expertise in the Chinese astrological calendar, he also wrote other explanatory books, one of which is *Science in ancient China*. Normally, when talking of world history of science, it is customary to start from Greece and then move directly to a focus on modern European developments. Although the contributions of Islamic civilization to science have been recognized recently, interest in the history of science and technology in China is still relatively low. Yabuuchi offers his explanatory volumes to fill the cultural gap as much as possible. Although the scope of *Science in ancient China* extends only as far as the Tang Dynasty chronologically, it represents a concise summary of ancient Chinese science in a wide range of fields, such as astronomy, medicine, and technology. Particularly noteworthy is the attention paid to Chinese civilization's particular type of autonomy or self-centeredness, which also gives it a relative isolation from other civilizations. In any case, Yabuuchi must have been tantalized by the fact that the majority of Chinese histories of science have been written by Westerners such as Joseph Needham. The historical relationship between China and Japan has been deep; Japanese researchers should be more involved in elucidating this history through scholarship, in the manner of Yabuuchi. *Scientific civilization in China* is a sequel of sorts to *Science in ancient China* that took Chinese scientific history to the present day.[63]

Yamada's *The space of black words* is a kind of biography of one of the most original thinkers of the Edo Period, Baien Miura. Yamada uniquely describes how Miura took an independent perspective and promoted the Chinese notions of dual cosmic forces, yin and yang, to an extreme, establishing his own original natural science. In place of the traditional conception of the five elements, he attempts to apply the yin and yang dichotomy to all things, working from the philosophy of Ki. After an overview of the scholarly, rather mundane life of Miura, Yamada centers on a detailed introduction of his major work: *Gengo* (*Deep Words*, including various versions). This work is overwhelming and powerful; I remember feeling dizzy after reading it.[64] As a layman when it comes to this period, I am unable to guess what a history of scientific thought in the Edo period would look like. Still, *The space of black words* shows that there are many unexplored themes in Japanese intellectual history and the history of science in Japan.

(7) I must omit neither Shōji Ijiri nor Kiyonobu Itakura.

Although a renowned geologist, Shōji Ijiri also embarked on a deep contemplation of Hegel for a time. Over a long period Ijiri held an important position as an academic authority within the Geological Society of Japan.[65] Let's examine his *Shimpan kagaku ron* (Science studies: A new edition, 1977). His work in this genre was one of the subsequent developments in the wake of Yuiken. Across the world, I doubt there are many geologists like Ijiri who have engaged in such profound, philosophical scholarship. The first half of *Science studies: A new edition* is divided largely into sections on methodology and epistemology. Ijiri classifies scientific methodology into seven different methods from low-order to high-order, comprising experiential methods, described methods, classifying methods, logical methods, theoretical methods, experimental methods, and contingent methods. Intuitively, geology can be understood as being more centered on descriptive aspects than other branches of physics; thus it is understandable how experimental methods might come near the end of the list. Also, there is the notable feature of contingent methods being last. In being assembled from things that require secondary conditions, and focusing on the situation-dependent nature of phenomena, this method is somewhat at odds with claims of "the inevitability of nature." In any case, I find it very interesting that due to his knowledge of the field, the characteristics of the science of geology have affected the author both explicitly and implicitly in constructing his theories of science. I believe Ijiri was sensitive to the domain-specific nature of individual sciences reflecting the differences of their objects, rather than contriving just one general approach.

Although this deviates slightly from our notion of the *histoire des sciences*, next I would like to look at the work of Kiyonobu Itakura, who theoretically guided science education together with Hiraku Toyama for a certain period after World

War II. The postwar science education reached a peak from the second half of the 1950s to the early 1970s. It was a counter to the previously prevailing norm of basing children's scientific knowledge on their ongoing experience of the world. More specifically, there was criticism of the "life unit learning" that was touted as a standard at the time. Itakura's *Kagaku to hōhō* (Science and methodology, 1969), *Kagaku to kasetsu* (Science and hypotheses, 1971a), and *Kagaku to shakai* (Science and society, 1971b) are important works that exemplify the kind of discussion of the day. At one point in time, Itakura's classes in hypothetical experiments had many devotees.

Apropos, although unrelated to science education, from the perspective of a chronology of scientific thought I would like to discuss Itakura's *Mohō no jidai* (The period of imitation, 1988). This describes the history of beriberi, which raged throughout the nation after the Meiji Period until the notion of vitamins reached Japan. The text serves as both a prehistory of the concept of vitamins, and it is also an excellent social history of the same era. Of most interest is Itakura's point that where beriberi most ferociously raged in the army and elsewhere, successful hypothesis-based symptomatic treatments like wheat diets were not given much credit by doctors who studied modern medicine. The resulting damage may have long-lasting: it is a well-known fact that decisions by Rintarō Mori (later known as Ōgai Mori) impeded the establishment of effective treatments for beriberi. This provides a good example of how the conflict between scientific understanding of disease and empirical treatment of disease were not helpful to the patient. *The period of imitation* may be considered an ancillary work in the career of Itakura, but I personally believe it to be one of his masterpieces.

*

At the risk of causing reader fatigue, I have so far gone over a great deal of the literature in these fields. As is already obvious, the history of science is the accumulation of the specific achievements in each individual area, which have made their own specializations. That is to say, the history of science itself, parting from any sort of justification for events from contemporary ages, has the unique feature of disclosing individual and specific analyses on the history of science. How much and to what extent the history of science reflects the elements of the histories of scientific thought requires a separate, detailed analysis and cannot be subject to hasty judgment. Nevertheless, even the document-based field of scientific history today, seemingly obsessed with the excavation of primary documents and factual description, involves an implicit selection process of historical facts. Because certain value judgments and assumptions are behind the selection process, the history of science, if it has reached a certain level at all, also contains some elements of the history of thought. However, we would go too far if we called all the aforementioned individual histories of science a history of scientific thought. Indeed, the more the details of scientific history are analyzed, the more the theoretical assumptions behind them emerge, but I believe the difference between histories of science focusing on research of documentary records and histories of scientific thought lies in the extent to which they set a value on the description of facts.

Of course, I do not intend to downplay the importance and the role of documentary records. I would like to confirm here that there was a solid translation of the primary literature that comprised a groundbreaking series with excellent commentary: in the 1980s, a series of twenty-one volumes called *Kagaku no meicho* (Fine books on science, Itō 1980–1989) was published. This should be one of the indications of the maturation of science history in Japan. It is only too obvious that a dense analysis of the original texts is necessary in order to decipher the history of science in a constructive way and clarify the delicate cultural context in which the originals were written. In many cases, the discourse space for histories of scientific thought is quite removed from readings of the primary texts, but this is not meant to downplay the significance of reading a primary text itself. Twenty or thirty years have elapsed since the publishing of *Fine books on science*, but to this day it continues to be an essential instruction manual for understanding Gilbert, Virchow, and Bernard, among others. It is regrettable that there have not been any translations of a comparable undertaking since that time.

3. The Rise of Paradigms

Along with the postwar factual accumulation of *histoire des sciences*, there was a current more proper to the history of scientific thought. Although other commentators may have a different perspective, I would say the most important development in the history of scientific thought after World War II is the rise of the idea of paradigms and of a new philosophy of science.

(1) This new philosophy of science began quietly with the birth of the concept of

the scientific revolution. That well-known concept is evident in the historian Herbert Butterfield's *The Origins of Modern Science* (1949), a chronology of the revolutionary developments in modern mechanics from Copernicus through Kepler, Galileo, and Newton. These developments that occurred in Europe from about the mid-sixteenth century through to the start of eighteenth century would have a seismic impact on world history. Although *The Origins of Modern Science* itself was not translated into Japanese until 1978, it was known among Japanese science historians well before then. For example, the discussion that takes place in *Kagaku kakumei* (Scientific revolution, 1961), edited by Mitsutomo Yuasa and others, was based on the original concept. Nevertheless, around the world as well as within Japan, it was the publication of Thomas Kuhn's *The Structure of Scientific Revolutions* (1962) that allowed the concept of revolutionary science to spread beyond the specific area of the history of science. Soon the concept of paradigm shift became a common term among a wide range of academic disciplines. Kuhn's idea denied the sequential view of science according to which, the inductive accumulation of scientific knowledge in each era is viewed from within a common theoretical framework. He introduced the idea of a paradigm as a particular framework for conceptualizing scientific knowledge that dominates a certain area for a period of time. In ordinary times, science will carry out routine work within the dominant paradigm. If everything operates smoothly under a particular paradigm, that paradigm will remain intact. However, if within the course of this ordinary research several phenomena arise that the dominant paradigm cannot explain, or if scientists cast light on a new meaning of phenomena that have been largely neglected, the paradigm itself will be reexamined. Sometimes theoretical upheaval engenders a new paradigm. This process is called a scientific revolution. Thus, the concept of scientific revolution, taken together with the idea of the paradigm theory, has replaced the simple scientific periodicity of Butterfield with a more structural understanding of scientific change. This led to the understanding that a scientific revolution is applicable to any time and in any area, not only to the period when modern mechanics was developed. Also, the concept was subject to the interpretation that, in a given area, paradigm A and paradigm B were entirely different phenomena, comprised of entirely different sets of foundational claims and terminology, and it made little sense to question which was superior. This is an issue of incommensurability. While it became entangled in the controversies of relativism, it was still a much-debated idea. Furthermore, I would say that at the time, Kuhn himself was opposed to discussions of incommensurability in the stronger sense of possessing relativistic implications.

In any case, in the United States and Europe from the mid-1960s and in Japan from the 1971 translation of Kuhn, it is difficult to deny that the idea of paradigm shifts, as well as the concept of scientific revolution as a structural understanding of scientific change, served to revitalize many related areas of the history of science and the philosophy of science. While this new paradigm theory intersects with the classic sociology of science of Robert Merton, in essence it partly comprises a sociology of scientific knowledge (SSK) that at its heart asserts that not only scientists, but scientific knowledge itself, reflects the social background of the contemporary era. Looking forward, the social studies of science and technology, especially in Europe and the United States in the 1980s, continued to radicalize discussion. Eventually, this led to vigorous rebuttal from scientists in the 1990s and the outbreak of the so-called science wars. For more details surrounding these events, please see my book *Saiensu wōzu* (Science wars, 2000a). For better or for worse, Kuhn's theory of scientific revolutions became material for a great number of debates within the history of science and the philosophy of science for several decades after its publication.[66]

(2) We got a little bit ahead of ourselves there. In the twenty or so years immediately following the translation of *The Structure of Scientific Revolutions* into Japanese in 1971, there were many individual scholars who made contributions to the history of scientific thought. In particular, I would like to touch upon four such individuals.

First, Shigeru Nakayama is the scholar who translated Kuhn's book into Japanese. Nakayama was actively involved in scholarship through participating in, for instance, *Kagaku shi* (History of science, 1967) by Isao Sugimoto (ed.); but his introduction to Kuhn preceded more vigorous academic activities. He wrote *Ten no kagaku shi* (The history of science of the heavens, 1984a), *Shimin no tame no kagaku ron* (On science for citizens, 1984b), *Kagaku gijutsu no sengo shi* (The postwar history of science and technology, 1995), among other works, and became well-known worldwide. Also, from the mid-1990s, he began to publish *Tsūshi nihon no kagaku gijutsu* (A historical overview of Japanese science and technology, 1995–1999), an important historical overview of a broad range of industry trends that brought together a large number of disparate researchers. A work of this scale, spanning topics related to the history of science and the history of industry, was unprecedented, and it has not been equaled since. Nakayama, along with physics historian Kunio Gotō, Hitoshi Yoshioka and others, played a key role in overseeing the entire endeavor. *On science for citizens* includes a number of interesting essays. For instance, "Ochikobore no kagaku ron" (On science for dropouts, pp. 7–22) concerns the process of knowledge production in the fields of science and technology and how this process inevitably becomes fiercely competitive and challenging, thus producing many discouraged dropouts. Cutting-edge scientific or technological knowledge is difficult for the lay public to fully comprehend, and in the case of corporate or military controlled knowledge, even the principle of openness that pervades other aspects of science is missing. In such cases, the first line of defense may be the assessment by citizens. However, this evaluation process could be a mere tragedy without any intellectual joy for a member of the lay public caught up in a debate on the placement of nuclear power plants, for example. In the first place, Nakayama says, rather than proceeding from the premise that science and technology are rapidly advancing, we should start from the perspective of ordinary life.

It was also an expression of his reservation concerning the discussion that Japan should become a scientific and technological nation, on which a national dialogue was beginning at that time. Nakayama offers the concept of "Tozasareta enkan" (The closed circle, pp. 212–246) as his view of the sociology of science; therein, instead of a concept of a quasi-closed circular ring to represent the production structure of scientific knowledge, he proposes a perspective that focuses on the usage and evaluation structures of that knowledge, putting forth a triangulated model of science, consisting of academic science, systemized science, and science service. Academic science is the production of scientific knowledge based on evaluations and assessments among colleagues. Systemized science is concerned mostly with industrial uses—science that follows from the evaluation and usage of sponsor organizations. Finally, science service is the kind of science that is for public evaluation. Naturally, Nakayama was fully aware of the difficulties inherent in science service, and the structural problems of this remain even today. However, the ideal is well worth upholding. This perspective is not anti-science, but it is the perspective of a science historian with a critical consciousness. It can be said to be a politically reasonable and orderly program. Nakayama's attitude is vigorous; he was never satisfied with his contribution to Japanese academics of introducing Kuhn; rather, he continues to work internationally even though he has reached a very advanced age. I have a great deal of respect for this kind of energy.[e]

The second person I would like to discuss is Yōichirō Murakami, who is known beyond the scientific community. Amid the popularity of the notion of paradigms through the field of the history of science, Murakami most forcefully argued that one of the theoretical implications of incommensurability was to deny the unambiguous determinism between the empirical observations and their theoretical interpretations. Some believe that a theory exists for the purpose of explaining phenomena, but when new facts or observations emerge that cannot be explained by theory A, an experiment is conducted and that experiment will result in the complete refutation of that theory. But this idea is not supported by historical facts. Theories can launch a sort of auxiliary device that prevents them from ever seeming to fail. When theory A fails, or when theory A is replaced by theory B, it is more accurate to say that it is superseded by the complex summation of multiple factors than by an unbiased rebuttal in light of facts or phenomena. There is definitely room for discussion as to whether we can identify the structure of paradigm shift with irrational or psychosocial processes. In any case, Murakami observed that the simplistic positivist idea that a theory becomes sustainable through verification, or collapses through rebuttal, could not explain the history of science, and this was taken as an important assertion, actively driving further scholarship in this area. Murakami was actively involved in the introduction of Paul Feyerabend, Norwood Russell Hanson's famous notion that observation is biased by theory, and of Kuhn himself. Over the decade or so starting in the late 1970s, these ideas featured prominently in Japanese history of science and philosophy of science, and became collectively known at the new philosophy of science.

Of Murakami's prolific body of work, I would like to highlight here: *Kindai kagaku to seizoku kakumei* (Modern science and the revolution of the sacred and the profane, 1976), *Atarashii kagaku ron* (The new theory of science, 1979a), *Kagaku to nichijōsei no bunmyaku* (The context of science and the quotidian, 1979b), *Kagaku shi no gyaku enkinhō* (The inverted perspective of the history of science, 1982), *Bunmei no naka no kagaku* (Science within civilization, 1994a), and *Kagakusha to wa nanika* (What is a scientist?, 1994b). *Modern science and the revolution of the sacred and the profane* calls into question the historical perspective that takes continuity after the scientific revolution for granted, and foregrounds the discontinuity inherent in modern science. Murakami calls that discontinuity the revolution of the sacred/profane distinction. Specifically, he gives a historical retrospective regarding the gradual development and implications of the idea that the mind of God is expressed clearly in the natural world—that is, the idea that knowing Nature is to arrive at Truth, and thus we don't need God. It was the secularization of truth and knowledge. To make his point, he conducts an analysis of eighteenth-century thought that adds depth to modern intellectual history.

In the first half of *The context of science and the quotidian*, there is a subtle analysis of the structure of the everyday world and our way of living in it. The context-dependent notion of object recognition by understanding a variety of things while positioning them within an unconscious context is elucidated. Murakami first analyzes the context in relation to objects and then to people. For example, the contextual-bound and binding mode of an ashtray are quite different from those of an accelerator. After describing the structure of the everyday world, Murakami then moves on to his main theme, an analysis of the scientific world. As is obvious in the example of the accelerator, it is natural that, when the scientific world and scientific objects are involved, the nature of the context becomes more important. Where the premises underlying knowledge are not shared, things that are in fact the same are not recognized as such. These relationships with the other within the scientific world have their own characteristic norms as well as unique self-structures. Although they are not often substantively distinct from the everyday world, there is frequently some functional distinction. In the everyday world, such objects have multilayered contexts. In the scientific world, theoretical language acquires meanings under certain codes. From an everyday perspective, Murakami argues that this theoretical language enjoys more syntax freedom, and that it cannot entirely shake off the background of everyday language; in some cases, it has a certain impact on the semantic meaning of everyday language and indeed fosters a complex interaction. In the process, Murakami attempts to construct a model whereby the theoretical language of science can be linked with the everyday world. This was Murakami's way to reserve judgment on the "thesis of the independence or the isolation of science" that was all the rage in the late 1970s, and that issue should be kept distinct from the debates on the sociology of science taking place in the West around the same time. It was a work of great originality and creativity.

It should be noted that in his early days Murakami also authored such interesting works of Japanese history of science as *Nihon kindai kagaku no ayumi* (The advancement of Japanese modern science, 1968), though he has a strong image as one of the adopters of the new philosophy of science. Also, in recent years, he completed works such as *Anzen gaku* (Safety science, 1998) and *Kōgaku no rekishi to gijutsu no rinri* (History of engineering and the ethics of technology, 2006), involved with the regulation school. Murakami is a refined gentleman with excellent cello skills, who has held concerts. He is mild-mannered and gentle, but he also shows an occasional austere glimpse of academic rigor that has impressed many subsequent scholars. When I had just entered my university training, I remember vividly the fascination I felt listening to Murakami's lectures. He has now passed seventy years of age, and continues to perform research at the forefront of the history of science.

Shuntarō Itō is the third person I would like to discuss. Itō has deep knowledge of the ancient history of science prior to the advent of modern mechanics and the non-European world of the middle ages, in particular Islamic history of science. Additionally, he attempts to present numerous viewpoints that generally capture the role played by the various major civilizations in world history. In short, Itō has a low-resolution perspective on the history of science, defined by a broad world-historic view on the dynamics of civilization. Of course, from the perspectives of the various experts in particular areas, this may give the impression at times of being too rough. But few individual writers can put out a broad historical view of the dynamics of various civilizations like Itō. He is justifiably well-regarded as an authority in comparative studies of civilizations. There is an atmosphere of dedicated scholarship that surrounds him, and contact with it leaves one feeling somehow purified. His way of opening discussion on an issue is clear and fair from beginning to end, and he also fully considers the perspectives of others. This holds not only for other leading academic authorities but also for young students. There are many people who love his inclusive personality. His works include *Bunmei ni okeru kagaku* (Science in civilizations, 1976), *Kindai kagaku no genryū* (Source of modern science, 1978), *Kagaku to genjitsu* (Science and reality, 1981), and *Shisōshi no naka no kagaku* (Science in the history of thought, 2002), with Murakami and others. *Science and reality* is a collection of essays, from which I would like to note "Kagaku teki hakken no ronri" (Logic of scientific discovery, pp. 235–261). As is seen in the examples of Reichenbach and Popper, etc., the standard philosophy of science that deals with scientific discovery can perform a posteriori reconstruction of why a certain creation was able to exist, but cannot deal with the developmental process of creation itself. This represents the so-called distinction between justification and discovery. He argues that discovery is a subject of psychology and sociology, not of scientific philosophy. Certainly there is no way to follow a particular procedure or algorithm in order to wind up with some great discovery or creation. However, on the contrary, Itō opposes regarding the creative as something totally irrational that should be attributable to intuition and coincidence, because there should be good reasons for bringing about creative hypotheses. It is not right to reduce the creative to purely psychological and sociological phenomena. To establish this argument, Itō goes back to the past, to the work of three men who studied the logic of discovery: Aristotle, Peirce and Hanson, in particular focusing on the *apagoge* of Aristotle. Peirce translated that idea as abduction. While abduction does not have an absolute certainty like deduction, it has the ability to expand thinking. Itō sees a certain type of revelatory thought there. Nevertheless, it is characteristic of Itō that he does not end there. He proposes a classification of methods of discovery in the background of facts related to the history of science—induction, deduction, and idea. Further, Itō created four sub-classifications under idea: analogous, universal, reductive, and systematic. Of course, the mechanical application of those categories will not result in the realization of new discoveries. Nevertheless, in this manner, he tries to explore abstract patterns in what is called the discovery of new perspectives. To reiterate, few individual writers can put out a grand view of civilizations as Itō can. However, it must not be forgotten that a wide range of discrete cases and a fair and objective analytical perspective underlie his views.

The fourth and final person is Masao Watanabe. He had a deep knowledge of the period concerning the establishment of modern dynamics, particularly Kepler and Newton, and he was the person who most exactly introduced the periodic concept of revolutionary science to Japan. This can be understood by reading, for example, *Bunka to shite no kindai kagaku* (Modern science as culture, 1991), in which Watanabe specifically demonstrates that when scientists made scientific inquires, they were led by the core notions of philosophical initiatives and religious concepts. Watanabe's works naturally reveal that binary formulas like "philosophy as empty speculation versus empirical science," or "religion that delves into the sacred world but pays little attention to nature versus scientists as free thinkers who regard religion as a useless shackle," oversimplify historical facts or are narrow scientific worldviews based on ideological bias. Science is itself a part of culture, tangled and interlaced with other complex cultural elements. There are many poets and writers who have been artistically inspired by contemporary science. To illustrate this point, Watanabe compiled *Amerika bungaku ni okeru kagaku shisō* (Scientific thought in American literature, 1974) and *Igirisu bungaku ni okeru kagaku shisō* (Scientific thought in British literature, 1983). His work was to bring the history of science closer to the history of culture, and in some sense embodied as an essential element in the history of scientific thought. *Scientific thought in American literature* specifically takes concrete works and thoughts from American writers and analyzes them in the context of the history of scientific thought. This work skillfully analyzes the thinking of writers such as Emerson, Hawthorne, and Poe on nature. This book contains the essay "Meruviru to kujira gaku" (Melville and the Study of Whales, pp. 145–172) by Eiko Kuroda. Melville, the great author of *Moby Dick*, had not received a formal scientific education. His career as a sailor allowed him to acquire an empirical, practical understanding of the science of whales. Historically, this era was also the peak of the whaling business. The thrust of *Moby Dick* concerns the fateful obsession of a boat captain to kill a white whale, as narrated by the protagonist, who is also on board. In the last battle against the white whale everyone except the narrator is killed. In order to break the monotony of the plot, Melville relies on whaling textbooks of the time for description. The skillfulness with which he kneads such standard scientific description together with the novel is outstanding. The revenge of the captain on the whale is "the same fiery emotion accumulated within the Leyden jar of his own magnetic life" (p. 159). It is interesting to see this story told in such scientific terms. The immense white whale is also a symbol of the indifference of physical forces to humanity. Overall, while referencing other works of Melville, Kuroda skillfully highlights an awesome contemplation of science. *Scientific thought in American literature* also includes a lineup of works by other authors, employing different approaches.

Watanabe is also an author of the small book *Nihon jin to kindai kagaku* (The Japanese and modern science, 1976). This work chronicles Japanese modernization, and was essentially an introduction to Western science, through the examples of Kenjirō Yamakawa, Morse, and Asajirō Oka. A particularly unusual facet is the discussion of *makyō*, a Japanese magic mirror in which light somehow reflects the design on the back. I remember picking up this book as a college student, and this passage about *makyō* remained long in my mind.

This concludes my discussion of these four individuals.

Although this is a digression from my discussion of individual academics, I would like to take the time to offer praise for the publisher Kousakusha, which, for almost forty years, has been introducing and constructing a wide compilation of knowledge across the sciences and humanities, including translation of literature on the history of scientific thought.

The publisher had many brilliant editors, such as Harue Sogawa, who served for a long time as editor-in-chief, and Seigo Matsuoka, who is widely known in the publishing industry. Their enthusiastic vivacity, rare in this field, has made it a continual delight to work with them in the pursuit of knowledge. Mainly in the 1970s, I stockpiled several of the booklets known as Planetary Books, and enjoyed their lively air very much. One book among those, *Kagaku teki yukai o megutte* (On scientific amusement, Sogawa and Matsuoka 1979), I have treasured for more than thirty years; even now, it quietly sits on my bookshelf. I hope the publisher continues to prosper far into the future.

(3) Partly fueled by the rise of the history of science, a fresh wind blew through the field of philosophy of science at the same time. With an intellectual background rooted in late Wittgenstein, Shōzō Ōmori created a unique philosophical world that extended beyond mere annotation. Wataru Hiromatsu had a strong presence through the 1970s and into the 1980s as a leading Marxist theorist; Keiichi Noe made himself an early master of the "new philosophy of science," which interlaced the philosophy of science of the Anglo-American world with the "new philosophy of science" that had originated in the history of science. The works of the scholars mentioned above are all significant contributions to "the history of the history of scientific thought." Works such as Ōmori's *Mono to kokoro* (Objects and mind, 1976) and *Shin shikaku shinron* (A new theory on new vision, 1982), Hiromatsu's *Kagaku no kiki to ninshiki ron* (The crisis of science and epistemology, 1973) and *Sōtaisei riron no tetsugaku* (A philosophy of relativism, 1986), Noe's *Kagaku no kaishaku gaku* (A hermeneutics of science, 1993a), and *Mukonkyo kara no shuppatsu* (Starting without a foundation, 1993b) are all important works in the history of science and scientific thought.

Ōmori originally devoted himself to the introduction of the philosophy of science during the postwar period, and his name appears in *Kagaku jidai no tetsugaku* (Philosophy in the scientific age, Aomi, et al., 1964), a trilogy put together by Jun'ichi Aomi and others. Afterwards Ōmori gradually began making his own scholarship, first emerging with *Objects and mind*. This work is a collection of papers, but there is a consistent awareness of the issues running through it. Ōmori himself describes it as an attempt to break down symbolic dualism, and offers in its place an "emerging" monism. A typical essay is represented by "Kotodama ron" (On the soul of words, pp. 103–154). Emerging monism, had it been followed seriously, had the power to significantly examine and radically modify the classic devices of philosophy such as consciousness, symbolism, and the world. Ōmori has several followers who are active in various fields, but unfortunately none of them seem to have achieved their mentor's forceful impact. In later years, he attempted to build his own theory of time based on the "emerging" monism. I am sorry that I can't claim Ōmori as one of my mentors. In his twilight years, when I saw him at academic gatherings, his face gave off a bright and serene impression that remains with me even now, even though he was hampered by physical ailments.

Among Hiromatsu's works, I would like to take up *The crisis of science and epistemology*. In order to target the epistemological objectification of the presumptions in modern science, Hiromatsu reviewed the epistemology of Locke and Kant, reflected on the basic concepts of Newtonian physics, and outlined the epistemology of the theories of relativity, quantum mechanics, and particle physics. His aim to transcend the traditional epistemological scheme of the subjective and the objective is embodied through a concrete investigation of the history of physics. Since this work was created as a compilation of dialogues, one sometimes wishes the author would get to the point more quickly. Nevertheless, it is the reflection of a philosopher who chronicled physics up to the mid-twentieth century, and it has not been followed by many similar works since then, and so it continues to be a valuable resource even now. The book takes a radical political position, and Hiromatsu uses difficult Chinese terms just like a Buddhist monk. Although he was an extremely strict person academically, I miss hearing him laugh at his own jokes during class.[67] While his collected works were published after he passed away in 1994, this work unfortunately did not have much influence, perhaps because Marxism has lost its intellectual authority globally.

In view of the situation at the time, when the philosophy of science in Japan was seen almost in the same light as logical positivism and that scientific view was presumed the natural view, Noe's *A hermeneutics of science* sympathizes with the idea of the "new philosophy of science" and challenges some of the underlying ideas of a scientific view akin to logical positivism. For example, with regard to the presumed distinction between theory and observation Noe emphasizes that all observation is always already theoretically-informed, and he advocates a scientifically hermeneutic program against the agenda of logical positivism. Specifically, he clearly put together discussion of the aforementioned arguments of Kuhn, Hanson, and Feyerabend, as well as Wittgenstein's notion of the aspect perception. Here we can see Noe's desire to frame the issues in terms of a more multi-layered human culture, in contrast to the scientism and reductive theories of nineteenth century physics. If you think about the emotive directionality of his thought, it is natural that Noe subsequently expanded his topics of interest to include a discussion of Kunio Yanagita, leading to a more narrative, descriptive conception of philosophy. Even today, Noe repeatedly engages in the editing and planning of philosophical books, consolidating his position as an authority of the field.

I have one more person to mention—the important philosopher of science Hideo Kawamoto. He is not someone who can be classified easily, so I'll treat him in this section for the sake of convenience. When I said earlier that, as a matter of principle, I would not discuss the philosophy of science in this introduction, what I had in mind was Carnap, Quine, and Kripke, proponents of the so-called American style of philosophy of science. However, Kawamoto's philosophy of science rests on a quite different intellectual foundation. Originally, he called attention to works that have been considered marginal in the history of science from an orthodox perspective, such as Goethe's theories of plants and colors. From the beginning of the 1990s, Kawamoto made efforts to establish a theory of autopoiesis in Japan. First, he dabbled in the translation of scholars associated with the field. Then, after completing basic introductory works, he gradually attained mastery of the subject. This is illustrated with works such as *Ōtopoiēshisu* (Autopoiesis, 1995), *Ōtopoiēshisu no kakuchō* (Extension of autopoiesis, 2000a), *Ōtopoiēshisu 2001* (Autopoiesis 2001, 2000b), *Metamorufōze* (Metamorphose, 2002) and *Shisutemu genshōgaku* (Phenomenology of systems, 2006). His description of the coordinated operation itself can be slightly frustrating if one is not acquainted with phenomenology. Inspired by the study of the science of mental disorders, Kawamoto recently seems to have a deepened interest in occupational therapy and physical therapy, developing his own frontiers of theories of action and of physicality.

(4) Throughout the 1970s and 1980s, there were many people engaged in important activities that I have not mentioned here. When viewed from the present context, I believe that Japan's history of science, philosophy of science, and history of scientific thought peaked with the "new philosophy of science," built around the criteria of the concepts of scientific revolution and paradigms, when the secondary themes inspired by these concepts were actively discussed. This occurred mostly from the second half of the 1970s through the mid-1990s. The evidence for this fact is present in the numerous series on the field compiled during that time. For example, the history of scientific thought accounts for a considerable portion

of Yōichirō Murakami's seven-volume *Chi no kakumei shi* (A history of revolutions in knowledge, 1979–1982, of which only five volumes were published), and the sixteen-volume *Shin Iwanami kōza: tetsugaku* (New Iwanami lecture series: Philosophy, 1985–1986), which was put together by Shōzō Ōmori. Additionally, there is a work whose title hinted at a shake-up in the conventional conception of paradigm theory as a somewhat infallible doctrine; the four-volume *Kagaku minaoshi sōsho* (Reevaluation of science series, 1987–1991) compiled by Ei Shimosaka and others. Here we find some overlap with the kind of postmodernism that arose at that time, and this work took a novel approach from earlier work that sought to establish a foundation, provide justifications, or follow in the footsteps of other work. Anyone associated with general histories of thought would not be able to let work of this kind fade into oblivion with the decline of postmodernism. When fashions of every era ignore or forget the accumulations of the past, they become a simple list that can no longer be called a history of thought, and the case of the history of scientific thought is no exception.

That is why this period was a peak. In taking on Japan's history of scientific thought and the chronicling of the history of this field, Yuiken and the Kyoto School scholars perhaps represented the first peak. This period described above was the second peak. Conversely, since the latter half of the 1990s, the history of science and scientific thought has entered a period of decline,[68] although others may have a different perspective on whether it can actually be referred to as a decline. Paradoxically, this was a change that can also be called "the dissolution of development" or "a turning back." In any case, I shall address how to understand this change in the next section. This also means revealing my expectations for the history of scientific thought in Japan. In describing these prospects, this very long introduction can finally come to an end.

4. Reflections from Scientists

Before entering directly into the issue of "decline," we need to take a little detour. Although the third section focused on a survey of the *histoire des sciences* and looked at the aforementioned peak in the history of scientific thought grounded in the fashionable "new philosophy of science," it ignored "scientific reflections," as these do not lend themselves easily to the discussion as it unfolded. Therefore, at the end of this section, it makes sense to touch on several individual scientists who contributed to this ideological debate from roughly the mid-1970s onwards. Atsuhiro Shibatani shall be first. In the same era that Shibatani was driving rapid development in molecular biology, *Seibutsugaku no kakumei* (The revolution in biology, 1960, 1970) models the shift from descriptive science to theory-driven science as a difference between molecular biology and conventional biological knowledge as modes of knowledge. Looking back, Shibatani noted that this book would later introduce many young people to molecular biology. Afterwards, from the time of *Han kagaku ron* (An essay on antiscience, 1973), he wrote books of general sociological interest. In *Anata ni totte kagaku to wa nanika* (What does science mean to you?, 1977), he is critical of the "go-it-alone" aspect of paradigms, and throws cold water on the so-called "rise and fall of scientific theories" argument. On the other hand, Shibatani also criticizes scientists who turn a blind eye to "the political study of science." Though a scientist himself, he maintains an exquisite sense of distance, retaining his position as a moderate critic. This sense of distance may also be related to the fact that Shibatani spent a long time conducting research in Australia. *Wareware ni totte kakumei to wa nanika* (What does revolution means to us?, 1996) is a kind of academic autobiography. Interestingly, Shibatani spoke openly of the fact that, with the combination of the intrinsic development of molecular biology and the growth of the university system (and its self-enclosure), he was not as successful in his efforts at reform as he would have liked. I can feel his hidden wish to fulfill the social responsibilities of a biologist, and for this I have the utmost respect for him. He withdrew from social activities ten years before his death in the spring of 2011.[69]

Like Shibatani, Itaru Watanabe was also an eminent scientist directly involved in the development of molecular biology. His perspective was slightly different from that of Shibatani. His discussion was often based on the assertion that the unprecedented knowledge of molecular biology contained the power to change traditional views of life and human beings. It also amounted to a criticism of classical philosophy. He had a number of works, including *Ningen no shūen* (The end of man, 1976) and *Atarashii ningen kan to seimei kagaku* (Life sciences and a new view of man, 1979). In fact, I had the opportunity to talk to him together with several colleagues during his last years, when I believe he was close to ninety years old. In retrospect, he related to us young scholars some impressive and serious academic reminiscences. *The end of man* is a manifestation of a sense of crisis in many ways. It illustrates a crisis related to the directionality of science itself as well as a crisis when science interacts with the rest of society. Of particular interest is the section titled "The End of Man" (pp. 163–193). This essay has the contemporary neo-Malthusian discussion in mind. If survival becomes difficult due to population explosion, the choice of whether socially successful people try to survive to the detriment of others, or whether they choose to coexist with the weak, such as the elderly or handicapped, becomes a big issue. The former is the war of all against all; the latter would be the domain of those having lofty ideals. Neither of these worlds would be our current world where "we should love ordinary human beings." In that sense, Watanabe concludes that the end for humanity as we know it may be unexpectedly close.[70] It is a profound theory of civilization that offers us a glimpse of some of the future difficulties facing humans who have come to understand our biological nature as we try to deal with the realities of the world today.

Next I will discuss Keiko Nakamura. Nakamura has been active for a long time at the Mitsubishi Kagaku Institute of Life Sciences.[71] Against the background of the rapid development of modern biology, such as molecular biology, she gradually began to show an interest in forms of knowledge that differed slightly in nature from integrated analytical and objective accumulation of knowledge. Nakamura advocated not the life sciences, but biohistory. Her great works include *Seimei kagaku kara seimei shi e* (From life science to biohistory, 1991), and *Jiko sōshutsu suru seimei* (Self-creating life, 1993). (1993). In *Self-creating life*, she attempts to supplement the externalist (exo-type) scientific viewpoint, in the sense of analytical, reductionist science and objectification, by taking an internal (endo-type) survey of this viewpoint that utilizes both subjectivity and intuition. This work sets life as the central concept in creating an overarching worldview rooted in specialty. As can be inferred from the word "shi" (to jot down, as in a journal— here translated as the "history" in biohistory), she is trying to see life as having a kind of historicity to it. Since the history of life involves an accumulation of small changes, a view of life as self-creating, not as self-replicating, is required. Nakamura's strong desires are obvious in her writing, in which she tries simultaneously to build a new, integrated kind of knowledge while also engaging deeply with other disciplines. It has been about twenty years since the publication of this work. Since that time, the human genome has been completely published, and the life sciences have become more and more analytical, combining with engineering techniques. In contrast to Nakamura's notion of DNA as the connection of life, others are rushing to use biotechnologies on "lower forms of life." On the other hand, the ongoing study of epigenetics is showing that the nature of DNA is more dynamic than is otherwise believed. I would like to hear Nakamura's thoughts on the current state of life science and on other theories concerning life, in the context of their coming actualization.

Shigeo Miki was an unusual anatomist. When I read *Taiji no sekai* (The embryonic world, 1983) with no prior knowledge of the work, I was so enthralled that I forgot to get off the train at my stop. Although Miki apparently never worked as an anatomist, in his last years he created a unique concept of the world in which it was not clear whether he was writing science or poetry. His recordings of lectures with pediatric nurses[72] have a light and festive atmosphere, with the whole room full of laughter. His early death is sorely missed; his tenure at the Tokyo National University of the Arts has already become legendary. Furthermore, Miki's *Seimei keitai no shizen shi* (A natural history of life forms, 1989) is one of the strangest books we have encountered in our chronicle of the history of scientific thought in Japan.[73] Miki's world unfolds around the polarities of food and sex, animals and plants, the contrasts between animal functions and plant functions within animal bodies. I would recommend taking up *A natural history of life formss*, looking at the numerous intriguing anatomical drawings, like life's forms. More than anything, Miki offers a quasi-Haeckelian overlap between present and past, reminding us of the phylogeny around individual organisms—his quasi-poetic theory of biomemory, described with specific examples such as chickens and lampreys, takes us to an astonishing imaginary plane. I believe that this is natural philosophy at its best, perhaps even a kind of poetry that surrounds nature.[74] It fills me with deep emotion to realize that such a person existed.[75]

Perhaps it is a sign of our era that all the people I have discussed thus far have come from the life sciences. There are two more people I would like to mention who come from outside the life sciences, then I will be finished with my illustration of scientific essays. Physicist Takafumi Matsui has succeeded in offering a fascinating, relativization of human life by calling us "aliens." Through the advent of agriculture, humans were able to escape the conventional biosphere and build an anthroposphere. Matsui offers a philosophical illustration of the implications of the anthroposphere on the larger timelines of existence. His works include *Wareware wa doko e iku no ka?* (Where are we going?, 1989), *Chikyū rinri e* (Towards a global ethics, 1995), *Uchū jin to shite no ikikata* (How to live as aliens, 2003).[76] *How to live as aliens* is a brief introduction drawn from Matsui's own *Towards a global ethics*. Due to the full recognition of the special nature of the anthroposphere, and because of the fundamental fact that it is changing the earth, Matsui argues that it is meaningless to use terms like "earth-friendly" when talking about global environmental problems. If one looks at the grand scale of things, the earth will not necessarily continue to maintain the conditions necessary to support life. Moreover, it is clearly impossible for the anthroposphere and society to continue as they existed in the twentieth century. Whether to head in the direction of an Arcadian past or a utopian future is a decision we must ultimately make, but Matsui avoids offering his personal opinion. He states that humans built the anthroposphere in order to recognize the universe; I believe this idea touches on the essence of human existence, making this a book that it as profound as it is clearly written.

Satoru Ikeuchi is a writer with similar expertise to Matsui. Not only did he write educational texts such as *Gendai uchūron o yomu* (Reading the modern cosmology, 1992) and *Kagaku wa ima dō natte iru no?* (What has become of science?, 2001), but also works concerning the culture of science, such as *Tenmongaku to bungaku no aida* (Between astronomy and literature, 2001) and *Terada Torahiko to gendai* (Torahiko Terada and the modern times, 2005). Rather than continuing Terada's academic tradition, Ikeuchi's work has a feel that can be likened to a sort of modern analog to the unconventional approach of Terada. Here, let's look especially at *Between astronomy and literature*. Ikeuchi's older brother, Osamu Ikeuchi, is a renowned scholar of German literature. Perhaps that is one reason why he did not settle for being an ordinary scientist, and instead sought out a new natural history in order to integrate the sciences and humanities, heretofore kept far apart. In the case of this essay, one might infer from the title that the subject matter concerns astronomy, but that is not the case. To be sure, the essay takes up some topics like the sky full of stars in *The Pillow Book*, but it mostly discusses pearls, morning glories, red spider lilies, bamboo, bonito, and many other subjects unrelated to astronomy. Its particular feature may be the way Ikeuchi brings literature and folklore into a relationship with his knowledge base of science, walking through, nonchalantly but quite consciously, the "self-enclosed intellectual world." This is truly an essay on a new kind of natural history with a rich, intellectual atmosphere.

We have taken an overview of the work of many people working in the tradition of scientific essays that holds great interest for the history of science and scientific thought. Overall, especially throughout the 1990s and later, there have been remarkable achievements in information technology, and the social discourse has undergone a significant transformation in the sense that science and technology play a bigger role, while at the same time there is a growing trend for scientists to use their expert knowledge as a weapon with which to make statements and proposals concerning culture and society. In that sense, Japanese society today enjoys the richest collection of "reflections from scientists" in the modern history of Japan.[77]

Section 4. The Infiltration of "Scientific Politics" and the Disputes Surrounding It

1. Decline or a Turning Back?

To reiterate, we have had a wealth of scientific reflections which have brought a high degree of public interest to science and technology. As might be expected, the approaches and perspectives on science and technology are highly varied. Nevertheless, I wrote previously that, from the late 1990s, the history of science and the history of scientific thought went into a phase of decline; originally, there was more or less an overlap between scientific reflections and research traditions concerning the history of science and scientific thought. What exactly does that mean? Did the two diverge at some point and taken different paths?

If one were to assert that the history of science and scientific thought have actually entered a phase of decline since the mid-1990s, one would be rebuked by historians of science. It is not so simple. Looking closely, no one will deny that high-quality studies continue to be published. For instance, Ken Saitō's *Yūkuriddo 'genron' no seiritsu* (The formation of Euclid's 'Elements,' 1997), Ken'ichi Satō's *Kinsei nihon sūgaku shi* (A history of mathematics in early-modern Japan, 2005), Tōru Sakano's *Teikoku nihon to jinrui gakusha* (Imperial Japan and anthropologists, 2005), Ken'ichi Takahashi's *Garireo no meikyū* (Galileo's labyrinth, 2006) are all masterpieces that combine substantive material with high levels of expertise. My *Kagakuteki shikō no kōkogaku* (An archeology of scientific thought, 2004b), framed by initimate engagement with the specific tradition of epistemology, was written with the intent to create the kind of history of scientific thought that I thought we needed.

It may be true that it is too soon to declare the period from the late 1990s a phase of decline. First, to be precise, I stated that the change can be called a decline, a dissolution of development, or a turning back. That is to say, the possible position that the field takes in society itself began to change so drastically that mere tracking of the intrinsic development of the history of science or scientific thought has proven insufficient. There are many reasons for that change, but I should point out the following first. Probably because the speed at which science and technology are developing has become so rapid, and its impact on daily life has become so profound that everyone is aware of it, the issue of science and technology is no longer a subject for historical analysis but has become a contemporary problem. Or at least, even among experts in the relevant areas, the shift in such a direction has begun to be considered to be more socially relevant; the contemporary response to the problems of science and technology is a more imminent problem than the history of science or scientific thought. Biotechnology, the rapid development of our information society, the issue of nuclear power plants, environmental problems, food safety issues surrounding chemical additives and genetically modified organisms, and other contemporary problems, all have powerful associations with science and technology. If the social implications or consequences of these problems have negative aspects, it is no wonder so many people involved in the history of science and scientific thought have come to the conclusion that it will be more meaningful to respond to contemporary issues by making social statements rather than to search for an answer buried in ancient documents. Consider, for example, Yoshihiko Komatsu. Originally, he was a historian of nineteenth century physiology with a focus on Claude Bernard; now he is known as a bioethicist. In books such as *Shi wa kyōmei suru* (Death resonates, 1996) and *Nōshi/zōki ishoku no hontō no hanashi* (Honest talk about brain death and organ transplants, 2004), he offers a consistent argument against organ transplantation. With an appealing narrative and intense political criticism, he played a central role in the Bioethics Roundtable and a series of protests against the 2009 amendment of the organ transplantation law. As a historian of science, did Komatsu represent a "decline," a "change in career," or "a turn-back"? Or, is this issue a small event that has been exaggerated? Do all these descriptions boil down to the same thing from society's perspective? And, more than anything, I wonder what prospects Komatsu has for his own academic background in terms of direction and future development.

What all this means is, in one sense, self-evident. But the response today is simply not an academic problem. The different origins, norms, and value judgments between each sector are inevitably intertwined when it comes to political problems of discussion and organization. The problems of science and technology are becoming less the concern of the history of science and the history of scientific thought and more than ever becoming the object of a sociology of science or a scientific study of politics.

Nevertheless, it is important to add that the sociology world in Japan is an important academic circle that boasts a very large number of researchers. In spite of this, the research tradition of sociology of science is relatively poor, although there have been some individual efforts, such as those of Miwao Matsumoto. This is not for any simple reason, but due to a variety of multilayered factors. The first possible reason is that the subject called sociology itself established an identity by breaking off from areas of scholarship such as philosophy. This process came about through a form of recognizing the need for a "scientific approach to societal events."[78] The problem of how to scientifically isolate religion and politics, or customs and cultural practices—that is, the question of first how to collect objective empirical data, decide what kind of scientific technique to apply, and what scientific concepts to use in analyzing them—was the very nature of sociological work once it had at least achieved conceptual clarity. In that sense, it is clear that there is an important difference in dynamics between targeting, for example, religion for analysis and targeting science for analysis. Moreover, a sociological approach that targets science always ends up like a Mobius strip. The reason a sociology of science is quite difficult to establish is that it seeks to examine its own academic origin. Another difficulty is that a heterogeneous variety of cultural factors may be inadvertently added to the mix. In short, a sociology of science in Japan faces some difficulties in developing its own knowledge. This seems to be an interesting issue to address. In any case, because this really deviates from our purposes in this chapter, I will leave off such discussion here.

To more clearly highlight our entire discourse, I would like to complete a certain formulation: "from the history of scientific thought to a scientific study of politics." I believe this is the pattern of intellectual shift that has been remarkable in this area since the late 1990s. Nevertheless, while in some sense it is unavoidable, this pattern itself ignores a variety of historical facts. To begin with, the fact that science and technology are social problems is true of any age, even before the 1990s. The promotion of science and technology under the total war regime is an example to some extent; the postwar efforts to democratize the research institutions of science and technology represented by Democratic Scientists Association (Minka) are another. The problems from pollution and drugs that plagued society from the 1950s through the 1960s, the energy issues of the 1970s and the subsequent technological responses to them—in retrospect, there were numerous issues that occurred at the interface between science and society in all ages, and each age faced demands for new knowledge with new forms and styles. To claim that there has been any important turning point since the latter half of the 1990s is only a naïve assessment, reflecting an oversimplification of the distant past and our excessive investment in more recent times—I feel I can already hear the critics saying so.

2. "The Political Nature of Science"

Instead of giving a quick response to this question and pursuing my own issues, I would like to mention four researchers who, within or around the academic system comprising the history of science and scientific thought, have responded sensitively to the problem of "the political nature of science."

First, we will discuss Jun Ui. He exhibited skepticism towards the mainstream response to the difficult problem of Minamata disease, and from 1970 has continued to offer an open night course at the University of Tokyo on the elementals of pollution. He sought to set an example for the public on how one might find ways of resisting the judgments of professional scientists with their specialized knowledge. Although in Ui's case, his movement itself has stronger ideological implications than his work, some of his writings were published in 1971 as *Kōgai genron* (The elementals of pollution) and then republished in 2006 as a one-volume edition (Ui 2006). Nevertheless, it is now a well-known fact that Ui labored in obscurity for a long time at the University of Tokyo, School of Engineering, under the shadow of an overall trend to shield industry from outside criticism. Becoming familiar with the huge social changes transforming science and technology from a young age, he refined, as his lifework, his opposition to those scientists gaining intellectual and social power. Ui did not stop with taking on the issue of Minamata disease; he also drew attention to Shōzō Tanaka's series of noble activities, and was quick to critically address issues of contamination and environmental pollution such as the Kanemi rice oil disease incident and the Kōchi Raw Pulp Concrete Affair. His work makes for fascinating reading; even now the opening lines of *The elementals of pollution* resonate in my ears

Since we have discussed Ui, it now makes sense to touch on Jinzaburō Takagi. Takagi had extensive knowledge of nuclear chemistry, and engaged in work related to the growth of the nuclear power industry. Nevertheless, he could not get used to the secretive corporate culture, and he resigned in order to return to college, where he pursued a doctorate, and thereafter worked at Tokyo Metropolitan University. Up to this point, Takagi's background is typical, but in 1973, when he was in his mid-thirties, he resigned his university position to seek different ways of producing scientific knowledge. Since that time, though struggling financially, he independently led the Citizens' Nuclear Information Center, and took a critical stance on national nuclear policy. The Citizens' Nuclear Information Center was intended to provide a model of independent information, depending neither on the government nor on any academic institution. In later years, Takagi explored the possibility of amplifying his methodology, referring to his activities as "citizen science." Although he passed away about ten years ago, the closed nature and self-righteousness of nuclear policy has since continued unchanged, and this was prominently on display after the Tōhoku earthquake in the spring of 2011. From the events of the Fukushima Daiichi nuclear power plant, it became clear that large-scale man-made disasters were possible. That accident is not over; a large amount of radioactive material has been released and is still a problem. I wonder what Takagi would have thought of it all, were he alive. Nevertheless, to only view Takagi's thinking in the context of these events may narrow our perspective. Whether or not we agree with Takagi's general ideas, he tried to maintain a style of knowledge production that was free of external control, and which has become an important reference when we think about the political study of science. Takagi has many publications, but here I would like to cite *Purutoniumu no kyōfu* (The terror of plutonium, 1981), *Waga uchi naru ekorojī* (My inner ecology, 1982), and *Shimin kagakusha to shite ikiru* (Living as a citizen scientist, 1999). *Living as a citizen scientist* is a kind of intellectual autobiography by someone who knows he has cancer and is looking back over his life. Takagi regards the huge scientific advancements and nuclear power that were practically forced into being by national policy, along with the political apparatus that facilitated them, as being problematic in terms of physics, ecology, and politics, etc.; his attitude to life speaks of his desire to continue to prosecute this empirically. Although the word "citizen" has a nice ring to it, the degree of difficulty that this kind of criticism experienced, emerging as it did from a minority position, can be seen by reading between the lines, and is an issue that is thrust readily before the reader. In his final years, he came up with the idea of de-nuclearization,[79] something with which we are now confronted.

These two people were outside the realm of the history of science and the history of scientific thought. Then, wasn't there any scholar who raised awareness of the need for a debate on the political study of science from within those fields of study? At least since the late twentieth century, scientific research has required large sums of money as well as large numbers of scientific personnel; this has to some extent come to acquire positioning within a political context. As a result, discussions that secondarily touch upon the politics of science are probably too numerous to detail. Here I would like to mention Shōhei Yonemoto and Hitoshi Yoshioka, two researchers who gave a more conscious and consistent consideration to the political study of science.

Shōhei Yonemoto has long been active in the Mitsubishi Kagaku Institute of Life Sciences. Initially his work concerned difficult themes with political overtones, including the history of European vitalism or eugenics,[80] and from the late 1980s his focus switched to more contemporary problems such as bioethics and environmental issues. This work was crystallized in publications such as *Baio eshikkusu* (Bioethics, 1985) and *Chikyū kankyō mondai to wa nanika* (What is the environmental problem?, 1994). Yonemoto also produced more radicalized work from the standpoint of the politics of science, such as *Chiseigaku no susume* (Introduction to the politics of knowledge, 1998) and *Baio poritikusu* (Biopolitics, 2006). In *Biopolitics*, Yonemoto describes the tendency of bioethics to depart from ethics and veer towards the political, becoming a vehicle for collective compromise of interest. Within this context, he discusses contemporary issues such as genome analysis, tissue banks, and assisted reproductive treatments. When analyzing these and other individual topics, he consistently attempts to connect the analysis with policy recommendations. At length, his work is not academic, but its critical consciousness is wise and sound, and as often as not, borders on academic. It should be noted that in recent years, Yonemoto translated Hans Driesch's *The History and Theory of Vitalism* (2007). Several translation errors are in evidence, possibly due to urgency. In spite of this, this book is of historical importance in the history of vitalism and of biology, and coupled with the brilliance of Yonemoto's exposition, is still an important work. Research on vitalism and eugenics continues to be Yonemoto's academic home. If not interrupted by work at Mitsubishi Kagaku Institute of Life Sciences or other social activities, he should have been able to create a lasting legacy of achievement for future generations. Of course, Yonemoto undoubtedly had various beliefs which led him to focus so much of his energy on policy analysis or political suggestions, and this kind of work should be of social importance. In spite of this, seen purely from the perspective of the history of scientific thought, I believe he could have well pursued an alternative, more academic career.

In contrast, Hitoshi Yoshioka's work comes from within the academy. He has mainly focused on the historical analysis of nuclear energy policy. In the sense that he has actively participated in government work while maintaining his critical position, he, like Yonemoto, attempts to bring the results of his academic work into the policy-making world. Yoshioka's style of composition is neutral in tone, but there are critical motifs that remain consistent throughout his work. When speaking, he talks very slowly but to the point, without any empty content, repetition or hesitation, sounding more like written text. His works include *Kagaku shakaigaku no kōsō* (Outline of a sociology of science, 1986), *Kagaku kakumei no seijigaku* (A political study of scientific revolutions, 1987), *Kagaku bunmei no bōsō katei* (Burnout of scientific civilization, 1991), and *Genshiryoku no shakai shi* (A social history of nuclear power, 1999). *Burnout of scientific civilization* takes on a broad problem, as it tries to criticize modern science and establish the theoretical framework of our scientific and technological society at the same time. It is a grand attempt to target the macro-structure of science and technology, namely the overall structure of the technology-promoting apparatus of research and development, for the purpose of criticism. To this end, Yoshioka directs most of his energies into establishing classifications and following the reproduction mechanism of the structure broadly. However, he does not focus extensively on specific details. In that sense, this work established Yoshioka's notions of the sociology of science and technology. This book can be positioned as the starting point for his academic initiative. Afterwards, many similar works by other authors appeared,[81] but there was little overlap in terms of political inclination; this produced the expectation that Yoshioka will give a more concrete version of his sociology of science and technology. Nevertheless, it is unfortunate that there have been no subsequent steps taken. I am eagerly awaiting a true academic sequel. Of course, having witnessed this recent nuclear accident, and as a longtime critic of nuclear power administration, he will probably begin to clarify whether the social and political base underlying special interests is what caused the accident.

Many researchers have long been deeply committed to the political study of science. Then, is there any sound reason to say that a decline in the history of scientific thought has occurred since the late 1990s, or that the intellectual focus has shifted from the history of scientific thought to the political study of science?

3. Science, Technology, and Society

I am not completely confident about my own claim that these developments mark a comprehensive change in the structure of knowledge. Even if the history of science and scientific thought play only a minor role in society, something like a "comprehensive change in the structure of knowledge" should be experienced in a profound way by all those involved in science. Nevertheless, I am not sure whether or not those active in the history of science or scientific thought (including myself) actually saw events of those twenty years or so as a radical experience. Of course, it could be that when people involved do not experience a crisis that conversely we have proof of a crisis.

(1) Anyway, there are certain movements in this field. In addition to the aforementioned overall inroads made by science and technology into society, there are a variety of additional factors at stake. For example, let's recall the deregulation of the university act in the early 1990s. Looking at the issue from a specialized perspective, one might wonder whether this is the root cause of the collapse of the faculty of liberal arts. Actually, at a number of universities throughout the 1990s, organizational changes were made that eventually reduced the importance of liberal arts curricula relative to more technical coursework. The "social utility" of the history of science, for instance, remains relatively obscure to outsiders. It was originally a minor course that did not draw many students. However, the reduction in courses such as introduction to science and the history of science in liberal arts faculties has spurred this decline. Basically, those with advanced degrees in the history of science found themselves facing poor job prospects (It seems this trend was happening in other fields as well, but for the time being I would like to focus on the history of science). Students became reluctant to follow this academic path. With this reduction in new researchers, the field lost a great deal of freshness and vitality. The impact of these changes gradually become stronger over time. Since the second half of the 1990s, this trend seems to be continuing, albeit at a slower pace.

As science and technology came to have a more pronounced role in society, it became clear that the research productivity of the national universities was insufficient, prompting the nation to begin to seriously address the issue of making improvements in this area. The Science and Technology Basic Act was passed in

1995, laying the groundwork for an institutional basis for the idea of converting Japan into one of the world's most science and technology creating countries. In the first and second phases, significant investment was made in science and technology, even as budget cuts happened in other fields. Because of that, science and technology in Japan is in pretty good shape. Of course, the amount of funding for each field varied widely. Fields that were allocated only small amounts were thrown into crisis, with the methods of selecting priority areas for distribution being less than clear. The decision-making process for these allocations by political leaders was at times problematic. Nevertheless, overall funding increased, and the aforementioned problems of allocation could be perceived as internal issues pertinent to only a small number of fields.

On the other hand, in addition to positive effects, there were negative aspects to the new focus on science and technology. It also led to highlighting many of the adjustments that needed to be made between various disciplines. This focused attention on the plethora of problems in information science, reproduction technology, medicine, the environment, and energy; advocates of science and technology, as well as policy-makers in related fields, made new attempts to direct the scattered intellectual resources of society to these ends, rather than to leave them unutilized. At that time it became apparent that there were some questionable areas that seemed to have no immediate applicability and whose experts were declining in number and ageing. Some might have wondered whether historians of science should be appointed as investigators in charge of the contemporary problems of science and technology, but I can't say the question was ever explicitly raised. In any case, the pool of experts in the histories of science and scientific thought were forced, through societal pressure, to become involved in a more aggressive push towards analysis of contemporary issues. And ultimately that is how the history of science was mobilized to solve problems in contemporary society.

(2) And what's wrong with that? One wonders if the history of science, which was once a useless academic discipline, had finally begun to contribute something to society. I can almost hear the objections that people may have to this idea, but I myself have some sympathy towards it. If we recall that this kind of social mobilization was present at the initial formation of the History of Science Society of Japan, we can see that is it merely finally bearing fruit, something which I believe is to be welcomed.

Looking back, it is interesting to note that, even in the flourishing period starting from the 1970s, the history of science and scientific thought in Japan did not introduce the tradition of the sociology of scientific knowledge (SSK), which was extremely radicalized in Europe and the United States in the 1980s. From the late 1990s, several colleagues and I engaged in a retrospective on research history and research advances, published as *Saiensu wōzu* (Science wars, Kanamori 2000a), which I mentioned earlier. *Science wars* has a strong topical focus on America, and I knew from the outset that it would be meaningless to attempt to introduce that material into the intellectual climate of Japan without some explanation. Through this book I wanted to expand knowledge of the sociology of science research tradition, and to inspire more people to participate in discussions of the problems involved in social, political, and ethical analysis of science and technology. Perhaps because my own presentation of these issues was poor,[82] the discussion never reached the level I had hoped for, and eventually just died out without exploring the issues in any depth. As mentioned, the sociology of science has since not shown a marked growth. Certainly, there were extremists in the sociology of scientific knowledge (SSK) tradition, and one couldn't expect to simply mimic them without serious problems arising. In any case, I think the sociology of scientific knowledge (SSK) could have been repositioned in a Japanese context for a closer examination, and it could have been an agent of active discussion like the "new philosophy of science."[83] However, it simply passed through low-level discussion, and superficial stereotypes like "the view of science as relativistic" were bandied about. All in all, this was quite unfortunate.[84]

What appeared instead was the so-called Science, Technology and Society (STS). STS was formed officially in 2002, and since that time it has focused mostly on developing activities centered upon science and technology communication. An important feature is that among its activists are numbered not only scientists and engineers but also policy makers and bureaucrats. Literature produced includes Yūko Fujigaki's *Kagaku gijutsu shakai ron no gihō* (Techniques of science, technology and society, 2005), Tadashi Kobayashi's *Dare ga kagaku gijutsu ni tsuite kangaeru no ka* (Who thinks about science and technology?, 2005), and Hideyuki Hirakawa's *Kagaku wa dare no mono ka* (Who does science belong to?, 2010). *Who thinks about science and technology?* describes the consensus development conferences from Kobayashi's own experience. This is a typical representation of the relationship between scientists and non-scientists that is often brought forward in the field of science and technology communications.

Science, technology, and society is a contemporary structure of knowledge designed to solve many of the social problems at the intersection of science and society. It includes the science cafe and the science agora, among others, that seek to build a system for improving the scientific literacy of citizens. Of course, there is a certain social function to those activities, because in a daily life that is becoming increasingly governed by science, it is apparent that having a certain degree of scientific literacy is becoming quite important. Additionally, to return to the topic at hand, many historians of science have found reasons to relocate to science, technology, and society programs. While society also requires a history of science, historians of science also need to participate in society, given both the instability of their social position and the insecurity regarding the social meaning of their academic endeavors. In that sense, mobilization occurred from both directions, and the results were mutually beneficial.

Nevertheless, when one looks at the subsequent science, technology, and society movements, their language at first glance appears novel, but in fact it is not inconsistent with the tradition of a classical scientific education. If STS goes well above the sphere of mere terminology and modes of discussion, future historians might position it as a megatrend of postwar science education that is comparable to the modernization movement in the postwar period. That would be a good thing.

However, the actual state of STS is not perfect. It has a strong tendency to be incorporated into educational activities in a wider sense, and in the worst-case scenario it may result in a somewhat uncritical pandering to contemporary national policy for the promotion of science and technology. In addition, I cannot help suspecting that science cafes are indeed just cafes with a different theme for small talk. The people who participate obtain merely the pseudo-satisfaction of problem-solving, while important social problems are reduced to inconsequential social chit-chat. Indeed, while the fact that the general public has the desire to meet scientists may be admirable, there is still a gap between the amateur and the professional, and for professional scientists themselves, it may not be a very rewarding experience. In contrast to scientists who are able to have a relatively stable sense of belonging to the scientific community, there is no guarantee that every citizen involved will feel a stable sense of belonging, perhaps because of the weak political base that comes with the idea of citizen participation. Some discussion and exchange of opinion should certainly be carried out, but conversations as equals is not always easy, particularly when there is an underlying dichotomy between a politically stable, powerful group and individuals who lack knowledge, political integration, and a base.

In general, society sometimes witnesses struggles and conflicts between various groups, and on occasion the source of underlying problems emerges through such conflicts. Of course, we generally prefer cooperation and harmony, and psychologically we can never enjoy struggle with others. Nevertheless, that kind of psychological load is just a particular negative for the parties involved in the struggle. Its social meaning may be found elsewhere.

Those involved with STS may in fact be something like flexible coordinators of social issues by drawing on a wide variety of conceptual devices. While sitting on the boundary between citizens and the government, they may inadvertently become a type of buffer. Also, the type of social adjustment that would arise out of this problem is likely to be tinged with a comfortable bias towards authority, and it may be hard to resist the tendency to settle for the solutions proffered by authority. I admit that social adjustment requires a great deal of effort, but what will this intellectual impact be, in fact, if where things will settle down is predictable from the very beginning? I cannot totally suppress my suspicions on this point.

There is a problem with the bureaucracy mobilizing many national intellectual resources to promote the national policy. Likewise, there is no particular problem with science and technology experts bringing enlightenment to the general public. But, if one looks at scholars of the history of science and the history of scientific thought, we must acknowledge that they have other social functions. I'm not saying there is nothing good about historians of science engaging in educational outreach activities. Yet the study of the history of science was from the beginning a complex discipline that internalized a variety of obscure elements, and its social function cannot be limited to simply politicized things like education. This brief historical overview should have provided a glimpse of the variety of diverse subjects this field contains. Nevertheless, intoxicated by the notion of social participation in the present, historians of science and scientific thought seemingly forgot about their role in building multi-layer problems, and jumped onto a more simplified scheme, possibly causing what may be the decline of the discipline. This is what I wanted to describe by the word "decline."

One of the purposes of this book is to present the original, complex nature of the history of scientific thought, along with some concrete examples. It is not intended to bring up anything novel. The objective of these essays is actually classic in a sense. This book again highlights the advantages of classic modes of the history of scientific thought covered in this introduction, and it shows an alternative to what we are currently facing, which is, greater and greater "direct social participation" and "mobilization for contemporary history." Below, I want to provide some analysis and rethinking of these two problems.

4. Is There a Future for the History of Scientific Thought?

(1) First of all, I would like to look at the current situation in the history of science and the history of scientific thought, which has been mobilized to serve contemporary history, and explain my idea about its implications for the history of science and the history discipline in general. Compared to the raging fire of contemporary issues on science and technology, discussion of the relationship between ancient science and thought may not seem particularly important. This is the theoretical justification for the aforementioned trend, but is this a reasonable path to take?

Indeed, in some cases it may be reasonable. New and unconventional problems are constantly arising. In cases where neglecting these problems would cause serious cultural harm or a deterioration in living environments, we must respond rapidly to mobilize the collective wisdom of society. Nevertheless, is there nothing we can from the distant past? Almost all phenomena in science and technology, religion, art, political institutions, and indeed society itself have their own "historicity." It is itself a lesson of history that trying to find a consistency or a regularity in historical facts often is not successful. In that sense, the individual events of history may seem to emerge in each of their eras from an unpredictable and illogical basis, sooner or later becoming a fragmentary, discontinuous link simply through immersion in the distant past. It may be impossible to establish strong causal or predictable linkages, to be sure, but if we are content with quasi-regularity in events, or a somewhat generic joining of them, in a manner of a loose chain of events that results in stereotypical development, then conversely, there are so many examples in evidence that it is difficult to enumerate concrete examples. This is why people who examine political history, literary history, and the history of warfare, etc., often become obsessed. The fields discussed in this book are no exception. Specifically, the generation and decline of particular theories in the history of science, series of events such as social acceptance or collective forgetting of a theory, subjects such as the conceptual relationship between scientific thought and Platonism with reference to the history of scientific thought, all leave a faint echo or shadow in the eras before and after them, while themselves fading away. Therefore, the determination that, for example, we are living in an era closer to Cartesian mathematics than classical Greek mathematics and therefore classical Greek mathematics has fewer lessons for our times, is a meaningless one. The distant past, like the recent past, has great implications for the present and for the future.

From this point of view it is truly regrettable that many specialists in the history of science and the history of scientific thought, driven by the pleasant sounding mottos of "get with the times" and "get involved in society" neglect their real work in historical research and thus contribute to the loss of diversity in research traditions that we are undeniably seeing today. For the record, I am not saying that current events are not important. I am simply saying that historical discourse has its own particular value.

(2) Second, I would like to offer a personal opinion on this idea to "get involved in society." Again, for the record, I want to say that I recognize the importance of social coordination of many sectors and educational outreach activities. I am merely suggesting that this is not the only thing that matters. Moreover, there are experts in the history of science and scientific thought who engage in collaboration with the bureaucrats responsible for science and technology policy. As a result of this, it is highly probable that their self-understanding of value of the history of science and scientific thought will be diminished. It is great to be "useful to society." The problem is that it is not easy to determine what is useful to society. In fact, it may be more accurate to say that, there are some things that we would expect to be of little social utility, but when seen in a historical context, may seem otherwise. Such predictions are far from definitive, and rarely accurate. Within science and technology, this notion sometimes takes the form of the famous dichotomy between basic research and applied research.

Capable scientists have stated time and again that to hastily deny the utility of basic research is detrimental to science and technology as a whole. I do not know to what extent such an analogy is appropriate, but specific research on matters related to the history of scientific thought cannot be said to be frivolous, recreational, or secondary simply because it does not take its cues from direct policy recommendations and contemporary issues. When people make important social judgments or cultural decisions, the various factors giving rise to these assessments and judgments are complex and multifaceted, and cannot be derived from a simple perspective such as one of "immediate utility." Try as one might, one simply cannot completely cover up "the utility of the history of scientific thought." Trained historians of scientific thought have the right, and indeed the obligation, to vigorously and thoroughly pursue subjects they are simply interested in, regardless of external considerations like whether or not this helps society. It would be better to become more sensitive to how crude the thinking is when people talk about "society and society," and to respond more prudently when confronted by those who brandish the idea of "social utility" like some magic wand.

*

I mentioned a prosopography of the literature in the beginning, and we have now looked into the faces of a great many works. As I said at the beginning, this is not really an analysis. Otherwise, this preface would have been much longer in order to handle a literature canon that exceeds the 650 or so books listed, including those in the bibliography. If a simple outline of the accomplishments of this literature has emerged from my description here, then that is enough. That I could carry this out to its completion is one of my utmost academic urges.

This introductory chapter is directed at the work of our predecessors in the minor academic field called the history of scientific thought. I will be happy if the reader feels a kinship for its significance, and for the spirit of those engaged in this work. Conversely, as has been presented above in the history of science and scientific thought in Japan, if we see a gradual decline or stagnation in this history, then we need to ask whether this is rooted not simply in external causes, but also in something intrinsic to the field. If the history of scientific thought casts aside the "closed nature" with which it has been unconsciously saddled, and actively seeks articulation and cooperation with other knowledge traditions in order to succeed in expanding the area of consideration and renewing intellectual devices, then this may forge a new future for the field. In fact, I feel that we are seeing the emergence of younger researchers producing outstanding work in the history of educational thought and other fields, excellent results are coming from those working at the intersection of social history and the history of science. We are seeing up-and-coming researchers who are globally active, such as Hiro Hirai and Akihito Suzuki. This is also grounds for hope.

Therefore, the time has come for the history of scientific thought to make plans for its own renewal and to form new networks. If the field fails to do so, it will simply be left out of Japan's intellectual community. Another possibility is that it could be reduced to an object of merely historical interest that has no historical role left for it, like some archeological gem in a museum. Shouldn't we hope instead, even wager on the chance that the history of scientific thought is not dead and gone but will continue on in some form? I am not sure that I was able to offer a hopeful vision of that future, or even one with a touch of positive nuance, but it is now time to bring this terribly long introduction to a close.[85]

Notes:

1) As you may know, a prosopography is not an in-depth investigation of a single person; rather it is an approach to draw out the general relationship of groups of people who are closely or loosely connected by mutual influence or other bonds within a given era. Thus, traditionally, it deals with a collective personality. This is why I have referred to this document as a "prosopography of the literature." I have omitted all honorifics, even for living persons.

2) A few comments are necessary here. Essentially, the scope of the philosophy of science should include, for example, the Neo-Kantianism that rose so prominently in the academy from the latter half of the nineteenth century to the early twentieth. However, normally in Japan, when speaking of the philosophy of science, we are in many cases referring to the British-American school of philosophy espoused by Quine, Kripke, Wittgenstein, and others; this is a school that has almost no relationship to history in a broader sense. A Neo-Kantian philosophy of science would, in some respects, overlap with a history of scientific thought, and while this is alluded to briefly below, it does not generally reference an American-style philosophy of science.

3) This may become clear in the final stages of discussion, but one aspect in the decline of modern history of scientific thought lies in the fact that the approach of the history of scientific thought is being gradually encroached upon by something akin to a sociology of science. This trend is described as a shift towards something like a political study of science. Anyway, this semblance to sociology of science has a strong connection to the field of the sociology of science in the broader sense, and it is that sense of the sociology of science that will also play a strong role in this chapter.

4) Conversely, works such as analytical textbooks that are an extension of the usual work of scientists, as well as the introductory texts that offer an easily-digestible rewording of particular themes, will not be covered. These, including the latter, fall within the wider domain of science itself and constitute too broad a body of work to be considered here.

5) Precisely because the history of thought in physics has traditionally been at the core of the history of scientific thought, paying insufficient attention to this field risks failing to get to the crux of the topic. However, in chapter one of this book there is a discussion regarding the theory of elementary particles, a central tenet of Takuji Okamoto's history of thought in physics, which compensates to some degree for this crucial defect. Additionally, the history of technical thought needs to be handled separately, and with the exception of a few books, it is not touched on with any depth.

6) Obviously, this is no more than a general statement, and I am in no way ignoring the fact that when considered from a historical point of view, numerous scientists have left outstanding work in fields corresponding to the history of science and to the history of scientific thought.

7) The subject matter, as well as a meta-view of this subject, may at times be difficult to understand, even obscure. This is not because the view is, in fact, obscure, but because scholarship in the history of scientific thought tends to run in that direction.

8) This work is James G. Crowther's *The Social Relations of Science*, New York, Macmillan, 1941. Given that the original title does not contain a phrase corresponding to *kagaku shisō shi* (the history of scientific thought), this book fails to meet the criteria as reference literature.

9) While perhaps an expression of extreme regret, Yoshioka generally offers a harsh evaluation of the consistently low standard of scientific thought in Japan. In comparing science and technology, Kunio Oka put more emphasis on technology as active intervention with the physical world, but Yoshioka concluded that the aimless continuation of technical knowledge had marginalized systematic, sophisticated scientific thought. For example, his idea is well reflected in the following passage:

"In accounts of the conception and struggles with inventions and discoveries, and in the memoirs of scientists throughout Japanese history, many simply record the incentive and origin of the invention or discovery, together with the final results, with no details revealed concerning interim experiments or observations, nor of theoretical considerations. This may be the result of the historical impact of a basic flaw in emphasizing techniques and looking down on scientific principles (one cause of scholarly stagnation), as seen in the old Chinese scientific treatises, and also as an indirect influence of the guild-like secrecy seen in Japanese histories of technology and science. In either case, there was a general tendency to focus only on those technologies directly useful in real life, and to overlook the science underpinning them. This is one proof of precluding the full awareness of the distinction between technology and science, and delaying the general spread of fully fledged scientific thought, that is, the awareness of objectives and methods" (Yoshioka 1952, pp. 19–20).

10) To reiterate, the philosophy of science in this case is Neo-Kantian in essence.

11) Furthermore, in later works such as on the logic of species, Tanabe broadened his area of concern to the extent that his writing appears to lack any direct association with the philosophy of science. However, he left behind a trilogy of works related to the philosophy of science (Tanabe 1954, 1955a, 1955b) in his final years. Indeed, in Tanabe's academic world the philosophy of science took on a pivotal role.

12) Additionally, I would like to touch on Hisomu Nagai, who is little known outside the specialized fields of medical philosophy and the history of medical philosophy of the Taisho Period. *Igaku to tetsugaku* (Medicine and philosophy, 1908, 1922), *Seimei ron* (An essay on life, 1913) and *Seibutsu gaku to tetsugaku to no sakai* (Between biology and philosophy, 1916) are all voluminous works that are well-worth reading. Nagai is one of those who embody the Taisho vitalism referred to by Sadami Suzuki (see Suzuki 1995). Rereading *An essay on life* and other works from a modern standpoint reveals that Nagai's argument simply focuses on the conclusion that both physics and chemistry based methodologies are essential to understanding life phenomena. Pondering on the further development of this field merely dredges up a certain obviousness and even déjà vu, provoking little interest. Of these three volumes, perhaps *Between biology and philosophy* still warrants appreciation today.

13) The first issue was published in November 1932, and the last, the tenth issue, in August 1933. This chapter generally focuses on books rather than on journals or essays, and builds its narrative around *A compendium on materialism*. In the process of examining this journal, it becomes obvious that a great many authors wrote under an assumed name, and indeed some used a variety of different names for different purposes. While in many instances the testimony of their contemporaries is sufficient to reveal the identity of the various authors, this is not always the case. Indeed, this fact unintentionally sheds light on how important freedom of thought is.

14) I have in mind the story of the renowned Tales of Miletus, who is said to have fallen in a ditch while walking, absorbed in his observation of the night sky.

15) Of course, he is a theorist of great importance in proletarian literature.

16) Although this information takes a rather meta-level form, the series of historical works by Shin'ichi

Funayama are valuable to any inquiry into the conventions of thought employed in both materialism and the theory of science. Some examples are *Meiji tetsugaku shi kenkyū* (Research on the history of philosophy in the Meiji Period, 1959), *Taisho tetsugaku shi kenkyū* (Research on the history of philosophy in the Taisho Period, 1965), and *Showa yuibutsu ron shi* (History of materialism in the Showa Period, 1968).

17) Although Akihide Kakehashi was renowned for his unique economic philosophy after World War II, prior to the war he released an important work, *Busshitsu no tetsugaku-teki gainen* (The philosophical concept of substances, 1934). He explicitly takes a realist's stance in recognizing the objective reality that is independent of human consciousness and in confirming that recognition is a reproduction of that objective reality. Kakehashi constructs a framework that connects this with Marxism. One of its characteristics can be found in the existence of a type of autonomous motion in the physical world, which is assumed to be an objective reality. This provides an explanation for the dynamic nature of the world and society, and offers a foundation for dynamic growth in nature. The task of propagating previous research on the natural history of materials also comes into prominence. *The philosophical concept of substances* is an ambitious work based on the above recognition and even brings Darwinism into discussion. Kakehashi's task, with its cross-sectional characteristics, was long ignored by mainstream Marxism and relegated to an isolated position.

18) Although his work is from a much later time frame, I would like to quote the physicist Hajime Tanaka, one of the scholars who essentially took up the mantle of the academic tradition of *Yuiken* after World War II. Tanaka's *Shizen no tetsugaku* (Philosophy of nature, 1973) was very popular at one time, and his philosophical background was very obvious. Taking the basic premise that matter itself is the primary existence in this world, and that there is a material world that changes and develops on its own power, Tanaka takes the viewpoint that the human spirit, which belongs to this material world, is simply the workings of the human brain. It is noteworthy that he persisted in quite a pure materialistic viewpoint during the 1970s. This is a dialectical materialism that acknowledges the dynamics of the material world as a fundamental characteristic. It accepts contingency as an inherent factor in the material world, and views contingency as manifesting itself in such ways as biological evolution and the freedom of human consciousness. Socially, it sees the driving force behind revolutions of oppressed classes as a result of class conflict. In essence, this standpoint prolonged the Yuiken-type tradition, and was augmented by Tanaka's knowledge of physics. His specific examples, such as criticism of the idealistic understanding of time perception, are easy to understand and have persuaded many readers. However, when viewed from a present-day perspective, subsequent changes in world affairs have resulted in a decline in the influence of dialectic materialism. Coupled with this, the issue of whether Tanaka's arguments are also in decline, or whether these arguments include content that can be claimed to be independent from social conditions, will continue to be an interesting point of contention.

19) Although the positioning in connection to Yuiken is clearly inappropriate, it is unavoidable due to the lack of some other suitable context. Since Ishii's name has made an appearance, I would like to make a brief comment on Asajirō Oka. Oka's *Shinka ron kōwa* (Discourse of the evolution theory, 1904) is essential when discussing the history of the acceptance of evolutionary theory in Japan, and although somewhat early in terms of the time period we have established, it was widely accepted in its day, with Oka himself revising and adding to it many times throughout the Taisho period. Therefore, we can regard it as having practical influence on the period. However, I have chosen in this essay to take note of several essays in which the varied phenomena of human society are discussed somewhat cynically, and of these I draw particular attention to *Saru no mure kara kyōwa koku made* (From a troop of monkeys to a republic, 1926). Oka saw natural selection as a centerpiece of biological theory, and discussed various aspects of human society, such as love, ethics, and history, on this basis. He could be referred to as a legacy of naturalistic cultural theory. However, the basic mood of his many essays should be called somewhat pessimistic rather than cynical. His observations on many widespread phenomena such as the decline of group spirit, and what appeared to him to be the foolishness of humanity in embracing spurious etiolo-

gies, drew him to conclude that human culture was slowly falling into irrevocable decline.

20) I would like to reference Gōichi Miyake's *Gaku no keisei to shizen-teki sekai* (The formation of scholarship and the natural world, 1940) and *Sūri tetsugaku shisō shi* (The history of thought on mathematics and philosophy, 1947) as probably belonging to a branch of the Kyoto school. These are admirable achievements supported by a profound knowledge of the history of philosophy in Europe, and it is regrettable that they are rather unknown. *The formation of scholarship and the natural world* features references to Plato, Descartes, Leibniz, Kant, and other giants of the history of philosophy, and in particular makes an intensive investigation into the underlying notions of their conceptual framework that are somewhat related to the structure of the natural world: time, space, infinity, and freedom. It also exhibits a certain uniqueness in featuring the natural philosophy of William of Ockham from the late medieval times.

21) Incidentally, Shimomura also participated in the famous roundtable discussion on "Kindai no chōkoku" (Overcoming Modernity), where intellectuals cooperated with the war effort (see Kawakami 1979). Although he made only a few statements, it is striking that he, as sort of modernist, expressed concerns about the ambiguity and risk inherent in the concept of "overcoming." Thereafter, when looking back on this round-table talk, Shimomura stated that he was nonplussed by the self-satisfaction of the participants, and came to avoid any friendly relations with them.

22) In fact, the recognition that scientific technology exerts immense influence on the conduct of war was already commonly acknowledged by countries around the world after World War I. From that standpoint, the approach of promoting scientific research as a national policy was clearly in place in developed countries in the 1920s. Note that Japan established RIKEN in 1917. However, in Japan the link between scientific knowledge and technology came relatively late, and it was only in the 1930s that the country began to recognize this and adopt more proactive policies to achieve a higher level of integration of science and technology. For example, the Japan Society for the Promotion of Science, a public organization intended to provide scientific research funding, was established in 1932, and academic research funds for universities became comparatively abundant in the 1930s.

23) Some may feel that the number of statements I have made here in subsection 3 is undeservedly high when compared to that of the statements for other renowned thinkers. However, I regret that trends of this type in thought during the war have been neglected for political reasons, and to some extent I would like to make up for that deficit by giving them more in-depth description. This disproportionately large treatment of the subject is therefore intentional.

24) For details, see my essay.

25) Of course, there was criticism during this period. An example of this is in chapter 4, section 3 of Toratarō Shimomura's *Kagaku shi no tetsugaku* (A philosophy of scientific history, 1941). According to Shimomura, talks on science and ethnicity, as well as science and political regulation, were simple digressions from the heart of the matter. To his mind, the creation of science only takes place in a discourse space that is independent of human interest. He says, "The underlying basis of science is indifferent to the fate of humankind" (Shimomura 1941, 1988, p. 295). In this context, Shimomura thought that the restrictive framework of the nation-state was a spurious issue.

26) However, it may not be appropriate to touch on Sakuta in this context. This booklet was put out as a report by the National Spiritual Cultural Research Institute. He bases his conclusion on the assessment that the citizens should be led by national science. However, he was not attempting to demarcate the natural sciences themselves by national borders. Instead, he argued that they should be aware of their own national characteristics in such fields as psychology, morality, politics, economics, and education. Therefore, in the case of Sakuta, it is more appropriate to broadly consider the "science" of national science as knowledge in general. National science is science that includes the life of the nation in its research purview. However, the doctrines of individualism, liberalism, and anarchism were carefully excluded, and Sakuta argued that this was simply science for the lives of the nation as a unit and as a group,

and for the nation itself on this axis. He refers to the notion of creating "science" as a "position of national intent." Although the argument seems incomplete, it should be deemed natural that it essentially reinforces the political direction of that time, given the social function of the National Spiritual Cultural Research Institute.

27) For example, in February 1945, in the closing days of World War II, *Nihon kagaku dō* (The Japanese way of science, 1945) made its appearance, co-authored by physicists Toranosuke Iwatsuki and Ichirō Watanabe, who left behind significant achievements in fields such as math education. *The Japanese way of science* is a large volume that virtually saturates the topic, making it difficult to give it a close reading. Note that while Iwatsuki played an active role at the Research Institute for Theoretical Physics, he perished in the atomic bombing of Hiroshima a few months after this book was published.

28) Yasusaburo Sugi can be counted as another scholar strongly influenced by Kunihiko Hashida, and Sugi's works include *Kagaku no furusato* (The hometown of science, 1943), *Kagaku to gakudō* (Science and academism, 1944), and *Kagaku no shukumei* (The fate of science, 1949). Probably due to the presence of Hashida, the field of physiology in Japan produced a large number of scientists who took part in work concerning the history of scientific thought. This fact may deserve special mention.

29) Written in August 1940.

30) As might have been expected, Takakazu Maeda whom I mentioned earlier also had an article on "Life and science" (pp. 15–37) in his work *Nihon kagaku ron josetsu* (Introduction to debates on a Japanese science, 1944), where he speaks again of the necessity of "science in living life." He argues that young peoples' associations in various places should be able to interact with simple machine tools.

31) Maeda's *Introduction to debates on a Japanese science* provides corroboration:, "Since the promotion of science was taken up as an important national policy upon the inauguration of the Konoe cabinet, journalistic discussions of science have become extremely lively" (p. 190).

32) Gundayū Aida, who made a name for himself in the study of glass and cathode ray tubes after War World II, published a book titled *Kagaku hyōron* (Science review, 1943). It comprises a variety of themes, including discussions similar to the life science theory mentioned above. In "Kagaku hyōron ni tsuite" (About science review, pp. 13–23) and "Kokumin shisō to kagaku bunka" (The nation's thoughts and science culture, pp. 46–56) etc., Aida presents an array of remarks that support this. Scientific awareness should not be the sole domain of specialists, but must permeate politics in a coordinated fashion if it is to really thrive in society. For that to occur, the public at large must participate. Only when politics, daily life, and science are connected in a unified, organized manner, does the science for national defense and a science of daily life begin to take shape. For instance, science does not exist solely for the purpose of inventing machines. It is when science is put into action in a broad sense in society, ideology, and in daily life in general that improvement of cultural standards is realized. These are the outlines of his arguments. However, in this context I would like to look at works such as "Kagaku kokusaku no juritsu "(Establishment of national policies on science, pp. 75–85) and "Kagaku shugi kōgyō no bekken (A brief view of scientific industry, pp. 135–141). Although Aida emphasizes the importance of promoting science at a policy level, he focuses particularly on the preeminence of research organizations such as RIKEN on an institutional level. At any rate, a national policy for the development of science was required. In that context, Aida places significant value on the science-focused industrial policies of Ōkōchi, something that seems only natural.

33) Incidentally, literature such as *Pour la haute intelligence française* (1925), trans. *Kagaku no dōin* (Mobilization of science, 1938), by the right-wing French author Maurice Barrès, also references an atmosphere of similar social situations, but goes no further. Obviously, given the total war consuming the nation as a whole, a great deal of intellectual energy was mobilized. I think that a series of historical works focusing carefully on this as accurate historical evidence, dissecting variants of that argument and linking this with periods both before and after, is very important both ideologically and politically.

34) If we consider the gathering together of people with similar interests and giving them a general objective

as being equal in importance to constructing new original knowledge, then Jun'ichi Sugai was surely an influential person during this period. Although originally an instructor at a military academy, at this time Sugai was an influential scientific bureaucrat with the Ministry of Education.

35) The reason I use the qualified expression "virtually the first" is, first, that "Tetsugaku to shizen kagaku tono kōshō" (Negotiation between philosophy and natural science, 1933) by Jun'ichi Sugai, which I mentioned previously, constituted part of the massive and inclusive *Iwanami kōza tetsugaku* (Iwanami lecture series of philosophy) published in the first half of the 1930s, and second that its several volumes included considerable material on the history of science and scientific thought. Even so, I am truly moved that philosophy, which had been introduced in earnest from the mid-nineteenth century onwards, had taken root among the Japanese in a short sixty or seventy years.

36) While it was simply a literal translation instead of an adaptation, Dannemann's overreaching tome on history, *Dai shizen kagaku shi* (six volumes), originally published as *Die Naturwissenschaften in ihrer Entwicklung und ihrem Zusammenhange* (The natural sciences in light of their development and connection), was also published during a similar period (1941–43). Immediately after World War II, this book was expanded, revised, and republished in ten volumes (1946).

37) It is worth mentioning that Keiichi Koyama carried out research into mathematical philosophy, publishing his magnum opus *Sūri tetsugaku* (Mathematical philosophy, 1937), after which he was also active as a poet. Possessing a formidable intellect, he roamed freely through the space between philosophy, mathematics and art.

38) This was published in the mid-1920s, but many more editions were released and it was widely read during the first half of the Showa period, thus fitting into our time frame. I used the 23rd edition, published in 1937.

39) Jun Ishiwara would have completed his lifetime career as a physicist had he not resigned his post because of a famous love affair; after this, he became a hard-hitting critic. *Kagaku to shisō* (Science and thought, 1938a) and *Shizen kagaku-teki sekai zō* (Image of the world of natural science, 1938b) are notable works relating to the history of scientific thought. Also, Ishiwara was originally a notable composer of *Waka* poems. After the love affair, Ishiwara was no longer rated as a professional scientist and was obliged to work as a critic unaffiliated with any organization, which no doubt rankled with him. *Image of the world of natural science* is a collection of critical essays focusing on the theory of relativity and quantum theory, as well as related theories on observation and contingency. In particular, there were many articles that showed traces of the uncertainty principle.

40) For example, collections of essays such as Morikazu Toda's *Omocha to kompeitō* (Toys and *kompeitō* sugar candies, 2002a) appear to be directly connected with Terada from their examples of *kompeitō* candies. However, I believe Toda's essential academic orientation is different from that of Terada.

41) One example of someone who was roughly the same age and similar to Terada is the meteorologist Sakuhei Fujiwara. Fujiwara produced the following works: *Kumo o tsukamu hanashi* (A story of grabbing the cloud, 1926), *Kumo* (Clouds, 1929), and *Kishō to jinsei* (Meteorological phenomena and life, 1930).

42) While I am uncertain whether one can refer to this as a "direct academic tradition," I would like to cite here Michitaka Uda's *Nankai hokumei* (The south seas and north oceans, 1943), which summarizes in essay form the author's experiences surveying these bodies of water. Uda's literary essay "Umi no ke" (Sea monsters, pp. 238–247), on topics such as mermaids, is quite fascinating. He also collaborated on volumes such as *Umi to seikatsu* (The sea and life, 1949) with Zen'ichi Yasui. I would also like to touch on the physicist Yoshio Fujioka. The eldest son of the literary scholar Sakutarō Fujioka, he was also connected with the administration of atomic energy after World War II. Although his *Butsurigaku nōto* (Notes on physics, 1942) is a general introduction to topics such as the development of quantum mechanics, it includes several essays on Terada. Fujioka himself admits that there are a surprising number of allusions to Terada in the foreword to the first volume of the second edition (1947). Small volumes such as *Kaminari*

(Thunder, 1947, volume I, pp. 19–25) are poems that offer references to everyday life in a blending of Terada- and Nakatani-like studies. Meanwhile, the physiologist Takashi Hayashi wrote collections of essays such as *Kagaku e no shisaku* (Contemplation on science, 1941), and left his mark on the history of mystery novels under the pen name Takatarō Kigi. He even won the Naoki Award for his novel *Jinsei no ahō* (Life's fool, 1936). Mystery novel enthusiasts are well-acquainted with Fujioka's artistic take on mystery novels. Incidentally, *Contemplation on science* contains an article entitled "Terada hakase no shi to kagaku zuihitsu" (The death of Dr. Terada and scientific essays, pp. 319–324). Hayashi notes there that Terada's writings are interesting because, while he at first appears to merely be writing about common daily life, there is an unshakable physical worldview and physical way of seeing things underlying his writing.

43) *Oto no bunka shi* (a cultural history of sound, 1949), a collaborative work by Ryūzaburō Taguchi and Osamu Tsukakoshi, begins with a type of musical theory that considers organisms in general. It first confirms the existence of three levels of music: the "music" that animals use to draw the attention of other animals for mating, the music that primitive people used in ritual and dance, and the music of civilizations that seek to establish musical theory and enrich their lives with art. The first section ends after a brief overview of Western and Eastern musical history. The second section takes a more engineering-oriented approach, and is—simply speaking—a technological history of devices that produce sound. The third section, "Oto no bunka mondō" (dialogue on the culture of sound), discusses dance and moves on to a physical explanation and exploration of the question of the nature of sound. If this volume has any Terada-like characteristics, it would be in how it deliberately mixes cultural phases such as music and dance with nearly pure physical explanatory phases. Gramophones and the tango, the songs of crickets— this categorically disruptive juxtaposition symbolizes a divergence in how sound and people interact. More recently, works such as Toshio Hayasaka's *Oto no rekishi* (The history of sound, 1989) should be seen as having different ideas and intellectual background, regardless of the similarity of their titles. Hayakawa's work can be almost regarded as a history of acoustic engineering.

44) I remember as a child reading about flathead harpoons (harpoons with flattened tips, used for whaling) and being struck at how interesting they were. Like any child, I gave no thought to who wrote the piece. Then 30 years or so passed, and when I was in my 40s, I discovered that it was written by Hirata. I felt as if I had dug up some buried treasure! That article, "Kujira ni mori o utsu" (Harpoon the whale), is included in this collection.

45) According to Tetsu Hiroshige's *Sengo Nihon no kagaku undō* (Scientific movements in postwar Japan, 1960), which will be touched on later, the Democratic Scientists' Association was so powerful for several years after World War II that "leaders in traditional academia felt threatened merely at the mention of its name" (p. 134). Initially, the Democratic Scientists' Association was split into seven sections: philosophy, political economy, natural sciences, history, art, education, and agriculture. The action policy of the organization was as follows: (1) Establish a scientific spirit and build up democratic sciences. (2) Fulfill, heighten, and mobilize the desire of the people for science. (3) Work against antidemocratic educational systems, institutions, and thought. (4) Train up-and-coming scientists. (5) Use science and technology to contribute to the welfare of the people. (6) Improve and maintain the occupational standing of scientists and technicians. (7) Gain total freedom for scientific activity. The *Gakusei sōsho* (Student series) edited by the Association struck a resonant cord at the time.

46) Although this is getting ahead of things by quite a bit, I would like to touch on Seiji Takada's *Kagaku hōhōron josetsu* (Introduction to scientific methodology, 1988) here. As will be explained later, it is becoming difficult to create an overview of science for social and institutional reasons. It is in these circumstances that Takeda's book carries on the tradition of the scientific overview. On the other hand, however, he breaks the "spell" of Neo-Kantianism, taking a completely different approach. One characteristic of this volume is how it explains the relationship between the natural sensory organs and artificial copies, making use of plenty of specific examples found in everyday life. It is my strong hope that similar

high-quality introductions to science will continue to be offered in the future.

47) These page numbers refer to the first volume of *Taketani Mitsuo chosaku shū* (Collected works of Mitsuo Taketani, 1968).

48) Although I am jumping ahead chronologically here, Jun'ichi Murata's contemporary works deserve mention. With a detailed intellectual foundation in phenomenology, Murata refined and developed the philosophy of technology in such works as *Gijutsu no rinrigaku* (An Ethical Study of technology, 2006a), *Gijutsu no tetsugaku* (A philosophy of technology, 2009), and *Kyōsei no tame no gijutsu tetsugaku* (A philosophy of technology for coexistence, ed., 2006b), while displaying a consciousness of social values. Murata's philosophy of technology was formed through deliberate investigation of the older layers of history, and it is philosophically sound. Considering how unproductive the debate on technology in Japan has been, there is a need to continue to develop theories and philosophies of technology such as those espoused by Murata.

49) As mentioned earlier, this often ends up just presuming the ways things "should be." Actually, it is possible that direct social utility could have been assumed as a requirement for a history of science from the outset. In that sense, from the perspective of the history of science, the purpose of science and technology advancement should not be located "outside" science itself.

50) At around the same time, Asahi Shimbun edited and published *Nihon kagaku gijutsu shi* (The history of science and technology in Japan, 1962). Although this is much smaller than the Dai-ichi Hōki version of the *Series on the history of science and technology in Japan*, it was nonetheless a great book that offered plenty of information in a single volume. Furthermore, Asahi Shimbun's work—which provides an overview of science and technology in Japan prior to the Meiji Period—functions like a complement to the *Series on the history of science and technology in Japan*, which generally focuses on the Meiji Period and subsequent eras.

51) A few words about a personal memory here. Probably around 1980, when I was first becoming interested in the history of science, I was foolish enough to slip into a class on the history of mathematics without knowing anything about the subject. Showing no ill will toward this amateur, Tamotsu Murata deigned to teach me a variety of things (Having said that, I inconvenienced the other members of the class, for which I should have apologized). During this class we read Cavalieri. Murata struck me then as something akin to an aloof mountain hermit.

52) Sasaki himself states that his public concern is not mere whimsy (Foreword to *Mathematical thought in the twentieth century*). More than once he has based arguments on his interest in social and political issues. For example, *Science, technology and modern politics*, a brief collection of Sasaki's lectures, expresses his political stance directly and clearly. He consistently criticizes neoliberalism as recklessly fanning the flames of interpersonal conflict and seeking to exhaust critical views of entire systems, calling for the establishment of a society that stresses alternative environmental resources. He also expresses his sympathy with the social frameworks of Katsuto Uchihashi and others, who have consistently engaged in honest criticism. More specifically, his plans include using natural energy in a proactive manner, heightening the awareness of workers, and creating collaboration between the critical citizen strata of society and workers. Sasaki refers to his framework as eco-socialism. It is worth referencing this as one aspect of the political left in the post-Cold War structure.

53) Some examples of very interesting historical overviews of sub-classifications in physics or related fields in this context include Toshima Araki's *Seiyō tenmongaku shi* (A history of Western astronomy, 1965), Toshio Watanabe's *Kinsei nihon tenmongaku shi* (A history of astronomy in early-modern Japan, 1986–1987), Kunitomo Sakurai's *Tenmongaku shi* (A history of astronomy, 1990), Hideo Kobayashi's *Chishitsugaku shi* (A history of geology, 1952), Motoharu Fujita's *Nihon chirigaku shi* (A history of Japanese geography, 1942), and Shintarō Ayusawa's *Chirigaku shi no kenkyū* (A study on the history of geography, 1948).

54) Works such as Juichi Matsuyama's *Nyūton to kanto* (Newton and Kant, 1997) must be seen more as the

pursuit of natural philosophical research traditions than as histories of physics. There are not many of them in Japan.

55) Incidentally, Tarō Kihara, Satoshi Watanabe, and Tsutomu Kaneko are three examples of authors who left us with reference materials that would be better classified as free and wide-ranging histories of scientific thought backed by physics, than as histories of physics. Kihara wrote *Bunshi to uchū* (Molecules and the universe, 1979) based on his final lecture at the University of Tokyo "Kikagaku teki shizen kan" (The Geometric view of nature). Since Kihara focuses on forms, his ideas may seem similar to those of Terada Torahiko. However, Kihara actually operates in a completely different world from Terada, as Kihara's theory of form develops while reviewing such topics as group theory and quantum physics. His ideas on situating cores in the middle of molecules (chapter 7), are full of amusing twists that deepen our direct understanding of quantum physics. A famous physicist and scientific philosopher Satoshi Watanabe left behind specialized contributions in fields such as thermodynamics and information theory, while at the same time performing work related to the history of scientific thought in time theory and life theory. Some examples of his writing are *Jikan* (Time, 1948), *Jikan no rekishi* (The history of time, 1973), *Toki* (Time, 1974), and *Seimei to jiyū* (Life and freedom, 1980). *Life and freedom* unexpectedly begins with a discussion of Buddhism by the physicist Watanabe. He then argues his position freely in a variety of fields including embryology, physics, and chemistry, before ending the volume with a discussion of his own theory of life. Life, he argues, is not a thing but a state, and is something immaterial that maintains its self-identity through change. After making this argument, Watanabe then states toward the end that the characteristic of life is found in freedom. Entropy is a living thing that has been reduced to a partial system; from this idea, he draws upon indeterminism and backward causality. One of Tsutomu Kaneko's famous works is *Ainshutain shokku* (The Einstein shock, 1981). This scientific cultural history covers a variety of events that occurred when Einstein visited Japan in 1922, the reaction to his visit in Japan, and the meaning of his visit.

56) While there is a risk of leaving behind the context of this introduction—which attaches strong importance to works intimately connected to the history of thought—it is worth touching here on Yasu Furukawa's *Kagaku no shakai shi* (A social history of science, 1989) as a valuable and high-quality sociological/socio-historical analysis. Although this volume is written from a comparatively general perspective, Furukawa is well-versed in the history of high-polymer chemistry, and is one of the leading chemical historians. For this reason, I would like to touch on Shigefumi Kurahashi's *Kagaku shakaigaku* (Science sociology, 1983) here.

57) The following references deal with subjects corresponding to types of sub-classifications in this area: Tamejirō Kawakami's *Shika igaku shi* (The history of dental medicine,1931), Sakae Miki's *Chōsen igakushi oyobi shippei shi* (The history of medicine and diseases in Korea, 1955), Yukio Tateno's *Hōshasen igaku shi* (The history of radiology, 1973), Atsushi Ishii's *Seishin igaku shippei shi* (The history of psychiatric disease, 1981), Takehisa Kōra's *Shiteki seishin igaku shi* (A personal history of psychiatric medicine, 1988), Hisao Nakai's *Seiō seishin igaku haikei shi* (The historical background of Western psychiatric medicine, 1999), and Waichirō Omata's *Kindai seishin igaku no seiritsu* (The establishment of modern psychiatric medicine, 2002). It is worth mentioning Toshiyuki Takizawa's *Yōjō ron no shisō* (The thought of discussions about nourishing life, 2003) as a volume that accurately summarizes the history of hygiene theory in Japan. Tadafumi Mizuno's *Taiiku shisō shi josetsu* (Introduction to the history of gymnastic thought, 1967) is an extremely interesting achievement that takes a unique approach as an extension of the curing theory.

58) Although this work is not a part of the period we are working in, it must be cited due to its overwhelming importance.

59) In discussing the history of medicine, Tachikawa often took an approach that portrays intellectuals fighting disease as a type of cultural history. He shed light on the lives of such cultural figures as Shiki Masaoka and Kenji Miyazawa from the perspective of illness. This is an interesting method of human

observation. Mahito Fukuda's *Kekkaku no bunka shi* (A cultural history of tuberculosis, 1995) also has a similar characteristic as a combined form of the history of medicine and cultural history. Taku Shinmura is another scholar who has left us with work specializing in the single-layer socio-historical approach. Two examples indicative of Shinmura's work are *Shi to yamai to kango no shakai shi* (The social history of death, disease and nursing, 1989) and *Kenkō no shakai shi* (The social history of health, 2006).

60) Sōda's *An illustrated history of Japanese medical culture* is a large-format, gorgeous volume full of illustrations. However, it is quite expensive and can only be purchased secondhand these days. This work covers Japanese medical science over a wide period of time stretching from ancient times to the beginning of the 20th century. Unequaled in the number and beauty of its illustrations, It contains many portraits of famous doctors from days past, as well as plenty of illustrations to aid in understanding surgical procedures and other topics. For information on modern medicine, the volume is especially noteworthy for the comparatively high amount of information related to military medicine it contains. Although such volumes are more suited for library use than private purchase, it is certainly a cultural asset of Japan.

61) Kawakita's *An introduction to medical science* contains the author's personal outline of the three phases of history, physiology, and pathology. Paradoxically, I feel that this volume unintentionally shows how difficult it is to write introductions to sciences like medicine. While detailed information is given for individual textbooks in each field, the discussion in this book reveals how difficult it is to provide a narrative of medical science on a level above the specific information itself, or on a general level. This can be said of any field of modern science, but it may be particularly apparent in fields such as medicine. Be that as it may, the health theories in chapter 16 exemplify Kawakita's exquisite abilities.

62) Although we do not have many works left to discuss in the history of scientific thought, I would like to touch on the work of science historians who are rather unusual. These works are Tetsuo Tsuji's *Nihon no kagaku shisō* (Scientific thought in Japan, 1973) and Hiroo Mita's *Yama no shisō shi* (The history of thought on mountains, 1973). While both volumes are low-cost paperback pocket editions, they are rich in content. *Scientific thought in Japan* does not look at science as a purely foreign idea that fell upon Japan, which originally had unscientific culture, but surveys ancient Japanese traditions to see what scientific, rational, and technological thought can be found there. While it is a small volume, it is full of content, and with every two or three reads I discover something new. I wish the author had written a larger, full-blown volume. Having said that, Tsuji has recently published a history of physics titled *Butsurigaku shi e no michi* (The way of the history of physics, 2011), albeit its subject is different. It seems there are few books similar to Mita's *The history of thought on mountains*, a splendid work that is therefore treasured by enthusiasts. The book takes selections from the writings of thinkers on the topic of mountains, and adds appropriate comments. Mountains have been seen as places of spiritual experience since ancient times—after all, the discourse space when discussing mountains themselves is extremely broad. Still, I wish he had written more. Incidentally, when Mita was young he was famous for his research on the history of mathematics (under the pen-name Yūichi Seta). His transition from the history of mathematics to mountains is itself interesting.

63) Nagayasu Shimao's *Chūgoku kagaku shi* (The history of Chinese chemistry, 1995) is a sort of small encyclopedia on China that surveys a wide range of topics including pottery, glazing techniques, copperware, ironware, salt production, paper making, brewing, and medicinal herbs. While it is of course based on the work of pioneers such as Needham, Shimao's ability to neatly cover such a wide variety of topics is certainly deserving of praise. It is also reassuring that the volume accurately covers the art of making elixirs, a very Chinese topic.

64) This book of Yamada's is worthy of translation into English. Surprisingly, a researcher in New Zealand called Mercer published an annotated translation of *Deep Words*. (Rosemary Mercer 1991) at around the same time.

65) I have heard rumblings that he was hurt by the acceptance of plate tectonics. However, this is a matter for geologists, and holds no interest for me. I am more impressed that a scientist of the first order with a

broad field of view such as Ijiri exists. Although Rironsha published *Kagaku ron* (On science) in 1954, the book was originally released in 1949 under the title of *Koseibutsugaku ron* (An essay on paleontology). Ijiri has also released *Ijiri Shōji senshū* (Selected works of Shōji Ijiri) in ten volumes (1981–1983).

66) Kuhn released *The Copernican Revolution: Planetary Astronomy in the Development of Western Thought* (1957 in the original language), a classical work on the history of scientific thought.

67) I will never forget receiving a sudden phone call from him when I was a mere idle graduate student. He encouraged me for around 30 minutes. We were not affiliated with the same research office, but he is one of the people I feel most directly and most deeply indebted to in my academic career.

68) On the other hand, the so-called philosophy of science—that is, the research tradition that has logical positivism as its origin—has assumed a solid position in Japanese philosophy. As mentioned before, the New Philosophy of Science diverged from the interworking between the study of the history of science, and it has maintained a subtle distance from the so-called philosophy of science. Since the latter half of the 1990s, the New Philosophy of Science has been recognized as accepted and it seldom becomes the subject of controversy. The philosophy of science following logical positivism has been touched on several times already, and I will avoid discussing it in more detail as it is outside the corpus of this introduction.

69) I will mention Kiyohiko Ikeda here, who is also versed in structuralist biology. Ikeda also made his appearance in the intellectual world as a proponent of structuralist biology at the end of the 1980s. He applies the concept of the arbitrary nature of linguistic symbols to the world of organisms, and seeks an antireductionist theory of life. In addition to theoretical works such as *Kōzōshugi seibutsugaku to wa nani ka* (What is structuralist biology?, 1988), *Kōzōshugi to shinka ron* (Structuralism and evolution, 1989), and *Seimei no keishiki* (The form of life, 2002), he has published many collections of light essays such as *Tadashiku ikiru to wa dō iu koto ka* (What does it mean to live properly?, 1998). Many of his readers enjoy his freewheeling style, marked by both venomous and frivolous talk. In *The form of life*, Ikeda argues based on concrete examples that, while organisms are basically dynamic systems that maintain an identity, the maintenance mechanism is not necessarily determined at the microscopic level, and thus organisms are arbitrary to some degree. One characteristic of this book is that, after defining science as a pathos that has difficulty describing identity, it then spends a great deal of time delving conceptually into what makes this "identity" work. Asking whether or not things and laws have an identity independent of human cognition is what philosophy is all about, so we can say that what Ikeda is really doing here is creating "a philosophy of identity" on the basis of his knowledge of biology. Although he has also published very interesting classification essays such as *Bunrui to iu shisō* (The thought of classification, 1992), I feel secure in saying that *The form of life* is his chief work. Of course, his recently published *"Shinka ron" o kakikaeru* (Rewriting "the theory of evolution," 2011) is a fantastic book full of essential claims couched in clear writing.

70) In other words, this means that it is impossible for us either to foolishly leap into a perfectly social Darwinist world like the former, or to achieve perfect coexistence with the weak. This also means that living in a kind of "incomplete compromise" is the condition of existence for humanity as a whole.

71) This was founded in 1971 as the Mitsubishi-Kasei Institute of Life Sciences. It was closed in the spring of 2010.

72) Miki's practically first work was *Naizō no hataraki to kodomo no kokoro* (The functions of organs and the heart of a child, 1982).

73) I have discussed Shigeo Miki briefly once before (see Kanamori 2004a, pp. 117–153).

74) It is typical for scholars such as Miki to remain individual masters of their art and to have difficulty establishing an academic tradition. However, he has many admirers in a variety of fields, and symposiums extolling him are held even today (in fact, I once spoke at such an event). Masatoshi Gotō's *Yuizō ron* (Organ-ism, 1999) is one example of an extremely interesting book that draws from Miki.

75) Anatomy is a peculiar discipline. One would expect it to be dry, but we sometimes encounter some very

interesting individuals in it. The anatomist Takeshi Yōrō has established a certain presence in the world of ideas with several studies that even include general philosophical implications divorced from his area of specialty. His works, such as *Katachi o yomu* (Read the shape, 1986) and *Yuinōron* (Brainism, 1989), are particularly important. He generally has a humorous and unique style that gives off a feeling of enlightenment. He was successful in reaching the general public, and even now is one of the most well-known mainstream figures in scientific culture. However, Yōrō's work after his mainstream success has declined in quality, and his essays may feel a little too light for those who have been following his work from his early days. *The Wall of Fools* (2003), which has been a popular success, is also merely a light work in which Yōrō's speech was transliterated into writing. It also includes some partial mistakes that cannot be overlooked. I am not sure how Yōrō himself feels about this, but I should not be the only one who feels disappointed in his transition. I would love to see Yōrō get back to serious work and write on clinical philosophy the way that only he could do (his *Rinshō tetsugaku* [Clinical philosophy, 1997] is merely a collection of light essays). I believe that Yōrō could write something really amazing if he would put his mind to it.

76) In some ways, cosmology is the field of science with the greatest sense of classical autonomy among the modern sciences, which show increasingly strong connections to industry. It is perhaps for this reason that the field continues to be seen as important in the scientific world. Other than Matsui, there are several well-known researchers such as Katsuhiko Satō (cf. Satō 1993; 2008).

77) However, an additional comment is required here. There are a number of figures in scientific culture who, with a solid scientific training in their field, opportunistically write some simplistic "reflections of a scientist" kind of essays. If such essays become too numerous, it could endanger their existence as scientists, and if they were originally allowed to make social statements because they were brilliant scientists, these scientists are engaged in social activities whose process could undermine their basis as scholars. First, it's detrimental for such scientists themselves (because "making money" ultimately should be a secondary matter). Second, this is detrimental for a general public that gets flooded with scientific discourse that is watered down and impossible to verify the truth of.

78) I am aware that this is a rather reductive judgment. The question of how to place positivism within sociology is not a given, but it is an open-ended problem; even an amateur sociologist such as myself is at least aware of the fact that many objections and different viewpoints have been raised over this. However, within this context I do not believe that it completely misses the mark to say that the construction and adherence to a certain kind of scientific stance is an important normative ideal of sociology.

79) This is *Toritachi no mau toki* (When birds dance, 2000), a sort of novel. His winning the Right Livelihood Award (sometimes called the "Alternative Nobel Prize") must have been some consolation given all the hardships he had faced in his life. I met him several times during his final years, and remember thinking how his quiet nature hid a powerful strength of character.

80) Yonemoto has put out more articles than books related to eugenics. However, works such as *Iden kanri shakai* (Genetically managed society, 1989) and *Yūseigaku to ningen shakai* (Eugenics and human society, co-written, 2000) show this side of his work. When we speak of the history of eugenics, the following resource must be mentioned: Zenji Suzuki's *Nihon no yūseigaku* (Eugenics in Japan, 1983).

81) Yoshioka calls "the sociology of science and technology (*kagaku gijutsu shakaigaku*)" "the social study of science and technology." This looks like the STS (Science, Technology and Society) that I will take up below, but one should recognize that its basic political stance is quite different.

82) "Science wars" is not exactly a shocking term for those familiar with the American style of debate. There are many examples of similar expressions, such as Darwin wars, Freud wars, and culture wars. Basically, any debate that is slightly heated they call "wars" in a rather journalistic way. Of course, "wars" may strike those accustomed to the ideological climate of Japan as an eccentric and radical expression. In particular, we shouldn't be quick to use such inflammatory rhetoric if it leads to a hardening of positions among scholars. Further, my manuscript was prepared as though there truly was a war going on, as it were. Even

if this is excusable as a common journalistic method, it may have been inappropriate for handling problems that require honest discussion and negotiation.

83) I suggest reading *Kagaku ron no genzai* (The present situation of science studies, Kanamori, Nakajima 2002), edited by Nakajima Hideto and myself, for the major currents in the development of the history of science, history of scientific thought, and sociology of science since Kuhn.

84) However, there is evidence that anthropological studies in the field, following the scholarly tradition of Latour—a French scientific theorist whom I discussed from my own perspective when I introduced the Science Wars—are beginning to take root to some degree in Japan. See for example *Gendai jinruigaku no purakushisu* (The praxis of modern anthropology, Yamashita and Fukushima 2005).

85) The list of references at the end of this book contains several volumes not mentioned in this introduction (I decided not to list them individually for brevity's sake). I feel this list of references is in and of itself an important source of information. Please feel free to use it as you wish.

a) After the publication of the Japanese version of this book (October 2011), the following books that include the words *kagaku shisō shi* in their titles have been published:

Sūkikyō berrarumīno no tegami: kagaku shisō shi e no hitotsu no tobira (A letter of Cardinal Bellarmino: A window on the history of scientific thought, Hiroshi Nishifuji 2012)

Gōrisei no kōkogaku: Furansu no kagaku shisō shi (Archeology of rationality: The history of scientific thought in France, Osamu Kanamori 2012)

Kagaku shisō shi no tankyū (An exploration into the history of scientific thought, Hidehito Sakamoto 2013)

b) "Sanshirō," a novel by renowned Meiji-era novelist Sōseki Natsume, features a teacher named Hirota who some say was modeled after Kōichi Kanō. Yojirō, a friend of the protagonist Sanshirō, nicknames Hirota "grand darkness" for the fact that he is a careful critic of both traditional and contemporary culture who seeks neither fame nor wealth but rather is content to live out his life in a "grand darkness."

c) The Michurin Movement was named after Ivan Vladimirovich Michurin (1855–1935). Trofim Denisovich Lysenko (1898–1976) created the movement in 1948 as a Marxist alternative to Mendel's genetics.

d) While Lysenko was influential in the USSR, there was a fierce debate between advocates of his theory and mainstream researchers in Japan.

e) Nakayama passed away on May 10, 2014.

CHAPTER 1
NUCLEAR AND ELEMENTARY PARTICLE PHYSICS: THE EVOLUTION OF A COMPETITIVE VIEW OF SCIENCE

TAKUJI OKAMOTO

Section 1. From the Inception of Quantum Mechanics to the Nobel Prize of Hideki Yukawa

When Japan was entering the Showa Period, quantum mechanics was beginning to take hold in Europe. After several years of delay, a movement to learn and research this new physical theory arose in Japan, principally among young people in their late teens and twenties. The effects of this were not immediately visible to this generation, but by the mid-1930s, quantum mechanics was being extended to quantum electrodynamics and applied to the study of atomic nuclei. The results of this were evident after World War II, as, in 1949, Hideki Yukawa (1907–1981) received the first Nobel Prize ever awarded to a Japanese national, an acclaim that was evident to all.

Japan's second Nobel Prize was awarded to Sin-Itiro Tomonaga (1906–1979), who, together with Yukawa, was working on cutting-edge studies on quantum mechanics. Coming slightly before Yukawa's Nobel Prize, the work for which Tomonaga won this award was related to fundamental theory in quantum electrodynamics. After Yukawa and Tomonaga, Masatoshi Koshiba (1926–) was awarded the prize in 2002, and Yōichirō Nambu (1921–2015), an American citizen, Makoto Kobayashi (1944–), and Toshihide Maskawa (1940–) were awarded the 2008 prize for research in elementary particle physics.

As of the end of 2010, among the fifteen Japanese Nobel Prize winners in natural sciences, seven have been in physics.[a] Six out of these seven are researchers of elementary particle physics, and five out of these six are theorists. Despite the strong trend of giving the Nobel Prize in physics to researchers rather than theorists, most of Japan's physics prize-winners to date have been theorists. This fact illustrates that, in the period when this research was carried out, Japan boasted its highest level of international competitiveness in the field of nuclear and elementary particle theory.

Japanese research in nuclear and elementary particle theory started with limited study on quantum mechanics, and before long, a wealth of accumulated achievements drew public attention and gained a firm base of international appreciation. All this process occurred during the period from 1925 to 1950, the first half of the Showa Period. The great strides forward that theoretical physics made in Japan is one of the most important trends that characterizes all Japanese science from this period. Moreover, during this same period, while not as eye-catching as winning Nobel Prizes, Japan's experimental physics research in nuclear and elementary particle physics was also world-class. For example, in 1937, a cyclotron with an electromagnet twenty-six inches in diameter was produced at RIKEN, making Japan only the second country after the United States to operate such an instrument. If a proposed sixty-inch cyclotron had been completed, it would have been the world's largest, along with a similar model at the University of California.

When one takes historical background into account, some thought-provoking features of the aforementioned nuclear and elementary particle research programs emerge. After World War I, Japan was considered one of the world's five major military powers; but during the early Showa Period, Japan was still economically challenged compared to the developed nations in the West (the phrase *senshinkoku* was often used at the time). It is difficult to understand why research in nuclear physics and quantum electrodynamics was promoted, as such subject matter would not have been very useful for industry. In addition, from the Manchurian incident through the progression of the Second Sino-Japanese War and to the onset of World War II, circumstances would have called for applications of science and technology with more direct utility for warfare. It is difficult to find a reason why the state and society supported such theoretical research, except perhaps for potential military applications of the energy that could be theoretically generated by nuclear fission (which most Japanese experts expected to be impossible). Nevertheless, except for a brief interruption in the final days of and immediately after WWII, research related to basic quantum mechanics and nuclear physics continued; resources that were in scarce supply in Japan at the time were allocated to the construction of the aforementioned cyclotrons.

This chapter explores why research on atomic nuclei, elementary particles, and quantum electrodynamics was maintained in pre-war Japan; it is an attempt to follow the attitudes and activities of physicists from the inception of quantum mechanics in Japan through the period of Yukawa's Nobel Prize. In particular, there will be a focus on the academic perspective of the individuals involved. What I would like to take up as the academic view are the motivations behind scientists choosing to engage in study of certain fields, and I would also like to focus on the successes the various scientists achieved thereafter. More specifically, what I am concerned with is the motivation behind learning and researching particular academic fields in a certain culture at a certain period of time, as well as the philosophies that are reflected in their achievements. Discussion as to what academism and science are or should be like in general are not a central topic here. The academic view in the sense I have mentioned above is not something that is often explicitly discussed once it is established at a certain period and accepted by a particular group. If scholarship in a certain direction is deemed to be a matter of course, there is no need for subsequent generations of scholars to reexamine it. Regarding the subject of this chapter, that kind of academic view was first established in the middle of the Meiji Period. It then went through some slight modifications and changes in response to the circumstances of the times and then was handed down to the generation active in the first half of the Showa Period. Accordingly, in this chapter, though slightly long for a pre-history, the establishment of a certain type of academic view in the mid-Meiji Period will be taken up first, followed by discussion focusing on some symbolic events occurring in the course of time through to the first half of the Showa Period.

There are other reasons to begin our discussion in the mid-Meiji Period. For one thing, in the first half of the Showa Period, the scientists who began their work from the mid-Meiji period were in some cases still performing research, and many were also in administrative positions to support research, with great influence over the actual conduct of studies. Also, giving a brief review of some events that started in the mid-Meiji Period and led up to the early Showa Period will lead to a deeper understanding of the events that occurred after the acceptance of quantum mechanics. That is, it will become easier to see why things that did not occur before the advent of quantum mechanics took place after quantum mechanics made its debut. Describing the academic flow from the mid-Meiji Period will provide an understanding of how the situation after the inception of quantum mechanics allowed for the realization of the ideals of those who aspired to scholarship in the mid-Meiji Period. Lastly, what many people had considered to be cardinal achievements of Japanese natural science up to the mid-1930s were accomplished by a generation of scientists represented by Hantarō Nagaoka (1865–1950) and Hisashi Kimura (1870–1943). The opportunity to discuss such figures would be still another reason to devote slightly more time to discussing the era before quantum mechanics.[1]

It should be noted that this chapter makes reference to individual research only where necessary; when doing so it only utilizes prior research to provide a brief overview.

Section 2. Establishment of a Competitive Scientific View: the Agony of Hantarō Nagaoka

1. Challenge to the West

Now in Japan, the situation where science has become rooted in a certain kind of society and culture is understood to indicate not just that science is learned as part of a basic education, but that there are people who undertake research independently and report the outcomes. In Japanese history at least, science became one of the main pillars of education after the Meiji Restoration, and shortly thereafter, there began to emerge people who engaged in research, and who shared the results with the world. It appears that this experience has led to an uncontested understanding of a certain idea—that the acceptance of science requires that research should include not simply learning, but also the outgoing transmission of knowledge.

If what we call science is a field in which people will immediately after learning wish to emulate pioneers and begin research, and in which, if they are able to obtain results, they will wish to announce these results to the world at large, then in Japan, where both state and society sought to introduce science from the Meiji Restoration onwards, it is no wonder that there have emerged people who embark on research and transmit such knowledge. Yet, is this actually how the transition occurred? Reflecting on this experience somewhat cautiously shows that even within Japanese history, there seem to have been many obstacles between practically applying scientific knowledge or learning of science and doing research on one's own based on acquired knowledge or publishing results internationally in foreign (mostly European) languages. Looking over these obstacles, it's easy to overlook what is necessary to make some conceptual leaps from learning to research and transmission in the course of the introduction of science.

The mid-Meiji Period was the first time Japanese people aspired to send achievements of scientific research to the rest of the world. What motivations did they have to move from passive learning towards research and transmission? What obstacles did they perceive, and how did they overcome them? In the case of Hantarō Nagaoka, there seem to be some clues as to how to unlock these questions. Examining them may reveal how Nagaoka's academic worldview was formed.

Nagaoka gained entry to the faculty of science at the University of Tokyo after attending the university's preparatory school. It is known that one year later, in 1883, he vacillated over whether or not to head down the pathway of studying physics. If Nagaoka were to elect to pursue this course of study, he found it unsatisfactory to simply pass on what was imported from foreign countries. Nevertheless, in the field of natural sciences, Nagaoka agonized during this period over whether or not an Asian person like him would be able to add anything new.

People in Nagaoka's generation who attended institutions of higher education such as the University of Tokyo, the Imperial College of Engineering, and the agricultural colleges absorbed scientific knowledge (not restricted to the field of physics) only recently imported from the West through Western textbooks in English, German, and French. There were no Asian scientists mentioned in such textbooks. Nagaoka was seriously concerned that perhaps Asians lacked originality, and that they had no choice but to simply receive the opinions of Westerners; he wondered if Asians lacked the ability to conduct scientific research, and if it was a field in which only Westerners should engage. Also in Nagaoka's era, early education, such as reading, writing, and basic ethics and morals, was studied at regional *han* schools, which were the precursor to primary education institutions. He was very much aware that much of the content that was then part of education at an institute of higher learning was not included in the scholarship that had been passed down through the generations in Japan.

Troubled by these realizations, Nagaoka took a year's leave of absence, during which time he read the Chinese classics, resolving to find evidence of achievements by Asians in the natural sciences. As a result of his search, he found an accurate accounting of solar and lunar eclipses in *Chunqiu* (The spring and autumn annals), and he encountered a description of a meteorite. He also knew that *Shiji* (*Records of the Grand Historian of China*) contained a description of aurora borealis. In ancient eras, Nagaoka discovered, it could be said that the Chinese had a more advanced understanding of the natural sciences than the West, and he was reassured to realize that their study of the natural sciences was not necessarily just trying to keep up with the West. In the end, Nagaoka decided to pursue physics. Nagaoka's examination of the Chinese classics continued even through graduate school. He began to realize that the writings of ancient China were worth reading, even though Sinologists discussed only ambiguous notions of how to properly govern nations (Itakura et al. 1973, pp. 39–44).

In graduate school, Nagaoka met Aikitu Tanakadate (1856–1952), a student five years his senior who studied in the United Kingdom. Nagaoka wrote a letter to Tanakadate in June 7, 1888, which reveals what motivated Nagaoka to continue studying physics. In a prior letter from Tanakadate to Nagaoka, it seems Tanakadate did not give a favorable impression of Western civilization and Western people, a sentiment with which Nagaoka seems to have agreed. More specifically, Nagaoka put forth the opinion that Westerners are not always correct (Nagaoka used the term "whites"), and criticized those who blindly adopted Western culture as cowards. He also stated that it was the clear duty of them to defeat Westerners and reveal their true natures, something he hoped would be achieved within ten or twenty years (Koizumi 1975, pp. 86–87).

Nagaoka's use of the word "defeat" may suggest war for some readers, but those young people who had experienced neither the First Sino-Japanese War nor the Russo-Japanese Wars probably did not share this interpretation. I believe the conversation between Nagaoka and Tanakadate was referring to overwhelming an opponent through research efforts. Nagaoka stated that this victory needed to be within ten to twenty years, as "There is no use of observing the victory of our descendents over the whites with the telescope from jigoku [hell]"—thus "[w]e must work actually with an open eye, keen sense, and really understanding, indefatigably and not a moment stopping" (Koizumi 1975, pp. 86–87).

What Nagaoka regarded as still more important was to inform Westerners of Japanese research. He believed that, whereas the words of Westerners were devoid of substance, Japanese scientists had substance but insufficient words. He determined that from then on there was no choice but to write in European languages, whether English, French, or German. In order to show this determination, Nagaoka wrote the entirety of his letters to Tanakadate in English, even though these letters were exchanged between two Japanese people (Itakura 1973, pp. 112–114).

What motivated Nagaoka to study physics was a desire to make new discoveries by himself and to challenge the West intellectually through such contributions. Nagaoka chose the field of physics, but looking at young people across Japan, a similar attitude motivated academics to engage in other fields.

Kazuo Hatoyama (1856–1911) was a lawyer and politician of the Meiji Period. His son Hideo Hatoyama also studied law in his father's footsteps and graduated from university with a law degree. When contemplating what future path to go down, Hatoyama's father advised him to be a university professor, though it was regrettable:

If you decide to follow an academic path, it means little unless you become a world-class scholar. However, this would be difficult in the field of jurisprudence. If the subject of the research is essentially worldwide, there is hope. However, what you are going to study is Japanese law. This is the difference between the natural sciences such as physics and chemistry and jurisprudence in terms of global worthiness. Of course, it could be possible to conduct research that would be of global value. Nevertheless, in making discoveries or research in which world-class values are to be acknowledged, there is a large difference in difficulty between natural sciences, whose subjects are mainly common all around the world, and jurisprudence, whose subjects are mainly confined to a certain country or society. In summary, jurisprudence amounts to discussion or research on Japanese law. Therefore, it is better to go out into the world with your academic knowledge and work more actively than to be a Japanese jurist (Hatoyama ed. 1919, pp. 46–47).

While scientific scholarship could move forward by disclosing its accomplishments to the world, the same is not true of the field of law. That this is possible in the natural sciences is an indication of their "global value." Hatoyama shared with Nagaoka the view that choosing academia was to throw down a gauntlet to the world, but he believed that law, which he had chosen to study, did not fulfill conditions appropriate to pose such a challenge in the world. After studying at Daigaku Nankō (which later became the University of Tokyo), Hatoyama traveled to the United States of America, where he received a bachelor of law degree from Columbia University, followed by a doctorate of law from Yale University. He became a professor at his alma mater for a time before changing careers to become a politician. Knowing both Japanese and American law, and with experience as a diplomat, Hatoyama believed that the law that he and his own son had mastered was inferior in places to the natural sciences in terms of "global value."

Similar circumstances befell Sōseki Natsume (1867–1916), whose story may be better known. Natsume also contemplated his future path from a young age. He began to write and manipulate the English language, and, prompted by aspirations to impress Westerners, he advanced to the department of English literature. Natsume received good grades, and he was given the opportunity to study abroad in the United Kingdom. However, while studying there, he began to believe it was deceptive to lavish praise on Western poems when he felt no inspiration from them. Natsume then received a visit from the chemist Kikunae Ikeda (1864–1936), who was in Germany at the time, and the two men exchanged ideas about the natural sciences. This event encouraged Natsume to aim at "more organized, solid study" instead of studying "ghostlike literature" (Natsume 1908).

Ikeda's visit to Natsume was also noted in a letter sent from Natsume to Torahiko Terada (1878–1935). In a paragraph before the description of Ikeda's visit, Sōseki compares science and English literature:

> If we are to live in the academic world, we should choose cosmopolitan fields. English literature lies behind the scenes; one cannot distinguish oneself in Japan or in England as long as one remains in this field. It could serve as a cautionary lesson for someone cheeky like me! You should pursue your study of physics. I read Professor Rücker's speech on Atomic Theory at the British Association. It was so stimulating that I became interested in studying science myself. (Natsume 1901)

Hatoyama referred to the natural sciences as having global value. Natsume described the same feature as "cosmopolitan." In any event, he offers the understanding that when one aspires to achieve academically, one also wishes to present the results of such study to the scrutiny of the world. It is difficult to achieve this in law or literature, but possible with the natural sciences. This academic dynamic is relatively clear in the case of Nagaoka, Hatoyama, and Natsume; there are also others in whom it lies in a less clear, more fragmented form. Kumagusu Minakata (1867–1941) studied at the University of Tokyo at the same time as Nagaoka and Natsume. In a letter on October 17, 1911 addressed to Kunio Yanagita (1975–1962), looking back on a day when he studied in the British Museum (March 16, 1897), he recalled how in a room he met Sun Yat Sen (1866–1925) and discussed the future of Asia. Sun Yat Sen asked him what he aspired to do in his life. Minakata answered, as he puts in his writing, "If only Asian people could expel all Europeans from Asia." Minakata related how Sun Yat Sen's face lost all color, adding "I now know he is not such a great man after all." (Minakata 1911, p. 162). It is possible to gain an understanding of Minakata's antagonism towards the West, as well as the fact, though less obviously, that this emotion served to motivate him in his studies.

Aikitu Tanakadate, to whom Nagaoka spoke about his sense of rivalry against the West, replied at a symposium held in later years when he was asked if he felt Japan could not rival the West:

I thought we could. (Laughing) Long ago there might have been people who thought we could not, maybe. Still, as you know, in the old days people were reckless. They saw Europeans as being inferior, as being more like animals. . . . They thought highly of sophism, but sophistry is an art that anyone can use after a little exercise. To do as the West has done, Japan needs to study practical sciences. In my youth, the goal of humanity was learning how to rule the world and the nation. . . . Nevertheless, they did not find such learning in the West that went beyond what they had learned in the East. That's when I realized there was no reason to study what we now refer to as humanities. Yet we lag behind in the fields they established, such as geometry or algebra. That's why I set about learning physics, but I still remain unable to do anything with it. (Tanakadate 1936, pp. 37–38)

Tanakadate believed that the East was not inferior to the West in terms of politics or ethics, and thus he felt no rivalry with the West in these areas. But in terms of physical sciences, Tanakadate believed the East was behind. Nagaoka also shared the same awareness when he was worried whether Asian people had any aptitude for scientific research. Like Nagaoka, Kōkichi Kanō (1865–1942), among others, is believed to have harbored doubts as to whether Japanese people possessed the ability to perform scientific research, and he chose this issue as the subject of his study. Kanō, a schoolmate of Nagaoka, was an academic administrator who studied mathematics first, then shifted to philosophy at graduate school, then studied Japanese academic history and history of thought while engaging in educational administration.

2. Concerning Industrial Application

It was widely understood that the introduction of Western science and technology was accelerated during the Meiji Period in order for Japan to keep up with Western military and industrial technologies and maintain its independence as a nation. The main benefits of the introduction of science and technology were expected to be practical, including by Nagaoka and his colleagues. Their perception of academia and science discussed above was somewhat colored by the fact that they did not take those who were studying medicine, engineering, or agriculture into con-

sideration. However, the introduction of science for the purpose of practical application was overemphasized, and it has been largely overlooked that there were
young people who were less concerned with practical application of science in Japan of the mid-Meiji Period, and that their behaviors were based on their unique
views on academism and science.

In reality, as detailed throughout this chapter, there was a not insignificant
number of people during the pre-war period who paid little attention to industrial
or military applications when they turned towards science and academism. There
are several reasons why this was possible, but I will offer one convincing point
which is closely related to the movement in support of the introduction of science
with the end application in mind.

It may be a little paradoxical that in prewar and postwar Japan, agriculture and
engineering had enjoyed high academic and social status, giving other fields free
rein to develop without concern for practical application.

During the Meiji Period, engineering and agriculture were seldom present in
the top institutions of higher learning (and subsequently, research) in the West,
but as a result of Japan's prioritizing the introduction of practical-based science
and technology, institutions dedicated to education (and later research) in those
fields were part of the former Imperial University. These fields were at the top of
regular education, with agronomist Yoshinao Kozai (1864–1934), and engineer
and naval officer Yuzuru Hiraga (1878–1943) subsequently appointed to the position of university president. Agriculture and engineering also enjoyed high
prestige, and scholars in those areas became eligible for doctorates (after the Academic Degree Order [1887]). Finally, engineering and agriculture graduates had a
constant presence in official circles and in business.[2]

The higher status of agriculture and engineering in Japan as compared to Europe and the United States is further evident in the experiences of Japanese college
educators who studied abroad. When physicists such as Tanakadate and Nagaoka
studied abroad, colleges in the United Kingdom or Germany had departments of
physics, where they attended lectures and conducted research. On the other hand,
most higher education institutes abroad did not have dedicated departments for
civil engineers who majored in water supply engineering or for bridge engineering, except for France, where Japanese civil engineers in the early-Meiji Period
studied; therefore, studying abroad meant participating in a particular project of
water supply works or bridge construction that employed what was then cutting-edge technology. With the exception of France, there were few academic pro-

grams abroad offering coursework in these subject areas, as there were in the case of physics. Upon returning to Japan, such individuals would often be awarded a doctorate by the Japanese institution that sponsored the trip abroad or would became a professor at an Imperial University.

Engineering and agriculture as applied sciences had been established both academically and socially since the middle of the Meiji Period in Japan. This allowed those who specialized in science (natural science) to develop an academic view that was not constrained by practicality. Nevertheless, with a responsibility towards his generation, Tanakadate wanted to apply the results of physics research to aviation engineering, and Nagaoka had a strong interest in applying his research to seismology, optics, and communications. While recognizing the import of practical applications of science, such practical applications of science were ultimately secondary for them, and when they discussed the essential character of scientific research, the major emphasis was on the intellectual challenge.

The fact that fields with major practical applications such as engineering and agriculture enjoyed relatively advanced social and cultural capital did not necessarily constitute an advantageous situation for the development of the relevant fields in the twentieth century. Furthermore, in regular education, Japan placed high emphasis on practical applications, reflecting the reality of the times, in which priority was given to maintaining military and industrial parity with the West. However, this was not always effective in the periods when the results of scientific research were directly applicable to technology.

For example, looking at the United States, R. A. Millikan (1868–1953), who was active around the same time as Nagaoka, introduced several of his associates who had doctorates in physics to technical development work at companies such as the Bell Telephone Company from the prewar period. During the first half of the twentieth century, Bell and General Electric, among others, were very eager to incorporate some of the new developments in physics and other fields of scientific research. Since the role of providing human resources in these fields often fell on the natural sciences, as opposed to the relatively underdeveloped field of engineering, the development of science was directly related to the development of technology. For example, the key development of quantum physics in the twentieth century rapidly led to applications in electronics, resulting in inventions such as the transistor (1947). Quantum mechanics was developed in Europe, and afterwards came to America and Japan. However, before the advent of the transistor, Japan had little communication between the disciplines of physics and electrical engineering, except for a period during World War II.

3. Features of a Competitive View of Science

Now I will discuss one particular feature of the young Nagaoka's scientific thought. Science is often understood as a discrete academic discipline. It appears to describe the natural order of things, but this would mean that Nagaoka selected physics for his career not because he had an interest in natural phenomena, but because he selected science from a raft of possible disciplines and then zeroed in on physics. During the course of his decision-making process, he turned to Chinese classics.

Additionally, young people at the time aspiring to academic life were also aware that they had to publish results of their research to the world by adding new findings to the existing academic systems. They also shared a philosophy that new knowledge would not necessarily be tied to usage or application, and that academism itself had value, along with addition of new findings to the academic system.

Publishing research results globally meant, in essence, revealing these results to the West. Even during the era of passive learning, an attitude to challenge the West in terms of scientific research already existed in a resolve to attempt dissemination of study results. At least some of the young people's intellectual self-respect was stimulated by the influx of Western culture, and they were determined to accept and stand up to the intellectual challenges posed by this new knowledge.

We cannot simply refer to this attitude in opposition to the West as nationalism. Nagaoka later came to respect Japanese pioneers such as Tadataka Inō (1745–1818); Nagaoka wrote that the reputation of China had dropped internationally, becoming only a shadow of its former glory. Nevertheless, at least in the middle of the Meiji period, Nagaoka's study of ancient China had been grounds for his self-worth as an Asian. In this sense, the intellectual self-esteem of Nagaoka and his colleagues was awakened and cast as a sense of intellectual rivalry with the West. Before the Meiji Restoration, Japan had been part of the Chinese cultural sphere, where intellectual aspects that drew on and established such a competition were not overtly existent.

Additionally, as mentioned before, Japan's confrontation of the challenges posed by the West in terms of the Western disciplines did not occur across all the Western academic fields that Japan at the time tried to absorb; it was understood that science was a suitable field in which to engage in this competition. Science from the mid-nineteenth century onwards, at least ostensibly, was comprised of methods, practices, and systems that did not discriminate among the participants in terms of language, cultural origin, or religion; therefore, it was possible for young Japanese people, who had embraced Western culture just twenty years before, to produce scientific results after certain preparation and to engage in competition.[3]

Prior to the Meiji Restoration, Japan had had a long tradition of Dutch and other Western academic influence, but when Nagaoka questioned the abilities of Asians in science, this historical influence did not come to his mind. In the light of his later focus on Tadataka Inō, it appears Nagaoka may not have been fully aware of the existence of this Dutch and Western learning in the Edo Period; if this were the case, it indicates all the more that Nagaoka's participation in the scientific research of the time was not an extension of the Dutch and Western learning tradition of the Edo Period. There was a major discontinuity between the dominant elements of learning, digestion, and assimilation of Dutch and Western learning of the Edo Period and the scientific research carried out by young researchers in the mid-Meiji Period; this discontinuity drove the competitive view of science that had developed within the influx of Western literature, forcing innovations throughout academia as a whole.

4. Learning and Competition

Thus far, we have discussed the motivations of Tanakadate and Nagaoka to study physics. I have also pointed out that the reason they were able to engage in science research in this competitive way was because the scientific fields generously accepted all participants. On the other hand, we can see from their communications that, though seemingly they were not aware of this at the time, the two men had to irreconcilably confront each other as they continued to engage in such a scientific competition.

As Nagaoka wrote to Tanakadate, in order to compete with the West, it was also necessary to get Western scientists to rely on Japanese research. Nagaoka argued that Japanese scientists had no choice but to learn the major languages of the West, though there was more than just language to learn. Even though science held very universal standards as to the rules of competition, there were no books which could render this standard readily learnable in its entirety. While so-called textbooks described the knowledge components of science, there were no handy instruction books that might allow one to make the leap from there to research. Since the rules of the game were not established in Japan, it was necessary for anyone who wished to take part to somehow learn these rules from the West. Nevertheless, the purpose of studying for these Japanese scientists was competitive, so they were not able to continue learning. Learning under foreign teachers hired from abroad, and learning from scientists from other nations while studying in Europe, both Tanakadate and Nagaoka were looking for opportunities for competition. At least in Nagaoka's case, however, his attitude was conspicuously meek and reserved towards non-Japanese, yet he had a strict attitude towards his fellow Japanese. He believed that if one person were to attempt to take on a scientific challenge without sufficient knowledge and were subsequently defeated, the damage to intellectual pride would be significant. As Nagaoka built up reserves of skill and looked for a worthy opportunity to take on a challenge, he himself swallowed his pride as he moved into old age, passing the mantle to the next generation.[4]

It was also difficult to determine what and to what extent one should learn. There were rules for competing, but there were no people or books available to provide a clear answer as to when such learning should be finished. Even though Nagaoka did not go so far as to assert the need to convert to Christianity, adopt a European language as his mother tongue, or marry a European,[5] he was aware that it was insufficient to simply master rules in order to become, for example, an excellent athlete. In scientific research, it was necessary to absorb the knowledge of previous generations, and to learn from excellent leaders. But how far should that learning extend? If it were necessary for Western education systems to be mimicked in order to achieve success in science, was it also necessary, for example, to study the human relationships, lifestyles, or worldviews of the West?

Furthermore, in order to make Westerners listen more carefully, the subjects of research should be aligned with this purpose. If Asians were to challenge Westerners, at the very least it was necessary to select universal, highly abstract topics that were of common interest to both. In some cases, there were topics that were interesting and had relevance to the West but almost no relevance to the East, which is why these became popular research areas.

Characteristics such as those described above, which arose out of learning, came to cast a constant shadow over the acceptance of subjects such as the theory of relativity and quantum mechanics in Japan.

5. Academic Expectations of the Nation

If it is assumed that young Japanese people had been attempting to challenge the West intellectually, it might be expected that this had the blessings of those responsible for the educational and academic policies of the nation. In practice, however, there was almost no involvement from the establishment in the movement among young people towards intellectual competition. In the middle of the Meiji Period, Arinori Mori (1847–1889) was the minister of education. Mori oversaw the enactment of edicts establishing elementary schools, middle schools, teachers' colleges, and the Imperial university system. In some cases he put his own mark on proposals for Imperial edicts, and he paid a great deal of attention to the curricular contents of various schools. He was a singularly unique minister who, if necessary, did not hesitate to state his academic views in front of faculty and students at the Imperial University. Nagaoka was once present at such an occasion (Nagaoka 1947), where Mori took the opportunity to speak about the nation's academic expectations. His words can be read as admonishments that Japan at that time should not participate in unnecessary intellectual competitions.

For example, in a speech that Mori gave at the Imperial University on February 7, 1889 just before his death, at which Nagaoka was present, Mori seems to advocate that all academic activities should be carried out for the benefit of the nation. More specifically, while it may be beneficial to learn from foreign examples in law and political science, it is necessary to focus on content that is in line with Japanese reality. Literature and history should also put emphasis on Japanese elements, and it would be harmful if students developed biases towards Chinese or Roman letters or knew every details of Western history while being unstudied in Japanese history. Even in science, engineering, and medicine, there was a need to know general principles, but, Mori argued, the focus should primarily be on things necessary for Japan; it was problematic to give priority to elements proper to foreign countries while neglecting issues urgent for Japan (Mori 1889).

Prior to this, in the second decade of the Meiji Period, Mori also prepared a document that seems to have detailed a major educational administration policy, in which he says science is divided into two categories: pure science and applied science; although both of these are necessary for a nation, in light of the specific situation of Japan, it was appropriate to emphasize the practical uses of science, while a small portal to the pure sciences would suffice (Mori, date unknown).

Known for his own conduct as a scholar, for establishing the Meirokusha (Japan's first intellectual society), and for his vigorous activities as a writer, Mori was aware that an academic discipline has a tendency to try and explore the universal truth for as long as it exists, and he understood that, as long as the core of academic endeavor was derived from the West, the interest of academics would consequently be focused on the West. Under such circumstances, Mori argued, Japan lacked the wherewithal for intellectual competition with Western counterparts, and thus, he felt that academic activities should be pursued for the sake of the nation. Although the academic administration of the state was not always as Mori intended, he seems to have captured exactly what was required by the Japanese of that time. Mori did not inspire young people to take on intellectual challenges; whereas Nagaoka and his peers had established a venue for themselves separate from the competition between nations that occurred through diplomacy, trade, and warfare, they were attempting to compete in a manner not associated with the demands of their country.

Section 3. The Development of Competition and the Fate of the Competitive View of Science: From the Saturnian Model of the Atom to Anti-Relativity

1. The Saturnian Model of the Atom

What were some of the concrete results of Nagaoka's mid-Meiji Period resolution to challenge the West intellectually?

From just before matriculating at graduate school, Nagaoka helped foreign teacher C. G. Knott (1856–1922) in his study of magnetostriction, while also measuring magnetic variation due to the Nōbi earthquake. After this, Nagaoka traveled to Europe to study from 1893 to 1896, where he was engaged primarily in the study of mathematical physics. For a while after returning to Japan, he conducted further research into magnetostriction before travelling again to Europe in 1900. At the International Congress of Physics, Nagaoka reported the results of his magnetostriction research, and at a general meeting of the International Association of Geodesy, he released the results of gravity measurements made in Japan. Both events were held in Paris. Nagaoka was asked to give a comprehensive lecture on magnetostriction, and thus it became clear that he was regarded as a leading researcher in this field. Nevertheless, for Nagaoka, it was impossible to miss the concentration of interest among physicists in Europe towards radioactivity and atomic spectroscopy, which were recent discoveries at that time (Itakura et al. 1973, pp. 212–221).

Nagaoka's publications in geodesy concerned the results of gravity measurements made in Japan, which he took over from Aikitu Tanakadate and Hisashi Kimura. Immediately after Nagaoka returned to Japan, some events occurred in this field that drew the attention of Tanakadate and Nagaoka. Because of significant errors made in the latitude observatory at Mizusawa, Iwate Prefecture, the headquarters of the German International Latitude Observation Service assessed Mizusawa as having less credibility than other observatories and requested an investigation be made into defects in its equipment. Although similar errors occurred in Russia, which were attributed to the use of a small telescope, the telescope in Mizusawa was large, and this request for investigation could be construed as casting doubt on Japanese management and maintenance of devices as well as their measurement techniques. Kimura, who was the director of the observatory, along with Tanakadate and Nagaoka, did not find any issues when he investigated the equipment. This left the measurement techniques as the only remaining avenue for investigation. If there was a problem here, there would be unavoidable loss in the perceived reliability of Japanese scientists, since the observatory had rejected Germany's suggestions to dispatch German observers.

Nevertheless, director Kimura examined the results of measurements at other observatories, and found a small variation occurring on a yearly cycle. This represented the discovery of the z-term. The results of this investigation were announced in a paper in 1902 and were recognized around the world (The editing committee of the history of 100 years of Japanese astronomy 2008, pp. 44–45). In the field of medicine, research such as that of Shibasaburō Kitasato reached international standards from the 1890s onwards; physics had not produced anything comparable to this. Nevertheless, Kimura's accomplishments showed that science in Japan was approaching the kind of quality that Tanakadate and Nagaoka had hoped for during their youth.

In 1903, Nagaoka himself threw his research open to the world for scrutiny, presenting his Saturn-type atomic model for examination. Before and after an academic meeting in Paris, Nagaoka engaged in research on subjects related to geophysics such as seiches and tsunamis. He continued work on magnetostriction, but over several years left research in both subjects in the hands of successors. While introducing the latest European work on electrons and radioactivity to Japan, Nagaoka himself engaged in the study of atomic structure. The results of his research were made public at an academic conference in 1903. These were published the following year in *Tokyo Sūgaku-Butsurigakukwai Kiji-Gaiyō* (Summaries of the Proceedings of the Tokyo Mathematico-Physical Society), and subsequently in *Nature, Philosophical Magazine* and *Physikalische Zeitschrift* (Physical Journal) (Butsurigaku shi kenkyū kankōkai 1969). Nevertheless, there are differences in content between what was published in Japan and what was published elsewhere.

In Nagaoka's atomic model, many negatively-charged electrons revolve around a positively-charged nucleus of a certain size, with the whole model resembling the planet Saturn; this is why it is called the Saturnian model. He claimed that this model was not a sheer speculation; in his understanding, this model could explain previous spectral observations and the phenomena of radioactivity, which were the only experimental results known at the time concerning atoms and molecules.

It was not only Nagaoka who arrived at the idea of a Saturn-type atomic model. When Nagaoka's manuscript was published in *Nature*, a British physicist G. A. Schott (1860–1937) had been considering a similar model of his own but had come to the conclusion that such a system would be unstable, given that it took account of only the electric force, following the inverse square law, and ignored magnetic force. Accordingly, Schott had not published his analysis, but now, in response to Nagaoka's thesis, Schott disseminated his intention to publish his results. This provoked a dispute between Nagaoka and Schott, but Nagaoka insisted that his own model, unlike that proposed by Schott, was not electrically neutral but rather was a hypothetical model for the atom that took into account the electromagnetic spectrum. Schott counterattacked by stating Nagaoka's model had been called unsuitable for describing even unstable atoms such as radium. Schott went further, offering calculations to show that Nagaoka's analysis was inconsistent with the quantitative properties of electrons and atoms that were known at that time (for example, the radius of electrons in the ring was deemed to be about 10^{-8} centimeters).

Nagaoka countered that, if the radius of the electron ring was assumed to be roughly 10^{-7} cm, then the stability of his model was assured. In addition, he repeated that his model was an ideal atom for representing the nature of matter, and not an attempt to describe reality. In a paper published in Japan, Nagaoka performed calculations using specific values for charge and mass. He also discussed the possibility of estimating the electron distribution on the ring, basing his suppositions on spectral characteristics; yet Nagaoka removed this argument in versions of his paper published in other countries. Schott did not overlook the areas that Nagaoka hid, where he had not found any definitive results (Itakura et al. 1973, pp. 275–283).

Nagaoka's atomic model was defective in the ways that Schott pointed out, but it is also undeniable that Nagaoka's argument was simply a stopgap measure. The publication of the Saturn-type atomic model was Nagaoka's first full-fledged challenge to the West, but from his perspective, although he attempted to compete based on an excellent idea, he was criticized for his unconvincing arguments, and forced to beat a painful retreat.

Nevertheless, Nagaoka's model differed significantly from that of J. J. Thomson (1856–1940), formulated in the same era, which proposed a structure consisting of electrons arranged in a sphere with a positive charge. For this reason, it was touched on by scientists such as the British O. J. Lodge (1851–1940), and the French J. H. Poincaré (1854–1912) and became well-known internationally. Especially through Poincaré, the Thomson model garnered particular attention in Japan as a global achievement through Hajime Tanabe's translation of *La Valeur de la Science* (Poincaré 1905), trans. *Kagaku no kachi* (The value of science, 1905).

Nagaoka's model was referred to in Europe for only several years after its publication, and it was the Thomson model, rich in material that could be used for describing properties of the atom, which was in practical use. Nevertheless, the atomic structure suggested by the 1911 experiment by Ernest Rutherford (1871–1937)—a small nucleus with a large positive charge and mass, with a large number of electrons rotating around it—was interpreted as in support of Nagaoka's model (Itakura 1976, pp. 186–190). Additionally, while the Nobel Prize began in 1901, recommendation requests for the awards in physics and chemistry were first sent to Tokyo Imperial University in 1905, which may have been related to the esteem accorded Nagaoka's atomic model[6] (Okamoto 2003).

The above is an evaluation of Nagaoka's atomic model. Thus had science emerged as a field in which participants from Eastern nations could compete on equal terms; and although scrutiny was severe, evaluation was administered fairly, based on results. Indeed, there are documents that relate the kinds of evaluation new participants actually received in cultures with long traditions of scientific research.

Rutherford conducted his experiments without being aware of Nagaoka's model; he was later informed of it by W. H. Bragg (1862–1942). In a postcard dated March 11, 1911 and addressed to Rutherford, Bragg wrote that he had heard from N. R. Campbell (1880–1949) that Nagaoka had proposed a large, positively-charged nucleus, but Bragg dismissed this with the words "but it was by [a] Jap anyway." Although at that time the word "Jap" did not have such a negative connotation, the word "anyway" stands out for its implied disregard for the Japanese people and their achievements (Itakura et al. 1973, pp. 340–341). It might have been assumed that, in a nation without a tradition of science, research would have been conducted on the spur of the moment, without any meticulous preparation or deep insight. Even if anyone could participate in scientific research, the task faced by newcomers—to win respect among colleagues who shared an accumulation of tradition—was of unrelenting difficulty.

2. From Competition to Harmony

Just as Nagaoka's atomic model became known to the world, the Russo-Japanese War broke out. Although it is possible to discuss Nagaoka's challenge to the West with his atomic model in the historical context of a Japan that had smashed a Western power in this war (Itakura et al. 1973, pp. 300–302), victory in the Russo-Japanese War brought about a change in the academic outlook of Japanese scientists. What really illustrates this change is the advent of the Japanese Society of Cancer Research.

After the Russo-Japanese War, Japanese physicians established independent research goals apart from the study of epidemic diseases such as tuberculosis and beriberi (of which the government had required urgent resolution), and these physicians set up organizations to achieve their objectives. They first took up cancer, and to that purpose they founded what is now known as the Japanese Foundation for Cancer Research. Research on treatment of cancer was not particularly advanced, and surgery did not ensure positive outcomes in many cases at that time.

International research had been conducted with collaboration between Europe and the United States, and Japanese scientists had also been invited by the German medical community to collaborate from even before the Russo-Japanese War. Nevertheless, the Japanese medical community at that time retained a reticence to conduct joint research with experts from developed Western countries; they did not reply to the invitation. The Russo-Japanese War changed this situation. At the beginning of the war, Tanemichi Aoyama (1859–1917) noted that, if Japan were victorious, "Japan would be numbered among the world's powers, together with those nations of the West, and would have no cause to be modest." This was the reason he decided to establish the Society of Cancer Research. Aoyama also said:

> We are in an age in which it is already impossible to receive sympathy and respect internationally simply in view of our military might. Similarly, such sympathy and respect cannot be received through monetary power alone. However, those nations that have made significant cultural progress will obtain respect and sympathy internationally. If we are able to obtain results in greater quantity or quality than those of the developed nations of the West, through research conducted by students at this Society of Cancer Research, then the respect and sympathy our nation receives internationally will be more than what we gain after using vast sums of money and risking hundreds of thousands of lives. (Aoyama 1908)

While Nagaoka was aiming to mount a successful challenge, Aoyama was trying to win sympathy and respect. Although they shared the goal of increasing Japan's ethnic and national status through achievement in scientific research, the competitive tone was fading in the case of scholars such as Aoyama—such was the effect of victory in the Russo-Japanese War. Nagaoka's adolescent outlook of science, full of rivalry, can be seen as a reflection of the tension felt at retaining independence of the nation before the Sino-Japanese and Russo-Japanese Wars.

Additionally, even though it is possible to think that national goals after the Meiji Restoration were for the most part reached through victory in the Russo-Japanese War, scientific research still continued. Reading between the lines, the language of medical scientists indicates that the objectives that scientists set were distinct and separate from the goals of the state. Accordingly, Nagaoka's comments in the same period on the Japanese situation after the Russo-Japanese War of being "numbered among the world's powers, together with those of the West" differed from those of Aoyama:

> With the end of the Russo-Japanese War, the Japanese people are proud to have joined the ranks of the great powers. In scientific research, Japanese

contributions remain quite unoriginal; Europeans sometimes praise us loudly for results that would not cause much excitement if achieved by Europeans. However, there is a reason for their compliment; once we could discern their true intentions, we should face them with strong sentiments such as anger or harsh criticism. (Nagaoka 1912)

That is, if the Japanese, with their pretensions of joining the great powers, were delighted at the praise offered for poor-quality research conducted by Japanese people, they would not understand the malice of the Europeans; Nagaoka insists that behind such European praise lay surprise that Japan, once an uncivilized nation, was able to embark on scientific research at all.

Before the opening of Tōhoku Imperial University, Nagaoka, who was appointed as its director, visited the countries of Europe from 1910 onwards, where he inspected laboratories. The report of his observations was released one year after his return to Japan. As can be seen from the passage cited above, its tone was that of a cranky old man, a persona often ascribed to Nagaoka. The passage shows a certain impatience with the Japanese situation when compared to that of the European academic physics community, which was then approaching a period of significant change.

The Europe that Nagaoka visited was still shocked by the implications of quantum theory and special relativity, which had been published a few years previously but only recently understood. Nagaoka compared this tumultuous state of "revolutionary revolution" to the commotion in ancient China, with rival chiefs defending their territories, deeming it to be like chasing deer through the fields. Although Japanese research was now notable, if likened to a celestial body, it was merely equivalent to a star whose existence is discovered only when viewed through a telescope. "Our academic status will not increase unless a star of the first magnitude appears in Japan," said Nagaoka, written in an appeal to his juniors during his return to Japan. "It is not appropriate that only Europeans benefit from the fortunes of revolution. The pessimistic idea that we must stand downwind of Europeans because we are Asian is still more cowardly. Even if Japanese people were unable to exert any force in this revolution, we should be at the forefront of the next one" (Nagaoka 1911).

Seen in close proximity, the work of European physicists affected Nagaoka's own reflections. When Nagaoka asked J. Stark (1874–1957) in Aachen Engineering University about the emanations and other characteristics of the hot springs in the Aachen region, the German physicist protested greatly that he did not do such low-level technical work himself. This reminded Nagaoka of his advisor A. A. Kundt (1839–1894). While he was in Europe for study, Nagaoka told Kundt that he had made measurements of magnetism in Japan. Kundt warned not to do such work, but then consoled that there could be no other choice in Japan, where study of physics was in its infancy. Considering the European philosophy of recognizing the supreme value of basic research, while technical work was relegated to the lowest stages, Nagaoka wondered if Japanese scientists might be mistaken in allowing geophysical measurements to be performed as an international operation. He lamented that, ten years later, even allowing for their tendencies as a "spiritual nation," the Japanese people would be assuming an inferior position to the West, and as a result, might be unable to overturn their reputation as a nation of imitators (Itakura et al. 1973, pp. 382–383).

After returning home from Europe in 1912, in response to the request sent to Tokyo Imperial University to recommend candidates for the Nobel Prize in Physics, Nagaoka concluded his letter of recommendation in favor of H. Kamerlingh Onnes (1853–1926), whom he knew during his time in Europe. "I regret very much not to name any of my countrymen. The scientific research in Japan is still in its infancy, and as most of the investigations bear the character of routine work, it will perhaps be in the coming generation that one deemed for receiving the Nobel prize will ever appear" (Okamoto 2000). Nagaoka believed that as long as unskilled work had to be referred to as research, Japan would not produce research at an international level.

Achievements in Europe in 1900 stimulated Nagaoka to release his atomic model, but the changes he observed during his visit in the late Meiji era also taught Nagaoka his own limits. Nagaoka had been able to introduce quantum theory at that stage to Japan, but to do any more than he had done was beyond his capabilities. An awareness of his own inadequacy, combined with an increasingly ill temper, spurred him to chide his juniors.

On the other hand, Japanese scientific research did achieve much internationally, as if to realize Aoyama's aspirations, between the Russo-Japanese War and World War I, when many studies were unavoidably interrupted. Such achievements included Umetarō Suzuki's (1974–1943) discovery of oryzanin (vitamin B1—thiamine), Katsusaburō Yamagiwa's (1863–1930) induced cancer in rabbit ears, which was supported by the Japanese Society of Cancer Research, and Kōtarō Honda's (1870–1954) research on magnetism and metallurgy. Although Nagaoka may still have been dissatisfied by these achievements, along with national stability, the level of scientific research improved as if it were intended to contribute to culture. The scientists who had been at the forefront of Japanese science up until that point began to discuss science with an air that was less directly confrontational. At the end of the Meiji Period, Aikitu Tanakadate, who had once likened Westerners to animals, was impressed with the ability of porters in the United Kingdom to deliver luggage at the train station without using tickets, and he referred to that nation as a "truly developed country" (Nomura 1959). In his 1915 Kōkūki kōwa" (Aircraft lecture) (Tanakadate 1915) at the House of Peers, Tanakadate noted that there was a spirit at the root of Western civilization, exemplified in Galileo (1564–1642), of seeking truth even when one's life is in danger.

As generations change, differences seem even more pronounced. Though they belonged to the generation immediately after Nagaoka, Torahiko Terada, Ayao Kuwaki (1878–1945), and Jun Ishiwara (1881–1947) produced writings and behaved in ways that showed little attitude of confrontation with the West in the field of science. Their writings are not without implication of the need to publically compete in science with other countries. For example, in *Hoppyōyō no kōri no yabureru oto* (The bursting sound of the Arctic Ocean, Terada 1933), written in 1933, when Japan experienced a time of "crisis" after the Manchurian Incident, there is the passage: "If Japan does not compete on the field of science, then it would be impossible for us to secure our existence as a nation." Nevertheless, while Nagaoka's position is that Japan should aspire to sincere intellectual contest with the West voluntarily, Terada here simply makes the claim that scientific and material competition with other nations is necessary for national survival. For those scholars who came into their adulthood at the time of the Sino-Japanese War, the fundamentals of Western culture were acquired at the Higher Schools. Furthermore, after the experience of victory in the Russo-Japanese War, the elements of Western Civilization had become a natural part of their lives, and science was beginning to become a natural part of this culture.

The competitive scientific view started to decline after the Russo-Japanese War, with this trend becoming even more notable during World War I, but Nagaoka alone continued to outdo himself.

3. "Academy Police"

In 1922, Albert Einstein (1879–1955) visited Japan. The welcome he was given illustrates well the situation in Japan following World War I. In 1919, Arthur Eddington (1882–1944) confirmed Einstein's general theory of relativity by observation of solar eclipses, whereupon Einstein suddenly became a global celebrity: he visited Japan and China, the United States, and South Africa. Einstein was informed that he had been elected to receive the Nobel Prize just before arriving in Japan, where he received an enthusiastic welcome. An Einstein boom, or a relativity boom, ensued, with Tanakadate and Nagaoka, as physicists with similar specialties, participating prominently in Einstein's welcome.

Among this unprecedented boom, one person bravely put forth objections to the theory of relativity. Uzumi Doi (1895–1945), while working at the First Higher School, was a young physics student continuing research under the tutelage of Nagaoka (Okamoto 2006a). As we will see below, developments surrounding Doi around the time of Einstein's visit to Japan speak to how multiple generations of Japanese physicists understood the standards of Japanese physics at that time.

The origin of Doi's anti-relativity was skepticism that the speed of light was a constant, an assumption underpinning the theory of special relativity. Even around the year 1920, this viewpoint was not an unusual one around the world. Whatever the case in the West, in Japan Doi's idea gained no supporters, meaning that his attitude of stubborn anti-relativity needed some justification. Doi's speech and conduct were somewhat eccentric,[7] and his real purposes were difficult to ascertain, but it seems that his desire to peg his self-worth as well as his academic reputation to some revolutionary discovery drove his anti-relativist position. Doi's anti-relativity claims were ostensibly based on his will to challenge the West; in Doi's journal, he likened himself to a lone genius, fated to the struggle of a Beethoven (1770–1827), a Galileo, or a Newton (1642–1727). He probably considered that he was a rightful part of the Western tradition, and dreamed of leaving his name among the academic giants of world history. Accordingly, Doi admired the worldwide fame of Nagaoka and asked him to be his advisor, wanting to follow in his footsteps. Doi also aspired to leave historical academic achievements from Japan.

In truth, Doi was missing a research companion who could elaborate upon prior research, and Jun Ishiwara and others pointed out some of the naïve errors in

Doi's work. Nevertheless, Doi believed he should be free to meet Einstein to exchange ideas, given that science does not supposedly ask qualifications of its participants. In fact, during a visit to the United States also, Einstein was presented with experimental results that seemed to be inconsistent with relativity. Nevertheless, Doi received pressure from various places, and his participation was nearly excluded just before Einstein's visit to Japan. The most influential attempt made to blockade Doi's topic for discussion was by his mentor, Nagaoka.

Nagaoka discouraged Doi from publishing his anti-relativistic idea by calling it a national disgrace, and Nagaoka commented that Doi was typical of a person from "Matsuzawa village."[8] Challenging the authority of the West was once one of Nagaoka's ideals, which he had spoken about with Tanakadate. However, Nagaoka now feared that exposing established Western authority to the naïve ideas of a student would lead to the discredit of all science in Japan. Nevertheless, Nagaoka himself had no ability to persuade Doi regarding the discussion on physics, so instead he presumably requested Ishiwara and Keiichi Aichi (1880–1923) to give professional criticism.

Nagaoka regarded discussion on science quite seriously, as a combative art. He did not think of a free exchange replete with errors and whims as worthwhile. In contrast to that, Einstein was previously aware of Doi's contention and did not consider it unreasonable—in fact Einstein described it as a serious discussion and told Nagaoka of his desire to interact with Doi. A dialogue in fact occurred after Einstein's lecture.

Doi also consulted Torahiko Terada. During Einstein's visit to Japan, an impressive array of elders of academia followed in his shadow. Even when Terada approached Einstein to have a chat, these academic leaders scowled, tense with anxiety as to what he would say. Terada called them the "academy police" (Terada 1935).

Nagaoka lacked confidence in the merit of young scientists in Japan, being afraid to embarrass himself. The values of the higher school education system burned in Doi: he dreamed of taking pride in the notion of the lonely genius, bringing intellectual challenges to the scholars of the world. In the middle of these generations, Ishiwara, based on his expertise, thought Doi's immature contentions reprehensible, but Terada found even humor in the tension of the older generation. The Japanese scientific community of the early 1920s had developed during the fifty years since the Meiji Restoration; its members comprised multiple generations that showed different kinds of self-awareness and international consciousness.

Section 4. The Advent of Quantum Mechanics

1. Learning a New Theory

In the early 1910s, Nagaoka looked at the changes occurring within quantum theory and relativity, and the "next revolution" that he anticipated took place in Europe from 1925 onwards. The quantum theory published in 1900 by Max Planck (1858–1947) was applied to Einstein's 1905 photon hypothesis, and this was expanded via Niels Bohr's (1885–1962) 1913 hydrogen model. Such theories were formulated over the years 1925 to 1926, after World War I, with the appearance of the matrix mechanics of Werner Heisenberg (1901–1976), Max Born (1882–1970), and Pascual Jordan (1902–1980), the wave mechanics of Ernest Schrödinger (1887–1961), and Paul Dirac's (1902–1984) transformation theory, which mathematically reconciled the two theories. As a result, the world's understanding of atoms and molecules further advanced, and the results were applied to research on the atomic nucleus and on physical properties.

The novelty of this new theory of quantum mechanics was such that even the founders had trouble in physically interpreting calculated results. Quantum mechanics enabled scientists to deal with substances at the very small scale. Physicists around the world had an interest in applying it to a variety of areas, and in developing fundamental parts of the theory—to draw on an earlier example, the incorporation of the tenets of special relativity. Nevertheless, given that this had drastically changed the frameworks in which research was carried out, it was now possible for researchers from nations with no prior accumulation of earlier scientific research to make important contributions in resolving specific problems.

From the perspective of Europe, the United States was only a minor contributor to scientific research before World War I. After the war, however, partly under the influence of support from serious institutions such as the Rockefeller Foundation, the United States made efforts to enhance higher education and scientific research, so that it became one of the centers of the new era of physics research. In 1932, American physicists contributed more than half of the many additional discoveries (including the enrichment of deuterium, the discovery of the neutron, the development of the Cockcroft-Walton accelerator, the development of the cyclotron, and the discovery of the positron) that encouraged further development in physics on top of the establishment of quantum mechanics. This year is often referred to as an *annus mirabilis* for modern physics, and it symbolized the newfound prosperity of physics in the United States.

The growth of American physics was rapid. The Dutch Physicist George Uhlenbeck (1900–1988) was in Leiden up until 1927, five years before 1932. In later years, he responded to an interview on the history of physics, saying that he considered the American journal *Physical Review*, which later became the world's leading physics publication, one of the "funny journals," and that he did not seriously review it though he infrequently browsed it. He added that it was "just like the Japanese" (Coben 1971, p. 456). In 1927, when theoretical research in quantum mechanics was among the leading topics in physics, Japan and the United States were seen as being at about the same level from the perspective of European theoretical physicists.

But how was quantum mechanics accepted in Japan, and how was it studied? Already from the 1910s, Ayao Kuwaki was making contributions to quantum theory which preceded the full development of quantum mechanics. Jun Ishiwara contributed a theoretical study; Toshio Takamine (1885–1959) and Masazō Kiuchi (1892–1967) conducted related experiments in spectroscopic analysis. After the birth of quantum mechanics, a relatively large-scale movement to learn the new theory, the Private Seminar on New Physics, commenced at Tokyo Imperial University. Apart from conducting exercises within the university and holding regular seminars on physics, young researchers were able to conduct study sessions at night by utilizing RIKEN's conference rooms. The Private Seminar on New Physics began in 1926, and the next year, *Butsurigaku bunken shō daiichi shū* (Literature on physics: First volume) was published by Iwanami Shoten, and this introduced topics such as matrix mechanics and wave mechanics from physics literature.

Although Nagaoka retired in 1925, in earlier practice at Tokyo Imperial University, he strictly evaluated students' publications. His reprimands apparently had students on the verge of passing out. While Nagaoka probably had no malicious intent, the younger generation regarded this as excessively authoritarian and organized journal club meetings outside of the university. Although Uzumi Doi was the oldest of the original organizers of these, afterwards, some of the older physicists such as Torahiko Terada were also recognized as participants—"recognized" because students determined participation by a yes or no vote. Terada referred to the participants as the "Colloquium of Heroes," and with the students' discontent with the university situation in mind, he remembered being impressed by the students' organizing spontaneously to study (Katsuki 1991).

At the same time in Kyoto, several young people formed their own club to study quantum mechanics, although at a much smaller scale than Tokyo's Private Seminar on New Physics. These were students in the laboratory of Kajūrō Tamaki (1886–1939) at Kyoto Imperial University, including Matsuhei Tamura (1904–1994), Sotohiko Nishida (1901–1949), Sin-Itiro Tomonaga, and Hideki Yukawa.

Tomonaga and Yukawa are well known to history, along with the circumstances in which they learned quantum mechanics and how they began their research (Okamoto 2006b). These two physicists became interested in the field called theoretical physics around the time of Einstein's 1922 visit to Japan. Einstein gave a lecture in Kyoto, where both Tomonaga and Yukawa lived at that time. Although the two were junior high school students, and thus did not attend Einstein's lecture, Yukawa was prompted by the enthusiasm in Japan to obtain Jun Ishiwara's textbook. Though unable to understand topics such as the relativity of time and space, the four-dimensional world, and non-Euclidean geometry, he was fascinated by Ishiwara's words. For the precocious junior high school student, not understanding books and theories can itself be attractive. When Yukawa found the word "quantum theory" in Tanabe Hajime's text at around the same time, it had a mysterious appeal.

Tomonaga and Yukawa were born a year apart. Tomonaga took five years to complete junior high school, and Yukawa took four years. Both attended Third High School, where they were in the same class. Because each learned a different first foreign language, they were not placed in the same classroom however. Tomonaga's brother-in-law, Takeo Hori (1899–1994), had just graduated from college in 1923 and was an instructor at Third High School. He was put in charge of lectures on dynamics, and his classes were where Tomonaga and Yukawa met. Hori's specialty was spectroscopic experiment with a deep association with quantum mechanics, and in his lectures on dynamics, he actively discussed new developments in physics. The issue of whether electrons are waves or particles was an old question; there was a completely new theory of matrix mechanics, but according to Hori, there was no one at Kyoto Imperial University who understood quantum mechanics. Influenced by Hori, Tomonaga elected to study physics there. For Yukawa too, with his already deep interest in physics, such discussion was fascinating.

Tomonaga and Yukawa enrolled at Kyoto Imperial University in 1926. Students chose a major in their third year. Tomonaga would have qualified for laboratory work, but he felt he was too frail to endure experiments, and instead chose to focus on theory. At this time, Tomonaga remembered hearing about quantum mechanics research from Hori during his time at Third High School, and decided to pursue studies in this sub-specialty. Nevertheless, at this time at Kyoto Imperial University there were no teachers able to guide Tomonaga. Masamichi Kimura (1883–1962), who specialized in spectroscopic experiments, was the closest match. The Tamaki laboratory's focus was on relativity. In the end, engaging in self-directed learning with a little help from the Tamaki laboratory, Tomonaga decided to study quantum mechanics. In the Tamaki laboratory, upperclassmen Sotohiko Nishida and Matsuhei Tamura were also reading papers in quantum mechanics.

With less hesitation than Tomonaga, Yukawa had already decided to study quantum mechanics when he entered university. While consulting Sotohiko Nishida, Yukawa taught himself quantum mechanics and perused the literature. Yukawa was also a member of the Tamaki laboratory in his third year.

Because these students were learning a new theory—a field without any textbooks—a great deal of time and effort was actually spent reading journal articles in European languages. In some cases, they were able to borrow journals from the university library, but in other cases, they had to order and purchase expensive prints from book stores. At times, they would place photographic paper on the pages and expose these to a backlight in order to copy the image, or they would copy material by hand. By mimeographing these and circulating these copies between colleagues, they managed to build up a collection of abridged editions of these texts.

They seemed to avoid discussion with each other, and they did not really read the same papers. Yukawa and Tomonaga have no memory of any direct conversations at this time. After graduation, both became unpaid research assistants in the Tamaki laboratory. Yukawa would often think while walking around the room, whereas Tomonaga would often escape to the library. Nevertheless, each was attentive to how the other was studying, and to what the other was reading. There is no doubt they were aware of each other's activities.

It is significant how the two groups in Tokyo and Kyoto each learned quantum mechanics at its outset in Japan. While conducting research alone, Uzumi Doi was wandering in an anti-relativistic labyrinth, but he found a venue for his activities in the Private Seminar on New Physics. Theoretical physicist Takahiko Yamanouchi (1902–1986) was somewhat older than Tomonaga and Yukawa. He said rather disappointedly in later conversation with Tomonaga that when trying to learn quantum theory, he had colleagues Chuji Tsuboi (1902–1982) and Seishi Kikuchi (1902–1974) who specialized in experimental physics, but no friends such as Tomonaga and Yukawa with whom he could cooperatively learn theory. Tsuboi and Kikuchi had joined the Colloquium of Heroes (nickname of the Private Seminar), but given that they were specializing in experimental physics, they could not effectively engage with pure theoretical physicists such as Yamanouchi.

Additionally, some of the trends in studying quantum mechanics in Japan, such as the changes to physics research as a whole stemming from this theory, and in particular the increasing independence of theoretical study, had larger implications for physics research in general. Around the time of the advent of quantum mechanics, a fundamental theory focusing on physical phenomena at the atomic level, there was an increase in the pace at which theory was developing, and these advancements were taking place in many fields. Accordingly, it became increasingly difficult for one physicist to understand the latest theories while simultaneously conducting experimental work. The movement towards the independence of theory that began at the start of the twentieth century gained momentum with the advent of quantum mechanics, and various attempts for studies and trials by beginners accumulated. In Japan, on the other hand, the educational system composed of the Imperial Universities and Higher Schools had reached its maturity through WWI and had produced a generation of students able to read literature in foreign languages and to study mathematics and physics in a self-directed fashion—in short, a generation that could operate at the cutting edge of theoretical research.

2. From Learning to Research

Intrigued by difficult new theories, Tomonaga and Yukawa began to study quantum mechanics. Their interest in this field was not to oppose the West, as in the case of Nagaoka, nor was it motivated by a desire to unravel the mysteries of nature.

For young scholars enthralled by such difficulty, it is important to have an environment that facilitates the attainment of these goals and desires. As both these men were born to academic families, it was not necessary to begin work immediately after graduating from university. Moreover, as they learned at Third High School and Kyoto Imperial University, they had developed strong interests in the latest achievements of the West and the ability to process and digest information. Tomonaga and Yukawa learned a theory that had no textbook by themselves. The field in which they were interested was an untapped area, and it appears that they understood that if they developed it, they would be at the cutting edge of global research. From the time they graduated college in 1929, the two began gradually to attempt their own original research. Nevertheless, these original studies in unestablished areas were often scooped by researchers in other nations before they could be published by Tomonaga and Yukawa.

As they turned to research, Tomonaga and Yukawa noticed particularly that researchers around the world seemed to have the strongest interest in two areas: the establishment of the foundations of theory that would allow quantum mechanics to respond to the requirements of special relativity and the application of quantum mechanics to the atomic nucleus. For his graduation thesis, Yukawa addressed the Dirac equation, which combined relativity and quantum mechanics, and took it further, summarizing some of his calculations for the hyperfine structure of the atom. He submitted it to Tamaki, who promised to examine it. Before that promise was fulfilled, Italian Enrico Fermi (1901–1954) published a more-advanced study in 1930. Tomonaga also was scooped by Fermi in research concerning hyperfine structure and the Hartree approximation. Since Yukawa also remembered being uncomfortable contemplating the idea of a wave function within phase space, he understood the significance of Jordan and Oskar Klein's (1894–1977) second quantization at the instant their thesis was published (Satō 2008). Such experiences, even when recalled with some frustration, seem to have shown Yukawa and Tomonaga that the path they had taken was not necessarily incorrect, despite the fact that they had taken it without anyone to show them the way.

Yukawa and Tomonaga were able to obtain more valuable information at lectures given by scholars visiting from overseas. Both Yukawa and Tomonaga remembered lectures from Arnold Sommerfeld (1868–1951), Otto Laporte (1902–1971), Heisenberg, and Dirac. Tomonaga gained confidence from the fact that he was able to understand these last two lectures in particular. He was inspired as well by the realization that Heisenberg and Dirac were still in their youth, only a few years senior to him.

Visits from lecturers from abroad were also opportunities for Nagaoka to give encouragement to younger scholars. At one Heisenberg and Dirac lecture held in September 1929, Nagaoka stood in greeting and honored these two young people for their success in developing new theories, and he spoke of his hope that their visit would serve to stimulate Japanese students, who, as Nagaoka described it, were interested in note-taking only to get through tests and boost their careers, and thus would probably not be capable of emulating Heisenberg and Dirac. While Tomonaga was unable to understand Nagaoka's doctrine eloquently delivered in English with a unique accent, upon hearing this he felt that this notable physicist appeared to have been vexed at the lackadaisical attitude of the young Japanese (Okamoto et al. 2006).

Take Sone (1887–1988) participated in the same lecture. Although Nagaoka was old enough to be Heisenberg's father, Nagaoka referred to the guest as "Heisenberg-*sensei*."[b] Sone was deeply moved to hear this because he remembered that Nagaoka said almost daily, "If one of my students produces truly great work, then I can call them my *sensei*." Nagaoka habitually told students that physics is a job for geniuses. Lectures from researchers visiting from overseas were a wonderful chance for him to show that geniuses in the physics field did actually exist, and that sometimes these geniuses were very young men who still had rosy cheeks, and who were even plagued by shyness as they addressed students (Katsuki 2007).

Yoshio Nishina (1890–1951), who worked at RIKEN, also assisted in the preparations for the two physicists' lectures but was left with different impressions regarding Nagaoka. The records of the lectures were published as a bulletin of Zaidanhōjin Keimeikai, an organization that provided financial backing for these events, but Nishina, who translated the lectures, wrote the following in the introduction:

> I frequently hear criticisms that scientists in certain categories in our country are only studying what has been left by Western pioneers, but I think it is partly because our academic world is lagging behind the trend of progress owing to our geographic situation. Therefore, I believe it is vital for our academics to invite scholars who are clearing pathways for these trends and to pay close attention to them. (Nishina 1932, 3)

This was not only a condemnation of the imitation of the West, but also an expression of the need to recognize the struggle of those individuals who are committed to improving the level of academia to allow Japan to catch up. In later years, Nishina's description here also caught Tomonaga's attention.

Nagaoka's attitude towards foreign researchers that he saw as performing high-level work was often one of unreserved praise, and he usually encouraged Japanese young people to pay attention to them and to learn from them. If this had happened frequently, students might have begun to see it as somewhat ridiculous, but it was very likely an important influence on them, too. At least, Nagaoka's utterances made it clear that what the senior academic scientist wanted was not any refutation of new theories, be they relativity, quantum theory, or quantum mechanics, but to accept these results and produce achievements that exceeded them. Whatever academic difficulties there were with following a new theory in Japanese academia, young students understood that they were being positively evaluated. Additionally, if one looks at the targets of Nagaoka's praise, it is clear that he was not praising the value of research for its practical applications. Also, his evaluative eye was just as strictly fair, as can be seen in his later activity related to recommendations for the Nobel Prize. Although the senior scientist seemed authoritarian, the presence of people who accurately assessed the results of scientific research and offered unstinting praise for excellent work provoked a certain sort of tension amongst younger people, which may have served to guide their research in a certain direction.

Lectures from Japanese researchers that touched on the latest achievements overseas were also valuable sources of information. Nevertheless, as Tomonaga and Yukawa had already studied such topics, they were able to evaluate the quality of the speakers. In 1929, there was a lecture from Yoshikatsu Sugiura (1895–1960), who had just returned from Germany. Sugiura tried to give research topics to Tomonaga and Yukawa. Nevertheless, the description of the experiment that Yukawa was allocated would clearly result in errors, and he declined Sugiura's recommendation. Tomonaga was provided with calculations related to molecular structure, to be integrated using a planimeter or graph paper. Even so, Sugiura's lectures consisted of his handing out printouts with formulae arrayed across them, followed by fast talking, which did not leave a good impression on Tomonaga.

In 1931, Yoshio Nishina lectured at Kyoto Imperial University. In a lecture based on Heisenberg's *Physikalischen Prinzipien der Quantentheorie* (Heisenberg 1930), trans. *Physical Principles of the Quantum Theory* (Carl Eckart and Frank C. Hoy 1930) with additional content added, Nishina, who had studied under Niels Bohr in Copenhagen for many years, confirmed that Tomonaga and Yukawa's research methods were not wrong, which was of deep significance to them, as their fumbling attempts were backed by a leading researcher. There were two others who were studying at the same university with the same interests who were also drawn to Nishina, although not in contact with Tomonaga and Yukawa: Minoru Kobayashi (1908–2001) and Shōichi Sakata (1911–1970) (Ezawa 2006).

3. RIKEN's Nishina Laboratory

At a lecture in Kyoto, Nishina took note of Tomonaga, encouraging him to come work at his lab at the Institute of Physical and Chemical Research (RIKEN). Tomonaga was hesitant, yet from 1932 he went to work at RIKEN first as a part-time, then as a full-time research student. That same year, Yukawa took a position lecturing on quantum mechanics at Kyoto Imperial University, then moved to the newly established Osaka Imperial University. These new bases set the stage for research that went beyond quantum mechanics.

Nishina's major as a student had been electrical engineering. After graduating from the Department of Electrical Engineering at Tokyo Imperial University, he had been conducting research on the electric furnace beginning in 1918 in the laboratory of Tsunetarō Kujirai (1870–1921). Before formally joining RIKEN, Nishina and Kujirai had been introduced to each other by Nagaoka. Nishina became interested in physics, which he was required to learn for his research, and this prompted him to attend graduate school at Tokyo Imperial University. In 1921, Nishina took over for Taiji Kikuchi (1893–1921)—who had died while in the United Kingdom on secondment from RIKEN—and studied there under Rutherford. Nishina's aspirations in the field of quantum mechanics were prompted by contact with Niels Bohr after a lecture in Cambridge. Bohr's lecture was dense but not particularly difficult to understand, which Nishina said provoked in him a desire to learn from Bohr. Of course, Bohr's theory was very esoteric, and this was compounded by his verbosity, but that made the subject attractive to Nishina, and as he was an international student dispatched from RIKEN, he was in an environment that accepted such academic desire (Ezawa 2007).

Nishina moved to research under Bohr in 1923. At first he was conducting research on x-ray spectroscopy, but in October 1928, just before leaving Copenhagen, Nishina and Oskar Klein developed the Klein-Nishina formula related to the scattering of electrons by gamma rays. For a while after returning to RIKEN in late 1928, Nishina was a member of Nagaoka's lab, and from 1931, he led his own independent laboratory. It was to this laboratory that Tomonaga came to work. Already, Ryōkichi Sagane (1905–1969) and Masa Takeuchi (1911–2001) had started working with Nishina.

At RIKEN, Tomonaga felt free to converse without restriction. The young researchers at RIKEN appeared to him to be very quick thinking. Although this was almost overwhelming at times, Tomonaga gradually made himself known in this environment and showed his abilities. It is commonly understood that Nishina brought back the free spirit of his laboratory from Copenhagen. Nevertheless, many of the young people who joined the discussion, including Seishi Kikuchi, were active in the Private Seminar on New Physics, and the generation of quantum mechanics can also be regarded as having shared a broad-minded attitude.

The research Nishina worked on was very wide-ranging. Nishina seems to have been bent on implementing most of the world's cutting edge research topics in Japan, especially after some striking discoveries were made throughout the world after 1932. Among his experiments were those targeting induced radioactivity and cosmic rays, the Van de Graaff generator, the Cockcroft-Walton accelerator, and the construction of a cyclotron in order to study the atomic nucleus. Besides this, theoretical research advanced around Tomonaga, who had begun to demonstrate his competence. Nevertheless, since Tomonaga's research was expected to support Nishina, Tomonaga was unable to pursue the research that he wanted to conduct. Tomonaga had calculated the cross-sectional area of atoms and ions excited by neutron bombardment, as well as the binding energy of deuterium, the results of which were published at the Physico-Mathematical Society of Japan between 1933 and 1935. Nevertheless, laboratory director Nishina could not find the time to craft these into academic manuscripts. In the meantime, foreign researchers such as Hans Bethe (1906–2005) and Rudolph Peierls (1907–1995) were able to publish exactly the same research. Tomonaga's own research also piled up in areas such as the atomic nucleus, cosmic rays, and quantum electrodynamics. One of Tomonaga's main achievements was the development of the super-many-time theory, sprouting from his interest around this time in Dirac's many-time theory.

4. Particles That Mediate the Nuclear Force

The Osaka Imperial University that Yukawa moved to was newly established in 1931, with Hantarō Nagaoka as its founding President. Nagaoka aimed to foster cooperation between promising young researchers, and appointed Hidetsugu Yagi (1886–1976) to head the faculty of science, an unusual choice given that Yagi was an electrical engineer. Yagi undertook some ventures such as inviting Seishi Kikuchi, who had won acclaim for conducting experiments on electron beam dispersion at RIKEN, to take up a post in 1934. As with Nishina, Kikuchi conducted experimental research centered on cosmic rays and the atomic nucleus, and turned his hand to the construction of large-scale experimental equipment, finally resulting in the construction of a cyclotron. Each lab at Osaka University was relatively independent, with the relationship between Kikuchi and Yukawa extending no more than to allow them to perform seminars in collaboration. In that sense, it was different in character from the relationship between Nishina and Tomonaga. Nevertheless, Kikuchi, who was already a researcher well-known worldwide for his study of electron diffraction, freely asked questions about even simple matters in the laboratory colloquium, and on seeing this, Yukawa appears to have decided to follow his example. Kikuchi also studied quantum mechanics in Germany, and Yukawa thought that, as with the Nishina laboratory in RIKEN, the atmosphere of Kikuchi's laboratory in Osaka University had been influenced by Kikuchi's experience studying abroad in Copenhagen and Germany, though Yukawa had never been himself. It can also be referred to as possessing the generational characteristics seen in the Private Seminar on New Physics.

Shortly thereafter, in a relatively isolated environment at the newly established university, Yukawa tried to produce some new achievements. From around 1933, he had narrowed his research interests down to the theoretical explanation of forces between protons and neutrons. At a meeting in 1933, he announced his hypothesis that electrons mediated the nuclear force, just as photons mediated the electric force, but that this idea was fraught with difficulties. In contrast, Nishina suggested that the nuclear force was mediated by particles in accordance with Bose statistics, but this assumption required the existence of unknown particles. At this stage, Yukawa was hesitant to push further. This hesitation was tossed aside by October 1934. In Kikuchi's laboratory, Yukawa published a theory predicting the existence of a new boson, with 200 times the mass of an electron. The results were again announced at the Physico-Mathematical Society of Japan the next month, and as an English paper the following year.

At the first publication of meson theory, only a few people, like Nishina, Kikuchi, and Tomonaga, showed interest. The idea of assuming unknown particles in order to explain known interactions in nature appeared too unconventional. Nevertheless, when Yukawa's theory was published, Tomonaga, who was almost the same age as Yukawa, thought, "He did it!" and "I cannot serve as an assistant to Nishina forever." Tomonaga himself closely examined Yukawa's theory from its very first publication.

The reaction in the West was poor. In 1937, through the efforts of Nishina, Bohr was invited to give a lecture at RIKEN and other places. When Yukawa attempted to discuss his theory, Bohr simply replied by asking him if he liked the new particles, to which Yukawa had no reply. In 1937, Tomonaga was to study under Heisenberg in Leipzig, but at that time, Heisenberg appeared to have recommended that instead of focusing on work such as Yukawa's, which he considered fanciful, Tomonaga should concentrate on something more plausible (Okamoto 2006b). This was a negative response, but it also showed that Yukawa's theory had garnered some attention.

5. Japan's Standing in Scientific Research

In the 1930s, within science, particularly physics, the standing of America was growing rapidly, while as of 1937, Japan's standing in science still remained low, as judged both domestically and internationally. On the other hand, voices that questioned Japan's standing in science surged from throughout Japan itself. As background to this, after World War I, Japan gained extensive colonies, having risen to a position as one of the world's three major naval powers and as one of the top five overall military powers in the world. In spite of this, it was perhaps considered internationally that Japan's culture had not kept pace with its military developments, and that there had been plenty of opportunities to demonstrate otherwise, if this were not the case.

For example, one such opportunity was the awarding of the 1930 Nobel Prize in Physics to the Indian C. V. Raman (1888–1970). Already, an Indian writer Rabindranath Tagore (1861–1941) had received the Nobel Prize in Literature in 1913; this new development, that an Asian had also won a Nobel Prize in a natural science, seemed to raise the self-esteem of the Japanese. The May 1931 (11th) edition of *Kagaku chishiki* (Scientific knowledge) reported Raman's Nobel Prize (p. 560); Raman commented on being awarded the Nobel Prize for research conducted in India, "For Japanese scholars in Asia, it is no longer essential to study abroad. It may well be time for more Nobel laureates from Japan." The November issue listed

Nobel Prizes awarded by country (p. 1350). In the following year, 1932, the preface to volume six of the journal *Kagaku* (Science) discussed the status of science within Japan and pointed out that the engineer Kyōji Suehiro (1877–1932), who had died recently, had praised the Indian science that had produced the physicist Raman and the botanist J. C. Bose (1858–1937).

Already from the late 1920s, there was some cynicism in Japan that there had been no Japanese Nobel Prize winner in the field of medicine. When the first winner of the Nobel Prize in medicine, Emil von Behring (1854–1917), died in 1917, the students of Shibasaburō Kitasato and others insisted that Kitasato deserved to have won jointly with Behring for the establishment of natural immunity. Further, after Danish scientist Johannes Fibiger (1867–1928) won the Nobel Prize in medicine for his research on the development of cancer, rumors spread that the work of Katsusaburō Yamagiwa, who produced similar results independently, had been ignored because Yamagiwa was Asian or Japanese.

In 1935, international physiology conferences were held in Leningrad and Moscow, to which Gen'ichi Katō (1890–1979) of Keio University was invited. One of the conference organizers, Pavlov (1849–1936), leaked to Katō the information that he, along with another Japanese scientist, Ken Kuré (1883–1940), of Tokyo Imperial University, had been nominated for the Nobel Prize, resulting in a recommendation battle being waged between the schools of medicine at Tokyo Imperial University and at Keio (Okamoto 2002). Over the next year, there was an interesting dialogue in the journal *Scientific knowledge*, wherein many Japanese scientists evaluated themselves and each other in terms of Nobel Prize worthiness. There were various recommendations made for Japanese Nobel Prize candidates from well-known individuals in many fields. The final results were published in the January 1936 issue (p. 82). In physics, the most recommended person was Kōtarō Honda (117 points), followed by Hantarō Nagaoka (107 points) and Hisashi Kimura (30 points).

In 1937, again in the journal *Scientific knowledge*, voting took place among various well-known individuals in many fields to determine recipients of the newly established Order of Cultural Merit. The results were published in the May issue (p. 609). From the top, recipients of votes included Kōtarō Honda (19 votes), Umetarō Suzuki (14 votes), Sohō Tokutomi (1863–1957) (13 votes), Taikan Yokoyama (1868–1958) (13 votes), Tōson Shimazaki (1872–1943) (12 votes), Hantarō Nagaoka (11 votes), and Kan Kikuchi (1888–1948) (8 votes). Nagaoka, Honda, and Kimura were the actual recipients of the very first Order of Cultural Merit in 1937.

Honored by the journal's recommendation of the Nobel Prize, Nagaoka received visitors from *Scientific knowledge* and gave an interview (*Scientific knowledge* 1936). In the article, Nagaoka stipulated that the UK was growing old, Germany had one foot in its coffin, and that American physics was growing prominent. When asked to comment on RIKEN laboratory equipment, Nagaoka responded, "There is no remedy for RIKEN." Many scientific journals were critically reporting at that time that Germany had lost a great deal of scientists through its persecution of the Jews. Talking about the Nobel Prize, Nagaoka said "That would be amusing, having a Japanese candidate." He revealed that he nominated one candidate every year, and of these, half were selected. He also said that prizes are an obvious trick, and that receiving the Academy Prize is too much of a good thing. By the mid-1930s, the appearance of quantum mechanics resulted in substantial research being carried out in Japan; but, as previously, the researchers who were acclaimed for having produced world-class work were the members of the old guard such as Nagaoka and Honda.

As the articles in *Scientific knowledge* demonstrate, for many years Nagaoka had put forth recommendations of candidates for the Nobel Prize. He began these recommendations in 1912, and from 1930, he received requests for recommendations every year. Up to 1938, his recommendations included Heisenberg, Schrödinger, James Chadwick (1891–1974), Frédéric Joliot-Curie (1900–1958), Irène Joliot-Curie (1897–1956), Carl Anderson (1905–1991), and Ernest Lawrence (1901–1958). No Japanese names were listed. However, evaluation reports amongst documents from the Committee on the Nobel Prize in Physics mentioned Kōtarō Honda and Seishi Kikuchi. In particular, the 1937 Nobel Prize in Physics was given for experiments that were similar to Kikuchi's 1928 electron beam scattering experiments, and that year's report subsequently included a detailed description of Kikuchi (Okamoto 2000). Nevertheless, as Kikuchi did not receive that year's recommendation, he was not a candidate.

The fact that Nagaoka knew Kikuchi and Honda very well personally and yet did not recommend them can be said to illustrate his high standards for the Japanese people. Nevertheless, judging by the Nobel Prize selection documentation, neither Nagaoka's vigorous encouragement nor the strenuous efforts of Yoshio Nishina and Seishi Kikuchi bore fruit; it could be said that, in light of international standards, physics research in Japan was still unable to generate such notable achievements.

Events featuring prominent invited foreign researchers were one venue at which the various leaders of science and engineering could complain about Japan's poor performance in those fields. With Bohr's lecture in Japan, Navy Vice Admiral Sadao Hatano (1881–1942) stated his dissatisfaction that Japan continued to "be a pale imitation of the 'advanced' foreign nations . . .", and that Japan, ". . . could only walk behind" in the academic world. (Hatano 1937) The director of Kagaku Chishiki Fukyūkai (The foundation to disseminate scientific knowledge), Nikichi Inoue (1868–1947) requested that "good-hearted young people" make strenuous efforts to bring some glory to Japanese culture and elevate the national prestige of Japan. This "pale imitation" of Westerners was an idea inherent in Nagaoka's usual speech, but at this time, he was involved in new fields of physics research at RIKEN and no longer made comments like this. Now such comments came from military personnel.

Section 5. Meson Theory, Cyclotron, New Weapons

1. The Breakthrough of Yukawa Theory

In 1937, immediately after Bohr left Japan, Americans Anderson and Seth Neddermeyer (1907–1988), Nishina, Masa Takeuchi, and Torao Ichinomiya (1909–1975) in Japan, and Americans J. Curry Street (1906–1989) and Stevenson published discoveries of particles ranging in mass between an electron and a proton. Already in the previous year, Anderson had discovered a particle in cosmic rays, the mass of which was between that of an electron and that of a proton, yet his 1937 report was more detailed; in particular, the results of Nishina and collaborators indicated that the mass of this new particle was somewhere between one seventh and one sixth that of a proton. This number was close to the mass of the unknown particle predicted by Yukawa—200 times the mass of an electron. Nishina informed Yukawa, Tomonaga, and Sakata of these results.

Before the revelation of Nishina and others, Yukawa pointed out that he had himself predicted the particles reported by the two groups in the United States. The Swiss physicist Ernst Stueckelberg (1905–1984) also agreed. The Americans J. Robert Oppenheimer (1904–1967) and Robert Serber (1909–1997) pointed out that challenges remained in terms of the saturation of the nuclear force and the magnetic moment of the nucleons, but that the revelations did not otherwise contradict Yukawa theory. It was thought that the overall direction of the theory was correct, but that there was some conditional room for improvement. Those interested in aspects of the atomic nucleus, whether within theoretical or experimental specialties, began to focus their attention on the Yukawa theory. Stueckelberg inquired about the possibility of coming to Japan to study with Yukawa (Ezawa 2007, pp. 31–32).

When Tomonaga was in Germany at the beginning of 1938, he wrote in his diary that he frequently heard the name "Yukawa" from Heisenberg's own mouth. Also in Germany, Yukawa theory came to be considered correct based on data from cosmic rays. Once, Yukawa had studied at the desk next to Tomonaga, and now Yukawa was being discussed by even Heisenberg. Tomonaga remembered that in a dream one night, after Bohr's wife expressed interest in Yukawa's theories, he responded, "Those who aim at such an achievement succeed just once in twenty years." Perhaps he considered such an achievement beyond his own abilities (Okamoto 2006b).

In Japan, Yukawa himself, along with Shōichi Sakata, Minoru Kobayashi, and Mitsuo Taketani (1911–2000), was working hard at developing his own theory. Japan's academic community also recognized the global significance of this theory. At the April 1938 gathering of the Physico-Mathematical Society of Japan, held at Tokyo Imperial University, discussion of Yukawa theory was permitted without the constraint of a time limit. In October 1938, the Yukawa theory was awarded the Hattori Hōkōkai Prize. Around the time of the press release, Yukawa became widely known as the scientist who predicted the new particle and had his name attached to it (at that time the new particle was sometimes called yukon). He was invited frequently to give lectures, contribute writings, and make radio appearances. Around this same time, Jun Ishiwara assessed Yukawa theory in the *Asahi Shimbun*: "It is an indisputable fact that such a fundamental theory, and of such importance, has not previously existed" (*Asahi Shimbun* 1938). Nevertheless, he pointed out that this appreciation of Yukawa was imported to Japan from overseas, and hoped for a future of original leadership from Japan.

In 1939, Yukawa was appointed professor at Kyoto Imperial University as the successor to Tamaki, who had died suddenly. That same year Yukawa left Japan to attend the Solvay Conference on Physics in Belgium and visited various places in Europe. The conference itself was cancelled because of the outbreak of World War II, but Yukawa visited various universities in the United States before returning home to Japan. At the end of the year, Jun Ishiwara reflected on events in the general scientific community for the *Asahi Shimbun* (1939a): he called it an "extraordinary honor" that Yukawa had been invited to the Solvay Conference on Physics. Even though Ishiwara was disappointed that the meeting had been called off, he expected many opportunities for Yukawa in the future.

Yukawa was first recommended for the Nobel Prize in Physics in 1940. Two people had recommended him: one was Dirk Coster (1889–1950) in the Netherlands, who had previously studied with Nishina; the other was Nagaoka. Finally, Nagaoka was able to recommend a Japanese physicist, acknowledging that results superior to any contemporary Western research had been produced by a Japanese scientist. Nagaoka called attention to the fact that Yukawa's theoretical work had come several years before the observation of the new particle, emphasizing the significance of Yukawa's research. It is not possible to detect much personal emotion in Nagaoka's recommendations from other years, but the letter of recommendation for Yukawa contained the following sentence in English: "It is for the first time that I suggest my compatriot as recipient of the Nobel Prize with full confidence." For the first time in nearly a quarter of a century, since his first recommendation of Kamerlingh Onnes, Nagaoka had deemed a Japanese physicist worthy of the Nobel Prize.

2. The Development of Large and Small Cyclotrons

When the RIKEN cyclotron was completed in 1937, it was described in the newspapers as the world's second largest, only after a cyclotron in the United States. In the *Asahi Shimbun*, in March and April, it was described as a "magic laboratory," a universal alchemic device capable of transforming any matter into gold (*Asahi Shimbun* 1937a).

The cyclotron came from the laboratory of its inventor, Lawrence, and was brought to completion using information obtained from Tameichi Yazaki (1902–1970) and Ryōkichi Sagane, with a donation of 150,000 yen from the Mitsui Hōonkai (Mitsui Foundation for the Return of Blessings), and a Poulsen arc electromagnet from the Japan Wireless Telegraph Company. Since before the completion of this three-MeV cyclotron, there had been calls for the construction of an even larger cyclotron. Nagaoka had been instrumental in terms of funding and equipment procurement for the cyclotron that had been already constructed. In March 1937, at the council of the Japan Society for the Promotion of Science, he pleaded the need for the construction of a larger cyclotron. Nagaoka argued that atomic transmutations were attracting international attention at that time. Although one cyclotron had already been constructed at RIKEN, this was insufficient for experimenting with all the elements. He declared that a department dedicated to the testing of atomic transmutations would be created within the relevant cosmic rays subcommittee and a budget of 110,000 yen would be allocated in order to establish a new device that would exceed ten MeV. It was planned that a generator that had been donated by the wireless company would be utilized, and to further offset costs, another 100,000 yen donated to RIKEN by the Tokyo Electric Light Company would be used. The installation would be at RIKEN, but instead of RIKEN's exclusive use, the equipment was to be made available to any qualified researcher (Nagaoka 1937).

The large cyclotron was featured in the newspaper in spring 1938, before operations began. It was reported that beams would be emitted in the autumn of that year (*Asahi Shimbun* 1938). This equipment was at the same scale as the cyclotron in the Lawrence lab at the University of California, and it was expected that soon the fundamental phenomena of the universe would be elucidated at RIKEN using the world's leading equipment.

Because it was difficult to acquire equipment during the Sino-Japanese War due to government control over goods, installation had to be carried over to February 1939; even so, the California cyclotron was still not yet running (It was reported operational the following June). From the design stage, Lawrence gave generous cooperation; the same iron that Lawrence had used for the electromagnet of his own cyclotron was purchased from the United States; in the newspaper it was reported that the world's largest cyclotron was now complete earlier than its counterpart in the United States (*Asahi Shimbun* 1939b). Nevertheless, the finished larger cyclotron did not exhibit sufficient performance. RIKEN's design had been the same as that of its successful smaller cyclotron but simply at an increased size, with the end result being equipment that was not operational.

When the assembly of Lawrence's equipment was complete and operations began, a full report was published by Ryōkichi Sagane in the Japanese journal *Kagaku* (Science) (Sagane 1939). It was stated that things had been somewhat stagnant with the RIKEN equipment, but it would be complete once the oscillator is ready. Yet even this estimation was wrong. On the other hand, it was known that Lawrence was now working on an even larger device, with an electromagnet weighing 2,000 tons. Nishina himself was forced to admit that, "It will be able to generate a

Yukawa particle, and advance physics to a new level" (Nishina 1940a). After that, the idea of a 2,000-ton cyclotron also attracted interest. For example, articles appeared in *Kagaku* in March 1940 (*Kagaku* 1940a), August 1940 (*Kagaku* 1940b), and April 1941 (*Kagaku* 1941). Details were gradually revealed: the diameter would be 184 inches, and the total weight 4,900 tons.

In the May 1940 edition of *Kagaku gahō* (Scientific graphic), an article called "Dai saikurotoron no zembō" (The whole picture of the large cyclotron) showed six-colored photos of the large cyclotron in California issuing a beam, as well as a concept diagram adopting a highly efficient resonance principle that was very different from that used in the RIKEN equipment. Tameichi Yazaki, who wrote the commentary on the back page, explained that Lawrence had further conceptualized a "super-large cyclotron" with a 4,000-ton magnet that would be able to generate artificial cosmic rays (Yazaki 1940). Also, it seems that RIKEN understood the key points of large cyclotron remodeling to some extent by that time. In September 1940, Nishina again sent researchers to Lawrence, asking for some guidance in remodeling the large cyclotron. With World War II looming, the United States had already started the mobilization of science to the war effort; therefore while in the United States, Yazaki's request for detailed drawings of the cyclotron was denied. However, he returned home with a conceptual diagram on the use of resonance, which had been the main cause of failure, and the large cyclotron was remodeled based on this.

Looking at two of Sagane's comments prepared in quick succession, one of the main areas of remodeling was understood to be the vacuum system. In January 1941, Sagane published *Genshikaku jikken sōchi* (The Device for Nuclear Experiment, Sagane 1941a). It included a figure of the cyclotron vacuum system before remodeling (Sagane 1941a, p. 35), which differed completely from that in a commentary written immediately after the outbreak of war between Japan and America[9] (Sagane 1947, p. 126). According to Sagane's commentary on the later description, "Everyone is using this method for new cyclotrons." The adoption of the quarter wavelength principle was a fundamental point for remodeling (Sagane 1947, p. 130). He also described this method in commentary prior to remodeling (Sagane 1941a, pp. 41–42), but it was not initially adopted in the construction of RIKEN's large cyclotron.

We can learn from Sagane's commentary that information on a huge cyclotron was brought to RIKEN together with information on remodeling of the large cyclotron. Publications after the war included, "A Prospective View on the University of California's 4,500-ton cyclotron" (Sagane 1947, p. 131) and "Photos during the assembly of the University of California's 4,900-ton cyclotron." Although clues as to the details were lost in the war, we can understand that there was great interest around Nishina in this kind of large experimental equipment. The aforementioned prospectus was also included in the commentary of the study on atomic nucleus published in May, 1942, by Michio Hatoyama[10] (1909–1993), who belonged to the atomic nucleus laboratory at RIKEN (Hatoyama 1942, p. 21).

For both the small and large cyclotrons, Lawrence's cooperation had played a decisive role right from design through to completion. Tameichi Yazaki, who once had studied under Lawrence, recalled that Lawrence had advised him when Bohr visited Japan in 1937: "if you want to be a great physicist, first become a good man." Yazaki thought Bohr was one such "good man," but he also had Lawrence himself in mind (Yazaki 1937). Nishina made similar remarks in April 1940, stating that the scientific prospects of the United States, which included first-rate scientists like Lawrence, were hopeful, and the promotion of American science would be to the benefit of world science. The development of science was not just a problem for heads and hands to solve, but it "depends on the personal qualities of the scientists involved" (Nishina 1940b).

After returning from his visit to the United States in order to make improvements to the large cyclotron, Yazaki submitted travel writing to various newspapers and magazines, and gave his own observations in round-table discussions. Among those contributions, in a roundtable discussion for *Kagaku gahō*, he said, "They say the cyclotron is available to use for national defense." When asked, "What do you mean?" Yazaki replied first, "I don't know," but later he explained the possibilities of utilizing the energy generated when slow neutrons collide with Uranium 235. Furthermore, he revealed that construction of a cyclotron with a 4,000-ton electromagnet was in progress at Berkeley on top of the large cyclotron already in operation, so that cosmic rays could be artificially generated; and in order to prevent the generated neutrons from harming populated areas, the electromagnet was put on a concrete platform at the top of a carefully-selected mountain (Kaburagi et al. 1941).

We can see the shortcomings in Nishina and his associates' expectations from the troubles in the construction of the large cyclotron as well as the limits of Japanese technology at this point in time, but we can also perceive the strength of will of Nishina and Nagaoka to both manufacture and use such world-class laboratory equipment. They believed that, if they did not have the required technology in

Japan, then they could purchase it from abroad, and if funds were required, they could obtain them through institutional means. They felt that such efforts were worthwhile, given the significance of building a large cyclotron. Although the cyclotron was also expected to produce results for practical purposes such as medicine, the main reason for construction was to perform experiments on the atomic nucleus. When the small cyclotron was complete, and when the project on the large cyclotron was launched, Yukawa's theory had still not attracted international attention, but international interest in the theory increased as the construction of the large cyclotron proceeded. While the large cyclotron of RIKEN remained unfinished, information regarding the progress of the construction of equipment capable of creating Yukawa's particles at Berkeley had made its way back to Japan, heightening the impatience of Nishina and his colleagues.

3. The Basic Science of Wartime Japan

On December 7, 1941, Japan attacked Pearl Harbor and entered into a state of war with the United States and Great Britain. Mitsuo Taketani wrote that there was a dinner party following a RIKEN lecture immediately after the attack, where Nishina, RIKEN director Masatoshi Ōkōchi (1878–1952), and Seishi Kikuchi discussed the relationship between war and science. Nishina said "something very pure" that "war with America has started, and things will be difficult from here. However, the important thing for us scholars is that, when the war is over, looking at American and Japanese academics, it will be very embarrassing if Japan is much inferior. In order to avoid embarrassing ourselves, we will need to do a great deal of pure research for the sake of Japanese prestige." Ōkōchi said that it had been necessary to devise means whereby torpedoes could be launched in the shallow waters of Pearl Harbor, and that this had been made possible through the research of Japanese scientists. After hearing this, Kikuchi stood up to deliver a speech: if Japan lost, there would be no room even for basic research (Taketani 1958, p. 345).[11]

Nishina announced his plan to conduct basic research whether a war was occurring or not. Ōkōchi preached that scientists could support the nation even in wartime if they fulfilled the responsibility given to them. Kikuchi concluded that in an emergency scientists should be engaged in war-related research. In the foreword to the March 1942 edition of *Kagaku* (Science), Nishina advocated for basic science during wartime. The primary reason he cited was that basic science would result in breakthrough technologies. The second reason was that there was no other country producing basic science within the Greater East Asia Co-prosperity Sphere—what Japan called its area of influence during the war. The third reason was as follows:

> The science of Japan developed through incorporating the results of research in Europe and the United States, but the war this time has made such an exchange impossible. Therefore, we must now craft the future science for our country from within. Because Japan has significantly fewer scientists, and because our budget and materials are more modest than those of the West, each scientist must make the effort of several in order to foster progress that can be compared to that of our Western counterparts. If it turns out that the science of our country would appear greatly overshadowed right after the war, it will affect our prestige, and this shortcoming will have a negative influence on the construction of a new order in Greater East Asia. Were that the case, I would truly feel small in front of the spectacular achievements of our Imperial Army. (Nishina 1942)

Nishina himself was not very optimistic about how the war would turn out. No matter how the war ended, subsequent competition in basic science would ensue. Competition between scientists could not be neglected because the nation was in a state of war. Whether Japan won or lost (although publicly expressing the latter opinion would surely be problematic), the nation's prestige would be reduced if it became clear at the end of the war that there had been no gains in basic science. This was Nishina's assertion. At the same time, Michio Hatoyama, who had been engaged in nuclear experiments at RIKEN using a Cockcroft-Walton accelerator, stressed that Japanese research must in no way be lagging behind when comparing the progress of Japanese research to foreign research after the end of the war, and indeed, it should be ahead of foreign basic research (Hatoyama 1942).

In fact, Japanese atomic nucleus and cosmic ray researchers were working on basic science issues before the Pacific War broke out. The biggest problem was that difficulties had begun to appear within Yukawa theory. Even before the start of the Pacific War, differences between the properties of Yukawa particles that had come to be called mesons and those of a new particle discovered in cosmic rays had been noted: the lifespan of the meson as indicated by Yukawa theory was about one one-hundredth of the new particle, and the observed value of the scattering of the new particle by the atomic nucleus was very small compared to the indicated theoretical value. Although there appeared to be room for improvement of the theory, that route was not really pursued. In June 1941, Nishina wrote a commentary in the *Asahi Shimbun* on cosmic rays, stating that the particles in cosmic rays are considered to be what Yukawa predicted, but the values for theoretical lifetimes and observed lifetimes were different; Shōichi Sakata's theory showed promise for resolving this discrepancy (Nishina 1941a).

During World War II, awarding of the Nobel Prize was discontinued, but letters of recommendation continued to be gathered. For the 1940 awards, Yukawa had been recommended by two people, including Nagaoka, but from 1943 to 1945, the only recommendations came from the de Broglie brothers, Maurice (1875–1960) and Louis (1892–1987), with a disclaimer that it was not possible to obtain enough information during wartime. Due to the sudden attention that came with the discovery of new particles, the correctness of Yukawa theory remained indeterminate (Okamoto 2000).

In August 1937, immediately after the discovery of the new particles, Nishina proposed an association consisting of theoretical physicists and experimental researchers specializing in the observation of cosmic rays; based on this, a study group was launched that gathered researchers from within Japan to discuss the meson. The meeting was developed into what was referred to as *Riron no kai* (theory society) in June 1941. Afterwards, even during the war, multiple symposiums were held: *Meisō kai* (meditation society) in April 1942, *Meson kai* (meson society) in December 1942, *Chūkanshi kondankai* (meson roundtable) in June 1943, and *Chūkanshi tōronkai* (meson debate society) in September 1943. Additionally, in November 1944, there was a presentation by a Subcommittee on the Theory of Elementary Particle Research, National Research Council of Japan (The Committee for Yukawa Hall Archival Library 1982, pp. 266–268). The proposed improvements in Yukawa theory that were discussed at these symposia were of three essential varieties. Yukawa aimed to recreate the quantum theory of fields from scratch. Tomonaga did not recognize a problem with field theory; his proposal was a theory of intermediate coupling with improved approximations considering reaction of field. Sakata, Takeshi Inoue (1921–2004), and Yasutaka Tanikawa (1916–1987) expanded on the theory that mesons are decayed into cosmic rays. Sakata and Inoue performed calculations in the case that the cosmic ray particles were fermions, and Tanikawa performed calculations assuming they were bosons. Which direction was correct for theory, or whether there was even another right way, was not settled during the war.

Trends in experimental research also attracted interest: it became well known that Lawrence's cyclotron under construction would allow for the artificial generation of cosmic ray particles, and this was reported in the newspaper just before the war broke out (*Asahi Shimbun* 1941a). In spite of the difficulty of surpassing the relatively well-endowed Americans in terms of funding, personnel, and technology, Nishina was considering the construction of a cyclotron which allowed for the generation of cosmic rays. Although it had appeared before the war against the United States, contributions to the tenth anniversary edition of *Kagaku* (Science) concluded with a passage extolling the need to settle the Yukawa theory by constructing a 4,000-ton class cyclotron capable of promoting research with cosmic rays (Nishina 1941b). When the war started, Nishina said, "Just a single destroyer will be enough," believing a cyclotron could be constructed with the iron from a sunken warship (Tomonaga et al. 1952, p. 188).

In reality, it was first necessary to complete the sixty-inch cyclotron, and this work was continued even after the war started. While the war situation deteriorated rapidly, the overhaul, including the design changes and replacement of the main body and vacuum pump, was completed by February 1943, and after some adjustments, RIKEN's large cyclotron issued a 16 MeV proton beam in January 1944. Nevertheless, great efforts continued to be expended toward maintenance and management, including the work of looking for and sealing vacuum leaks. At the same time, cosmic ray observation continued.

4. Military Research

When the war started, scientists advocating for basic research also had no choice but to attend to military concerns. In the end, even the completion of the large cyclotron was realized as part of a military research project called the Ni-Go Project. The Ni-Go Project was comprised of research and development efforts towards producing an atomic bomb (It was assumed that slow neutron bombardment would produce nuclear fission in uranium 235). Nishina's laboratory was made responsible for this; the large cyclotron was to be used as a source of neutrons.

The discovery that neutron bombardment produces fission in uranium was made at the end of 1938, and the fact that additional neutrons are generated as a result of this nuclear fission indicated the possibility of obtaining even more energy through the ensuing chain reaction. As already mentioned, Tameichi Yazaki had revealed that this process was being put to military use in the United States. In an *Asahi Shimbun* article in February 1941, he pointed out, "Ideally it should produce a chain reaction, but this is very challenging. There is also the question of controlling the reaction." Yazaki determined that such military use would be difficult to achieve (*Asahi Shimbun*, 1941b).

Nevertheless, the Japanese army had already been conducting an assessment on the atomic bomb from the year before. In 1941, the director of the Engineering Division of Imperial Japanese Army Air Service commissioned RIKEN to carry out a study. In the Navy as well, a consultation between Nishina and Yōji Itō (1901–1955) resulted in the Committee on Physics, where the possibilities of using atomic nuclei for military use were studied. In the Committee on Physics, it was deemed that production of an atomic bomb was possible, but that the United States would not attain it during the current war, and so the focus was moved towards research on electromagnetic waves.

RIKEN had received its research commission in 1941, but the roll-out of the Ni-Go Project was slow; substantial activities began in late 1942. The first step for research and development was the concentration of uranium isotopes. The Nishina laboratory, without the requisite accumulation of knowledge and technology, continued to struggle with the volatile uranium compounds, even though the army was actively providing funding and materials. In April 1945, the research facilities burned down in an air raid. The possibility of continuing research at an evacuation site was taken into consideration, but materials were no longer available, and after this stage, active progress on the Ni-Go Project was not seen.

On top of the Committee on Physics, the Japanese Navy asked Bunsaku Arakatsu (1890–1973), of Kyoto Imperial University, to research the development of an atomic bomb in 1942. This was called Project F, which was to separate isotopes of uranium by centrifugation. Hideki Yukawa and Shōichi Sakata joined this project, and the first meeting was held in 1944. Ultimately, it was too difficult to obtain uranium ore, and the last meeting was held just before Japan's defeat.

Also within Navy-related research, Seishi Kikuchi was working on radar development, and Tomonaga was working on theoretical elucidation of the magnetron oscillator mechanism and also conducting research on microwave transmission circuits.

5. Expectations for Nuclear Physics

In spite of the fact that details of military research were not particularly well-known, in wartime it was appreciated that prominent researchers involved in nuclear physics were also involved in the development of new weapons.

As described above, after Yukawa won the Hattori Hōkōkai Prize, his name became well known in radio and newspapers. In 1940, he won the Imperial Prize of the Imperial Academy, and around that time it was reported that he had become a candidate for the Nobel Prize (*Yomiuri Shimbun* 1940). Yukawa was also awarded the Order of Cultural Merit in 1943. At this occasion, Nishina explained that, by the discovery of the particles Yukawa had predicted, Yukawa theory had suddenly become the globally central problem for theoretical physics. Yukawa's achievement, Nishina added, "gave global weight to the status of Japanese physics" (Nishina 1943).

Since the mid-1930s, newspapers occasionally had been reporting on Nishina's observations of "mysterious cosmic rays" (*Asahi Shimbun* 1935) being carried out in various locations. After the completion of the small cyclotron, Nishina was also known as the director of the "magic laboratory." Furthermore, as the discovery of Yukawa particles in cosmic rays became widely reported, Nishina was also mentioned in connection with Yukawa theory and mesons. From early 1937, when the new particle was called "Yukawa electron" and "heavy electron," it was already being referred to as a "monster threatening the scientific community" (*Asahi Shimbun* 1937b) and as a "monster in cosmic rays" (*Yomiuri Shimbun* 1939)—the Yukawa particle was introduced as a mysterious particle deeply penetrating matter. Together with the cyclotron—the "magic laboratory" capable of destroying atoms—this monster had become a symbol of Japanese science and Japanese physics.[12]

From 1943 onwards, as voices calling for the mobilization of science towards the war effort became louder, newspapers referred to Yukawa's research to indicate that the level of science in Japan was not exceeded by that of the enemy (*Asahi Shimbun* 1943). They also cited Nagaoka's atomic model, Kimura's discovery of the z-term, Honda's research on magnetism and metallurgy, etc., but these were in already-established fields of research; therefore, there were high expectations for the young brilliant scientist Yukawa and his new theory.

When reports arose of the development of new weapons based on the destruction of atoms, the names Yukawa and Nishina naturally appeared. In January 1944, *Mainichi Shimbun* reported that Germany was in the middle of researching an "atomic bomb" that could blow a warship one mile into the sky with just a "matchbox full of uranium." It was reported that two cyclotrons, from Paris and Copenhagen, were now available for this purpose (*Mainichi Shimbun* 1944a). Junkichi Itō (1917–2009) of Osaka Imperial University also published commentary that, although this research was difficult to bring to fruition, the United States and Germany were both committed to it, and "it can no longer be dismissed as a dream." Yukawa and Nishina's names were not mentioned here, but in the House of Peers the following month, Aikitu Tanakadate issued a long-winded tirade about the importance of scientific research in wartime, mentioning both of these nuclear physicists; Tanakadate discussed cosmic rays that could penetrate a 20 meter-thick wall of iron and calculations that one-gram of radium could annihilate all the British fleet if the ejected energy could be utilized at a single moment in time. Tanakadate alluded that young and promising scientists were investigating these themes (*Kampō* 1944).

Leaving aside his remarks on one gram of radium, the reason that part of a cosmic ray can penetrate twenty meters of iron is due to very small interactions between the components of the ray and the material. To those who understood this point, it was obvious that cosmic rays could not be used as weapons of mass destruction. Nevertheless, Tanakadate did not appear troubled by this point, and he wrote a further detailed explanation in the *Asahi Shimbun* the following month. There he wrote that Japan was not falling behind in scientific research in order to cultivate a decisive battle force, and that while certain specialist fields needed large-scale equipment in order to outperform international researchers in nuclear physics, the discovery of the meson was made by the "young, most brilliant scientist in our country" using only "pen and paper," thereby showcasing Japanese superiority in this specialty (Tanakadate 1944).

Tanakadate continued with such remarks. On August 26th, 1944, in the *Yomiuri Hōchi*, he referred to the so-called "Ōdan incident," in which a student died after causing an explosion during an experiment in the laboratory of Tokyo Imperial University Faculty of Science member San'ichirō Mizushima (1899–1983). Here Tanakadate claimed that Japan's scientific staff members were not inferior to those of the enemy, and that Japan had a "trump card." (*Yomiuri Hōchi* 1944a). There were rumors among some people that Mizushima's laboratory was working on developing an atomic bomb, and it was inferred that this is what Tanakadate was referring to when he mentioned a trump card. In a speech made on October 15 at the Osaka Bachelor Association club, Tanakadate gave an example of "cultivating a decisive battle force" by not falling behind in science: along with the names of Yuzuru Hiraga, Hideyo Noguchi (1876–1928), and Kōtarō Honda, Tanakadate referred to Yukawa as the one who predicted the existence of the meson using only pen and paper (*Mainichi Shimbun* 1944b). Prior to this, in April 1944, an article was published in *Gakusei no kagaku* (Science for students), whose readers were mainly high school students. It referred to a uranium bomb as a future explosive with the power to blow a warship one mile into the sky." The article also stated that Japan's ally Germany would bring it to mass production (Yukawa 1944a). By around 1944, it was likely that knowledge of such a bomb had spread widely. The author of the article in "Science for students" was Hideo Yukawa, whose name may have been mistaken for Hideki Yukawa.[13]

It was also apparent indirectly that Japan's nuclear researchers were involved in weapons development. Nishina was appointed to be the founding director of the Radio Bureau, the Communications Institute, and the Ministry of Communications and Transport. The Bureau was established on April 1, 1944, and this appointment generated publicity because a private scientist was to spearhead a team of engineers in the development of radio wave weapons. Nevertheless, on September 13, Nishina was allowed to resign from this post. The newspapers and magazines reported his reasoning for this request as "to escape from the complexities of administration with a desire to focus on the rapid completion of a decisive battle weapon" (*Asahi Shimbun* 1944a).

Immediately after the outbreak of war, research using the cyclotron would perhaps not have been allowed to continue if the importance of basic science had carried no military appeal. Nevertheless, being at the cutting edge of research on the nucleus now attracted the attention of the military; there was no longer any need to loudly proclaim the validity of such research. Nevertheless, already at this time, Nishina took the progression of the war situation very seriously, and as a scientist, he was making great efforts towards research in order to halt such deterioration.

Additionally, there was the management of expectations, particularly those expectations that Tanakadate had generated. With no clear outlook regarding the military use of nuclear fission, but with expectations rising, Nagaoka felt a sense of crisis in the current situation. As he wrote in *Gunji to gijutsu* (Military Affairs and Technology) in December 1944: "Publicity came from the legislature, from magazines, and from newspapers, and the pubic became interested in the problem." In this article, Nagaoka analyzed issues to be resolved before military applications could be realized. Specific problems discussed included the manipulation of neutrons, securing uranium as a raw material, separation of its isotopes, the bomb's fuse, innovations necessary to effectively harness the large quantity of energy generated, mechanisms for the use of power, etc. These problems were concluded, in light of the actual situation, to be "totally unknowable unknowns." Nagaoka further explained in the appendix that "From now, I will have to conduct more research on weapons to gain time, so I will take the liberty of not responding to requests for interviews or to letters regarding this article" (Nagaoka 1944).

Nagaoka's discussion is detailed; not only does it show the main points of the problem faced, but it also indicates ways to resolve the problem. His intent is evidenced by the presence of occasional strong negatives and the elucidation of suspicions. Nevertheless, some readers had an impression that there were challenges but also prospects of solving them, but because it was during wartime, details were being hidden (Yamanaka 2001, pp. 792–793).

In fact, at the time Nagaoka's article came out, more realistic news about the atomic bomb had been published in the newspaper. The morning papers on December 29, 1944 reported, based on information from Lisbon, that Germany had possibly used an atomic bomb. The *Asahi Shimbun* further added that this bomb is considered to be a uranium bomb; with just "one match," worth of uranium having the power to blow a warship two kilometers into the sky (*Asahi Shimbun* 1944b; *Yomiuri Hōchi* 1944b). This news coverage, although of questionable accuracy, was based on an announcement made by the Germans and a description of a bomb by Swedish physicist Manne Siegbahn (1886–1978), which was reportedly published in the British newspaper *Sunday Express*.

Perhaps stimulated by the information that Germany had an atomic bomb ready for use, commentary on an atomic bomb became more frequently seen in early 1945. The January 2 Osaka edition of *Mainichi Shimbun*, reported that it was unclear whether the German bomb was a nuclear weapon or simply a superior conventional explosive. In any case it was reported that Order of Culture recipient Hideki Yukawa, along with his mentor Nishina, was surpassing "magnificent nuclear physicists of the other superpowers, and they devoted themselves to their studies" (*Mainichi Shimbun* 1945). On February 1, *Yomiuri Hōchi* described a German atomic bomb, reporting that their uranium bomb could blow a warship into the sky using a matchbox worth of uranium (*Yomiuri Hōchi* 1945a).

Most notable in this narration of the expectations for nuclear physics was an article published in the *Asahi Shimbun* on January 8, 1945 called "Dreams of Scientists in the New Year" *(Asahi Shimbun* 1945; Okamoto 2007). Those first dreams of the year about new weapons included those of Tsunesaburō Asada (1900–1984), who was engaged in the aforementioned research on radio wave weapons, Hideki Yukawa, famous for the Yukawa particle, and Mineo Yamamoto (1903–1979), who studied aviation engineering. In the article, which was intended to show "implications for a new offensive of Japanese science," Yukawa dreamed of a hard ray of radiation being emitted from a cave on a mountainside in Japan and destroying Washington. The particles with strong penetrating power are mesons, and in order to manufacture them, there was a need for an apparatus tens to hundreds of times greater in size than the contemporary cyclotron, but a huge chunk of iron hidden in a cave appeared in Yukawa's dream. The article ends where Yukawa imagines that this might be the cyclotron.

The cyclotron in the mountain represents the huge, 4,000-ton cyclotron at Berkeley, which had frequently been described in newspapers and magazines as capable of generating mesons. In 1940, when the details of this equipment were unknown, an imaginary diagram depicting it as a large facility in the mountains was published in a magazine (K. M 1940). After the outbreak of war as well, as described above, the explanation by Ryōkichi Sagane and Michio Hatoyama on the nuclear physics of the cyclotron (Sagane 1947; Hatoyama 1942) included an overall view of the equipment resulting from work immediately prior to the war.

Although the article was thought to be written by a journalist who was familiar with the trends in nuclear research, as in the case of Tanakadate, there was no consideration for the point that there was no promise in using a component with strong penetrating power in cosmic rays (at this point believed to be the meson) as a powerful weapon. Nevertheless, in other respects the article made statements that were considered scientifically accurate (for instance, the writer understood that a straight particle beam would not arrive in Washington intact). We can see that people with a certain degree of understanding of mesons and the cyclotron shared an expectation that these scientific achievements would result in weapons.

Tanakadate was continuing to implore confidence in the "science of Japan" well into the summer of 1945. He continued preaching that "Japan's weapons of science" could destroy "5,000 or 10,000 enemy planes" or "1,000 or 2,000 enemy ships" *(Shin Iwate Nippō,* 1945). Such was the speech and conduct of an old physicist, who was nearly ninety years old, but this was backed up by the track record of Japanese research on the atomic nucleus. This might have introduced a certain kind of magical expectation that was different from the wishful thinking of the *kamikaze* (divine wind).

6. Drop of the Atomic Bomb and Defeat

It is not easy to measure the impact of the press coverage, but Kazutoshi Handō, born in 1930, recalls Aikitu Tanakadate's speech made in wartime that "one matchbox of weapons can blow one ship into the sky" (Sakamoto et al. 2000, p. 199). It is unknown whether this is based on real memory or upon information obtained in a later date, but Handō mentioned an (incorrect) understanding revealed in a roundtable discussion that Yukawa's meson theory was needed to make an atomic bomb. Amongst the discussion he remarked, as his current understanding, that "Maybe Yukawa's winning the Nobel Prize was an atonement for dropping the atomic bomb on Japan" (Handō et al. 2009, p. 362). Hisashi Yamanaka, born in 1931, also remembers reading the aforementioned Hideo Yukawa's commentary when it was released (Yamanaka 2001, pp. 791–792). Kenji Yoshihara, born in 1929, also remembers hearing the story that "a bomb the size of a matchbox can be made which would devastate Tokyo" (Yoshihara 2010). This reveals that those who were teenagers at the end of the war were possibly aware that the Japan which was home to Nishina and Yukawa might be able to make an atomic bomb, though they did not believe it blindly.

On the other hand, in the setting of Tanakadate's remarks following the Ōdan incident, people who were actually involved in the development and those with professional knowledge did not think an atomic bomb would appear in Japan, Europe, or the United States until after the war had ended, though they were aware of Tanakadate's remarks and the Ōdan incident (Tajima 1995, pp. 75–76; Tomonaga et al. 1952, pp. 189–190). Nevertheless, as the war situation worsened, Nishina began to grow frustrated with the slow progress of military research, perhaps because he had taken the leading position in the mobilization of science and had often made official remarks (Ito 2002). In a calligraphy requested in July 1945, Nishina wrote "All things come from nothingness," and some researchers expressed concern that "the boss was going to die" (Tomonaga et al. 1952, p. 195). This writing may be interpreted as meaning that Nishina had become somewhat nihilistic; furthermore he wrote: "I cannot work, and our house is burned down,"

Rather, this should be construed as manifestation of Nishina's sense of responsibility and frustration because experimental equipment had been burnt in air raids, making the development of an atomic bomb nearly impossible even though the expectations of the military were unrelenting.

On August 6, 1945, the atomic bomb was dropped on Hiroshima. When this information went around, a sense of responsibility for military research began to overwhelm Nishina. The next day, on the 7th, he joined the investigative team organized by Imperial Headquarters. He was to go to Hiroshima, but he returned to Tokyo after an airplane failure. The beginning of a letter from the researcher Hidehiko Tamaki (1909–2013) speaks for the state of mind of the time:

> If Truman's statement is true, I think the time has come when those of us concerned with the Ni-Go Project should commit *harakiri*[c]. I will tell you about the timing when I come back from Hiroshima, so please stay in Tokyo until I contact you again. Truman's statement seems to be true, just as the prior figures that appeared in his previous statements were true. Whether it is true or not will be obvious when we arrive at Hiroshima tomorrow. The reports that have been delivered to the General Staff Office seem to support Truman's statement. Regrettably, what my sixth sense had told me was right with regard to this issue. In short, if this is all true, the researchers in the United States and the United Kingdom have acheived a great victory over Japanese researchers, that is, over the researchers in Building No. 49 of RIKEN. This means that the personal qualities of the researchers in the United States and the United Kingdom surpass those of the researchers in Building No. 49. (Nakane et al. 2007, pp. 1142–1144)

Per Truman's statement, the power of the atomic bomb dropped on Hiroshima was reportedly equivalent to 20,000 tons of TNT. This was consistent with what Tamaki had calculated a few years before (Yamazaki 2010). Through the press, Nishina was able to know the contents of Truman's statement soon after the atomic bomb was dropped on Hiroshima. With that Nishina was more or less convinced that what had been dropped on Hiroshima was an atomic bomb (Nishina 1952, p. 15), and he submitted a memorandum to support this claim.

We can see that Nishina was serious in his intent to perform *harakiri*, as he declared this at the start of his memorandum: he added that the timing would be determined separately. Though what other researchers around him actually had in mind was unclear, Nishina was enthusiastic about developing an atomic bomb from 1943 onwards. Nevertheless, it is not impossible that Nishina offered predictions to the military that America was unlikely to succeed in developing an atomic bomb.[14] He felt responsible enough to commit *harakiri* most probably because he was beaten by the enemy in terms of the development of an atomic bomb, and he discovered this fact in the worst possible way when such a bomb was dropped on his own country. More specifically, to whom did Nishina feel this responsibility, or who was compelling him to feel this way? As will be described later, it is possible to find answers to these questions from the circumstances surrounding why Nishina ultimately did not follow through with *harakiri*.

As can be seen in the next paragraph of Nishina's memorandum, it is clear that the great victory for US and British researchers over Japanese researchers, in particular over the researchers in Building No. 49 of RIKEN who were engaged in the Ni-Go Project, directly refers to the fact that the United States succeeded in developing an atomic bomb first. However, the next sentence shows that Nishina thought this was a victory of the personal qualities of the enemy's researchers over those of his countrymen.

Before the war, the observation of cosmic rays and the continual upscaling of cyclotrons, centering on Yukawa theory, had been major topics in nuclear physics, and issues such as the use of nuclear power and the development of atomic bombs had probably never been addressed by physicists. Nevertheless, during the war, physicists in each country were engaged in the development of nuclear weapons, and this was reported in newspapers and other media even in wartime. Faced by special circumstances and challenges, nuclear physicists around the world were engaged in attempts to solve a special but common problem, pitting their intellectual self-esteem against each other. As Nishina would have imagined, his mentor Bohr, Lawrence (who readily agreed to provide information about the cyclotron), Oppenheimer (quick to note the relationship between particles in cosmic rays and Yukawa theory), and Heisenberg (whom Nishina had requested to guide Tomonaga), were all scientists at the forefront of nuclear physics around the world, and all were working on this nuclear weapons problem.

The dropping of the atomic bomb on Hiroshima revealed to Nishina which country's physicists had won the intellectual competition to develop an atomic bomb. With regards to the idea that the personal qualities of the winners were superior to those of the losers, it can be understood that Nishina gained the deep-held conviction, which had been particularly inspired through exchanges with

Lawrence, that it was the moral character of the people involved that determined the success or failure of research.

After Hiroshima, an investigation of Nagasaki was performed. After the broadcast of the Imperial radio decree at the end of the war on August 15th, Nishina returned to RIKEN, saying, "The times have changed now." Concerned about the poor condition of the vacuum pump, he asked a researcher, "What has become of the leak in the cyclotron's vacuum pump?" (Tomonaga et al. 1952, pp. 195–196; Tajima 1995, pp. 89–90; Kimura 1990, pp. 46–47). This "sudden change" in Nishina had already been anticipated by people around him while he was in Hiroshima (Tomonaga et al. 1952, pp. 194–195).

Some attribute the surrender of Imperial Headquarters to the participation of the Soviet Union in the war, others attribute it to the dropping of the atomic bomb, and still others argue that both were necessary. In any case, in order to convince the military and the public that surrender was necessary, the dropping of the atomic bombs was given as the official reason[15] (Suzuki 2006; Iguchi 2010). Nishina, asked to investigate what kind of bombs had been dropped in Hiroshima and Nagasaki, may have sensed the atmosphere, which was shared by Hantarō Nagaoka, in Tokyo (Itakura et al. 1973, pp. 676–677). Trends centering around the Imperial Headquarters rapidly weakened Nishina's resolve to take responsibility, which may have meant committing *harakiri*. As the country moved towards surrender, Nishina seems to have become convinced that the military would not lay the blame at his feet. After the atomic bomb was dropped on Hiroshima, the responsibility that Nishina felt for failing to develop an atomic bomb was directed at the military, and the dropping had made the military move away from its position of holding Nishina responsible.

Immediately after the atomic bomb was dropped, people around Nishina had anticipated that the military might be unyielding in its pursuit of people to blame, and some feared that Nishina, who had left for Hiroshima, might be imprisoned (Tomonaga et al. 1952, p. 194). In addition, military personnel had visited RIKEN to ask whether Japan was also able to make an atomic bomb (Tajima 1995, pp. 87–89; Kimura 1990, pp. 45–46).

Even during the war there was press coverage of the mobilization of American science, and it was not unexpected that American forces might overwhelm Japan in this fashion. Moreover, the arrival of the atomic bomb had also been anticipated, although not so soon. After the atomic bomb was dropped on Hiroshima, Tameichi Yazaki expressed doubts as to the nature of the weapon, saying, "Thus far we have used the word 'atomic bomb' every time a mighty new (conventional) bomb makes an appearance, and I feel this is what is happening this time too." (*Yomiuri Hōchi* 1945b). Although Yazaki's judgment about the bomb dropped on Hiroshima was obviously in error, we can see from his remark that there was an awareness of repeated press reports regarding atomic bombs which were all shown afterwards to be erroneous. Nevertheless, once the nature of the bombs dropped on Hiroshima and Nagasaki became clear, people seemed to move to an understanding that America had overcome the many technological difficulties that Japan had been unable to resolve, and the atomic bomb was materialized, and more quickly than anticipated.

Section 6. Research on the Atomic Nucleus and Elementary Particles in Defeat

1. Researchers on the Atomic Nucleus Immediately after Defeat

After returning from studying Hiroshima and Nagasaki, Nishina's first concern was the adjustment of the cyclotron. Now that he was no longer shackled by military research, the first thing that came into Nishina's mind was the world of "basic science" before the war. The completion of the atomic bomb concluded a temporary state of research, in which nuclear scientists around the world shared the same challenge of military research. After this, it was expected that fierce competition would unfold around the meson again. Facing a competition on a stage different from the war between nations, Nishina did not appear to have been so concerned with the fate of his defeated nation.

Even though the scientific war had been lost, there were few voices raised in ire from the public attempting to hold scientists accountable. Instead of blaming scientists for the loss of the scientific war, defeat was attributed to the facts that military rejected the arguments of scientists, that confrontation with the Army and Navy prevented the results of science and technology from being leveraged to their fullest, and that scientific thinking had not permeated the nation or society in general. Conversely, some scientists expressed doubts at hearing once again arguments for the advancement of science, with some pointing out that this was what they had been told even while the war was being undertaken (Tsuboi 1946).

Remarks that the development of the atomic bomb could not be completed or that the dropping of the atomic bomb caused the loss of the war were difficult to come by, since reports concerning the atomic bomb were censored under the occupation. Nevertheless, in the January 1946 edition of the *Asahi Graph*, there was an article entitled "First Laugh of the New Year: Iroha Karuta,[d] New Edition," in which there were cards with proverbs like "First born, least clever: Fumimaro Konoe," "When force has its way, reason will retire: Mr. Tatsukichi Minobe," "Make assurance double sure in deleting anti-democratic contents in the government-designated textbook," and together with them appeared a picture card of an atomic cloud with a proverb, saying "Truth comes out of falsehood: an atomic bomb." Also, with the proverb "The proof of the pudding is in the eating," a photograph of Hiroshima taken from the sky after the atomic bomb was included without any commentary. These photographs were aimed less at the scientists who were directly involved in the development than as an ironic statement intended for everyone who had held hopes that a new type of bomb would instantly turn the tide of the war; still, these photographs must have been a deeply emotional sight for Japan's nuclear researchers.

Although there were difficulties after the defeat, it was no longer necessary to engage in military research, and the military itself had disappeared. The conditions were right for restarting research, and Nishina burned with the desire to do so. Nevertheless, it was no easy thing for him to again involve himself directly in research. After having escaped any damage by air raids, the large cyclotron was destroyed by the occupying forces in November 1945, along with the remaining wreckage of the small cyclotron. The detritus was dumped in Tokyo Bay, eliminating hope of resuming research. Moreover, immediately after the defeat, a movement to reform Japan's general research system in line with the intentions of the occupying forces gained momentum, and Nishina was obliged to play a central role. In 1946, he became the director of RIKEN after Masatoshi Ōkōchi was expelled from public office; here Nishina was compelled to struggle with maintaining and managing the entire institution amidst the chaos of defeat. In 1948, RIKEN was disbanded as part of a designated decentralization plan. When it was relaunched as a private company called Kagaku Kenkyūsho Co., Ltd, Nishina was appointed its president and thereafter became extremely busy. In 1949, he was appointed vice president of the Science Council of Japan; his role as a representative of the academic community also became more substantial. After the war, Nishina was responsible not only for RIKEN, but also tasked with the overall academic reconstruction of Japan; he was no longer able to take command at the cutting edge of research.

The young generation of physicists was also unable to resume research immediately after the war. Indeed, they seem to have been affected by the loss of the war more severely. Two months after the defeat, Yukawa was still refusing requests for writing and spending his days in meditation and reflection (Konuma 2006). In a meeting about the direction of the Nishina laboratory that was held immediately after the defeat, Tomonaga insisted that it was a pity that he had to stand by and watch while new attempts to use nuclear power would appear one after the other, but he was summoned by the Economic and Scientific Section of the occupation army when the cyclotron was destroyed after the war, where he was told that, rather than pursuing academic research, he might be better occupied by cooperating with efforts in reconstruction, such as in increasing food production.

Therefore, Tomonaga considered studying photosynthesis for a while (Tomonaga et al. 1961, pp. 123, 149). Before that, Tomonaga engaged in "work that does not really require the body or the mind," translating works that had been written in Japanese during the war into European languages, such as works concerning the super-many-time theory, reaction of field, intermediate coupling, magnetron theory, and s-matrix theory of three-dimensional circuits (Tomonaga 1956, p. 100).

Satoshi Watanabe (1910–1993) wrote in 1946, "What are Japanese scientists doing? They are doing nothing. Or at least, they're not doing any research." The first reason for this was the difficulty of their lives. However, Watanabe pointed out as an underlying reason that "there is no longer any driving force motivating their activities." They once had the research support of "capital and warlords," but now such were no longer able to provide funds (Watanabe 1946). In fact, some of these scientists had obtained military-issued equipment and started research immediately after the war, but the nuclear researchers had to deal with the fact that, in addition to the cyclotrons at RIKEN, the Osaka Imperial University and Kyoto Imperial University cyclotrons had been destroyed; they could not embark on any new research in atomic physics immediately after the war.

Nevertheless, it was apparent that overall academic trends in Japan did not change very much following defeat. Led by chemist Roger Adams (1889–1971), the US Scientific Advisory Group conducted a survey over the various parts of Japan in July and August 1947 in order to advise occupying forces on academic system reform in Japan. This survey surprised Japanese scientists, who adhered to basic science even in defeat (Scientific Advisory Group 1947). According to the

Scientific Advisory Group, "Much university research is somewhat esoteric in character. Mathematicians prefer such things as number theory to analysis or to work in applied mathematics." They observed that the motivation behind this was the idea of "cultured class," reflecting the philosophy that they should bolster Japanese honor by showing that Japanese culture is superior to other cultures in the world. Also, they reported that Japanese scientists consider as a point of honor that research activities of all sorts were carried out and all the fields of research known in other regions should also be worked on in Japan.[16] Additionally, it was pointed out that at the graduate and researcher stage, at least in the natural sciences and engineering, emphasis seemed to "fall upon work in pure sciences to an extent detrimental to applied science," and in light of the economic circumstances at the time, this emphasis was something that merited doubt.

The proposal of the American scientists was humble: while in the United States, where the application of science to industry was overemphasized and a shift to basic science was being stressed, the reverse might be more appropriate for Japan. The American scientists made a cautious suggestion that Japan should concern itself with the improvement of production methods, quality management, improvement in design and manufacturing, looking to methods for safety and management "[w]ithout abandoning the more romantic research in basic science."

This report of the Scientific Advisory Group was very similar in nature to the reactions of occupying forces members seen in Tomonaga's writings. At the end of the war, Japanese scientists did not feel it unnatural to return to the research from the pre-war period. However, American scientists hardly understood why they were pushing forward with basic science, given the nation's lack of food.

In fact, in the science laboratories deemed essential to start research anew, and even in Nishina's laboratory, attempts were made at research that would be of practical utility, such as the manufacture of penicillin and vitamin A, where the vacuum technology obtained through the construction of the cyclotrons could be utilized. Of these, they were able to utilize the results of prior research conducted by RIKEN's Katsumi Takahashi (1892–1925) in the study of vitamin A, and they were so successful that it aided in the postwar reconstruction of the nation (Sone et al. 2005).

2. Reconstruction of Research on the Atomic Nucleus and Elementary Particles

The interruption of research on the atomic nucleus and elementary particles did not last long. Japanese scientists, even those starving in ruins, were unable to allow unresolved problems to remain unresolved.

Previously, Tomonaga attempted to express Dirac's many-time theory within field theory, which he had found fascinating before he went abroad for study, and he had published his super-many-time theory in 1943, during the war. Now after the war, Tomonaga started new research with students in Tokyo, by rewriting quantum electrodynamics in the form of the super-many-time theory. Additionally, in 1948, working from Shōichi Sakata's theory of c mesons, Tomonaga arrived at the concept of renormalization, resolving a problem of integration divergence that he had noticed when studying abroad in Germany.

Contact with foreign researchers also resumed in bits and pieces. Oppenheimer asked Tomonaga to provide a report of his wartime quantum electrodynamics results written in English, which was published in *Physical Review* in 1948. In 1949, the discovery of a deviation from Dirac's theory of the energy levels of the hydrogen atom (the Lamb shift) was published in *Time*, but Tomonaga, who attempted to describe this through renormalization theory, was able to reproduce calculations of experimental results. Working from what little information they could obtain, Japanese researchers resumed their competitive approach to research immediately after the war, and sought to ascertain what their position in such research would be.

The successes overseas were more stimulating for research on the meson. In the United States in 1947, Hans Bethe and Robert Marshak (1916–1992) published their two-meson theory independently of research conducted during the war by Sakata et al. Immediately after that, Cecil Powell (1903–1969) et al. discovered the presence of two kinds of mesons in cosmic rays (The particles they discovered are now called pions and muons). In 1948, plans from before the war were put into action, and Eugene Gardner (1901–1986) and César Lattes (1924–2005) confirmed that a 184-inch synchrocyclotron was able to generate man-made mesons. As a result of this, it was discovered that the particle Yukawa had predicted was the pion, a short-lived particle that quickly disintegrates, and one product of this was the muon, a principle component of cosmic rays with high penetrating power.

Sakata's two-meson theory was correct, and, going back further, Yukawa's prediction was confirmed. This led to Yukawa himself being invited to the Institute for Advanced Study at Princeton in 1948, which was followed by a transfer to research at Columbia University the following year. Also in Japan, there was the confirmation of details of the nuclear force, determination of the nature of pions and muons, and fundamental modifications to field theory, which Yukawa had been working on from before World War II. Yukawa was already famous before the war, and in the September 6, 1948 issue of *Asahi Shimbun*, in an article called "Vox populi vox Dei," he and the swimmer Hironoshin Furuhashi (1927–2009) were featured as "Japanese people in the world who bring pride to Japan now" (*Asahi Shimbun* 1948).

Yukawa's 1949 Nobel Prize brought the widespread realization that physics in Japan had reached a level where it now led the world, but examining the process leading to the award in detail reveals a glimpse of the actual transition of international opinion with regards to Yukawa theory. Yukawa was recommended for a Nobel Prize by France during World War II, which was followed by recommendations from Gregor Wentzel (1898–1978), Jean Thibaud (1901–1960), and Marcel Schein (1902–1960) after the war. Yukawa continued to gather a small number of recommendations until 1949, when there was a surge in the number of people endorsing him for the 1949 Nobel Prize. He received the most nominations that year, with eleven endorsements, centered around researchers at the Massachusetts Institute of Technology in the United States, who were attempting to shift the focus of research to nuclear experiments. There were also recommendations from Nobel laureates Otto Stern (1888–1969) and Theodor Svedberg (1884–1971), who had a strong influence on the selection process. At the same time, eight prominent physicists including Fermi, Nevill Mott (1905–1996) and Charles Galton Darwin submitted recommendations in favor of Powell, who discovered the two particles. It can be seen that research on the meson attracted a great deal of attention during that same time period (Recommendations were sought in September 1948 for submission in January 1949).

The Nobel Committee determined to give the 1949 award to Yukawa and the award for the following year to Powell. Yukawa's award was for opening up an area of nuclear physics by predicting the existence of the meson, and, in advocating meson theory, for stimulating experimental research conducted by synchrocyclotrons. The 1949 selection committee consisted of six people, five of whom suggested a single award for Yukawa, with one person supporting a joint award with

Powell. Powell's achievement was the use of microscopes to analyze the results of using special light-sensitive material at high altitudes for recording observations, which was thought impressive because it suggested experimental work could be done without large-scale equipment. The results show that Yukawa was awarded the Nobel Prize the year after the significance of his theory really became clear. This was an unusual case of keeping with the intent of Alfred Nobel (1833–1896) as expressed in his will that the award should be given to contributions that were deemed significant in the year prior to selection. However, in the process of selection, there was a competition within experimental research, and this prevented unanimous selection.

From individual recommendations, one can read rather more lively evaluations. Millikan (who had built up a framework for physics research at the California Institute of Technology, the institution that hosted the two discoverers of the muon, Anderson and Neddermeyer) continued to recommend these two individuals each year from 1941, with the exception of 1943. In his yearly recommendations Millikan claimed that these two individuals had already expressed the need to discover new particles at an international conference in 1934, and that new particles had been shown in photographs of a published paper in 1933. He argued that these discoveries were from before Yukawa's prediction. Furthermore, Millikan highlighted the importance of the actual discovery of the particles, criticizing the fact that there are places in a 1935 treatise by Yukawa himself where the reader may gain the impression that Yukawa expressed that he is not convinced of either the theory or of the existence of the particles because the hypothetical particles had not been discovered. In his letter of recommendation for the 1949 awards, with discoveries after 1947, Millikan added that the significance of the discoveries of Anderson and Neddermeyer were now more apparent.

Arthur Compton's (1892–1962) letter did not identify a nominee, however when referring to Yukawa and Powell, he considered Yukawa's prediction to be no more than "a happy inspiration," pointing out that it did not lead directly to the discovery of any new particles. This was reminiscent of Bragg's 1938 assessment of Nagaoka's atomic model, although of course Compton's Nobel prize recommendation makes no statement that is equivalent to Braggs disparaging "by a Jap anyway" comment.

It was probably difficult to overturn the assessments for reasons of cultural sphere or racial affiliation, even though they were related to the results achieved by Nobel-class researchers. Nevertheless, Yukawa's victory at this time was for his achievement of fifteen years before, and Japanese research on the atomic nucleus and elementary particles in the intervening fifteen years had accumulated more than sufficient achievements to merit a single Nobel Prize.

3. Nagaoka's Catharsis

The results of the new postwar additions that Japan made to its atomic nucleus and elementary particle physics research from before World War II were clear to science students and researchers even before Yukawa won the Nobel Prize in 1949. Even though science and engineering did not enjoy the same privileges they had during the war, the popularity of physics departments remained high. Masatoshi Koshiba, who studied at the science department of the First High School, but whose poor academic performance in science led to rumors that he would go on to study humanities, was wholeheartedly resolved to undertake the "difficult" study of physics (Koshiba 2003). Moreover, after Yukawa's Nobel Prize, the media began to ponder whether Tomonaga would be next (Hanzawa 1983, p. 2).

What Yukawa's Nobel Prize brought to the people in Japan who understood research in the fields of the atomic nucleus and elementary particles was, therefore, not the surprise that such achievements and researchers were present in Japan, but conversely, the discovery and the delight that a Nobel Prize had been awarded to a Japanese person, and that the Western scientific community had been forced to recognize the achievements of Japan. Nishina pointed out in the *Asahi Shimbun* that the significance of Yukawa theory had become apparent in 1937, and the Nobel Prize was awarded as a matter of course, adding, "In any case, this is the first award for a Japanese. The enthusiasm that surrounds our nation's physics in the world means that we have finally returned to a world-class standard after the war, and it is also a great honor for our culture" (*Asahi Shimbun* 1949a). These thoughts seemed to represent the impressions of many physicists.

Nevertheless, it may be appropriate to consider the deep emotions of Nagaoka, who had spent more than sixty years at the heart of Japan's physics research since first setting his heart on physics in the middle of the Meiji Period; first he toiled at his own research, and then, when he was no longer able to keep up, he encouraged and supported his junior researchers in their work. Immediately after Yukawa's award, Nagaoka revealed with much joy in the *Asahi Shimbun* some details about his own recommendation. He said that he had written to the Swedish Manne Siegbahn twelve years before, "As an East Asian has never received the Nobel Prize, it is presumptuous for me to say, but Yukawa's achievements really deserve the Nobel Prize. Please take this into consideration." Nagaoka also said that when he consulted then-president of Tokyo Imperial University, Kiheiji Onozuka (1871–1944) on the matter, Onozuka worried that it might be "a bit too early," but now, the award had finally been achieved (*Asahi Shimbun* 1949b).

As far as can be verified, Nagaoka's letter recommending Yukawa was written in 1939, which was not twelve years before 1949, and the timing does not match that of the tenure of Onozuka as president of Tokyo Imperial University (1928–1934). Additionally, letters of recommendation are usually written to the Nobel Prize committee, and it is thus unnatural that the name Siegbahn should arise here. Furthermore, this is inconsistent with Nagaoka referring to his views on the Nobel Prize as described above in *Scientific knowledge* (1936). Perhaps the newspaper article was incorrect, or perhaps Nagaoka was pointing to some personal correspondence that occurred separately from the standard letters of recommendation. In any case, Nagaoka did not easily recommend Japanese names for the Nobel Prize, and in the last recommendation he wrote he became one of the first references in favor of Yukawa, although Nagaoka had no way of knowing this. It is understandable that Nagaoka disclosed such anecdotes with almost childlike happiness when Yukawa was finally given the Nobel Prize.

Nagaoka continued giving speeches and writing articles concerning Yukawa's Nobel Prize. On December 17, 1949, at a commemorative speech hosted by the Union of Japanese Scientists and Engineers, Nagaoka showed his sense of unconcealed rivalry with Westerners that had continued for many years. He noted that there was a disparaging stereotype that most advances in science and technology were due to "white people," and that the Japanese were good at imitation, like parrots or monkeys. Nagaoka celebrated that Yukawa's award washed this shame away and claimed that one could no longer accuse the Japanese of indiscriminate imitation.

Because Nagaoka's Saturn-type atomic model was the first atomic model with a separate nucleus, and it was also associated with meson theory, he was asked to write an outline for *Kagaku Asahi*. The editors of course had in mind the proximity of his atomic model and meson theory. However, Nagaoka had another idea. He recognized that, by giving the award to Yukawa, the Nobel Prize organization indicated that it did not discriminate based on race, nor did it discriminate against works based on the "yellow complexion" of their authors, thus correcting the misunderstanding that it would not award prizes to Asian people. Then Nagaoka published a translation of a letter to him from Ernest Rutherford, dated March 20, 1911. Rutherford's letter claimed that although his imagined atomic structure contained similarities to Nagaoka's own, which had been published a few years before, he had not read the details of Nagaoka's paper. Nagaoka rebukes this, saying that Rutherford had published many articles in *Philosophical Magazine*, the publication containing Nagaoka's treatise, and that he did not think that Rutherford could excuse himself by claiming to not have read it from 1904, when Nagaoka's work was published, through to 1911. Moreover, he mildly showed his resentment that his atomic model had been disregarded, by stating that, "the discernment of the reader is everything," with regard to Rutherford's own feelings in publishing his own atomic model, which was not so different from Nagaoka's Saturn model (Nagaoka, 1949). At this time, Nagaoka was eighty-four years old; what attracted him to scientific research until this age was, after all, his fierce spirit of competition with the "white race" as indicated in this article.

In August the following year, while temporarily returning to Japan, Yukawa gave a lecture at the University of Tokyo, where Nagaoka's shining face in the front row caught the attention of the newspaper reporters. Nagaoka passed away suddenly within four months of that event; perhaps he felt he had lived just long enough to see Japan defeat the white race in intellectual competition. Nishina, who was able to facilitate Yukawa's temporary return and his lecture, and participate in a roundtable discussion, became ill immediately before Nagaoka's death, and died himself a month later in January 1951. Aikitu Tanakadate, who made the "matchbox" comment during World War II, passed away the following year, in 1952. Within a few years from 1950, the individuals who had played key roles and had been a driving force in physics since the Meiji Period disappeared one after the other, and by this point, physics research in Japan was capable of promoting autonomous work beyond the capabilities of any one individual.

Section 7. Supporters of Basic Science

Nagaoka undertook physics research due to a sense of strong intellectual rivalry with the West. He initially followed the path laid down by physics teachers hired from overseas, conducting "everyday" measurements on geomagnetism and gravity; but feeling for himself the direction where Western research was heading, he altered the direction of his own research to match, and urged up-and-coming researchers to conduct research directly related to the most advanced subjects of Western research. Nishina had based his own research on quantum mechanics for many years; the treatment of this topic remained unclear even to Western physicists. Nishina's rivalry with his former colleagues and with newly ascendant American researchers appears to have provided motivation to advance his research. Nishina understood what needed to be done and what to be aware of while moving forward with research in order to put Japanese research at the cutting edge. He realized that there was no such system to achieve this easily in Japan, and he devoted the majority of his own energy to building this system.

Tomonaga and Yukawa admired the esoteric field of theoretical physics, and they started research drawn by the appeal of a new physics theory called quantum mechanics. The changes brought about by the emergence of quantum mechanics had the right characteristics for them to make an entry to this field. After the birth of quantum mechanics, there was a sudden expansion of areas of unique concern to theoretical researchers. For those who had been trained in language arts, mathematics, and physics in the educational system mainly composed of the Imperial Universities and Higher Schools, it was not impossible to absorb all this. From the late 1930s, Nishina aspired to catch up in terms of conducting massive experiments, keenly aware that research was associated with the technological standards and economic strength of nations. There were no such difficulties in the theoretical fields. Additionally, since quantum mechanics was a new field for science within any particular cultural sphere, whatever attempts Tomonaga and Yukawa were to make on their own would necessarily be the state of the art.

We cannot see any sense of rivalry with the West from Tomonaga and Yukawa's generation onwards, and it is not possible to see strong rivalry between fellow researchers. Nevertheless, since research progress had taken them to a world-class level, they enjoyed the trust and confidence of those who were aware of Japan's position in the scientific world. Accordingly they took on the role of fighting the fierce international battle that had been ongoing from the very beginning of the history of science in Japan. On finding that Japan's young researchers were at the vanguard of physics, Nagaoka and Nishina provided as much support and assistance as possible, Nagaoka from his position at the focal point of scientific administration, and Nishina as a research organizer.

Even though experiments failed to bring forth any new methods using high technology, already in the 1930s, Japan possessed ambitious scientists who were able to procure funding and technology to proceed with the construction and manufacture of the most advanced equipment, so long as the flow of information and material across national borders did not halt. If a technology was needed but did not exist within Japan, it could be bought, and if there were insufficient funds to do so, it was only necessary to convince the political and financial worlds. Some scientists assessed the situation in this manner and acted accordingly, and there were accordingly research plans underway that were under their guidance.

The competition with the West that began in Nagaoka's generation was also taken up by the Tomonaga/Yukawa generation in a sense, although motivations changed from era to era, and indeed, it could be said that a long-sought victory was finally achieved right before Nagaoka's death. Behind Nagaoka's determination to participate in this competition was a sense of intellectual rivalry with Westerners. Although this competitive view of science was not necessarily taken up in this specific form by the next generation, Nishina, Tomonaga, and Yukawa were motivated to start researching the latest Western physics theories, which were considered challenging. Put simply, in every generation, the international evaluation of intellect was one of the major forces driving research. A natural or materialist perspective that conforms to research can only be discussed after research progresses to some extent, and it can be said that research was not performed in order to elucidate a natural or materialist perspective.

These scientists also gave very little thought to benefits that research could offer to their society and nation. Rather, many of their targets for engaging in intellectual competition beyond cultural spheres over the long term were both abstract and highly universal, and these were unlikely to meet the concrete needs of industry and the military. Although cosmic rays and atomic nucleus research attracted special attention during the war, most of the leading researchers involved in such military research returned to pure science research immediately after the war.

It is significant that this venue of competition, which was removed from the direct interests of the nation, was defined as being separate from the competitive field in which the naked interests of nations collided, and that there were Japanese people engaging in this competition. If there had been no one engaging in this competition, Yukawa's winning the Nobel Prize would not have happened and could not have given hope to a nation overwhelmed by defeat.

Setting aside the individual qualities of the researchers involved, these factors were the reasons behind Japan's successes in challenging the world after the arrival of quantum physics: the situation in which the intellect was admired worldwide; young people with the intellectual pride to participate, and with the appropriate intellectual circumstances and wherewithal to do so, regardless of their motives; the fact that the appearance of new theories changed the rules of the game significantly, bringing about a situation in which the existence of an accumulated tradition had little effect on the ability to compete; and the fact that the international research situation created by new theories and their arrival was appropriate to young people trained under the education system of the mid-Meiji era and later. Even though it may not have been the desire to contribute to the welfare of mankind that led to the unlocking of the mysteries of the universe, it does not diminish the magnitude of such an achievement. The motivation to satisfy one's intellectual pride is an important force fueling academic expansion in any discipline.

Furthermore, the fact that Japan had such great achievements provided a valuable lesson at least for the Japanese, in terms of science and its evaluation system, as represented by the Nobel Prize. This fact showed that, even in a framework made by the West, and while learning from the West, it was possible for Japanese people to produce results that exceeded the West's best, and that such results could be appreciated beyond the racial and cultural sphere. At the same time this indicated that non-Western peoples could exert their abilities within that framework called science, and that competition within this realm can function across cultures and races.

Notes:

1) With respect to the issues that this chapter argues throughout, there is not much in terms of previous research. For the major characters in this chapter, Hantarō Nagaoka and Yoshio Nishina, *Nagaoka Hantarō den* (The critical biography of Hantarō Nagaoka, Itakura et al. 1973) and *Nishina Yoshio ōfuku shokan shū* (Correspondence of Yoshio Nishina, Nakane et al. 2006a, 2006b, 2007) can be cited as references. The first book is a biography; the second is a collection of letters with detailed commentary. Both are required reading for understanding the trends in Japanese science during Nagaoka and Nishina's era. There is a lot of description of the themes that are discussed in this text. If there is anything that this text can add to those works, it is the consideration of material discovered after the publication of *The critical biography of* Hantarō Nagaoka, and the attempt to describe a flow of history that is not always explicit in Nishina's correspondence.

2) Nevertheless, it was graduates from faculties of law that generally occupied positions of high status in official circles and in the business world.

3) It was known not only to those with academic leanings that science is a field of study with a high degree

of universality, while the same cannot be said of law or economics. For example, at the beginning of an instructive book written by a samurai Kiyoji Sako in Miyagi Prefecture in 1888, he pointed out that Prussian politics were not the same as those of France, legislation in the United Kingdom was not the same as that of Russia, and the US economy was different to Prussia's; however, science is the same in the East and the West, and from country to country (Sako 1888, Introduction pp. 1–2). For the academically inclined, the universality of the competition as a standard that assured prosecution according to fair requirements regardless of who was participating, was more important than the universality of science as knowledge.

4) However, an attempt was made when the Saturn-type atomic model was published.

5) For example, Arinori Mori, the first Minister of Education, belonged to a religious organization of a certain Christian denomination while residing in the United States during the Edo period, and is said to have encouraged foreign students to marry Americans before they returned to Japan. He also seriously considered adopting the English language as Japan's official language.

6) Nevertheless, Sweden was a neighboring country of Russia. The possibility of focusing on Japan under the influence of the Russo-Japanese War was high.

7) For example, in April 1922, he sent a manuscript to J. J. Thomson, eccentrically titled "Formidable Nonsense of Einstein's Theory of Relativity," which he hoped to publish in *Philosophical Magazine*.

8) While this discriminatory comment points at the Matsuzawa hospital, a well-known psychiatric facility, it was quoted because it plainly shows Nagaoka's attitude.

9) For example, the approximate time can be seen from the description "the current situation of the 4,900-ton cyclotron is unknown because of the US-Japan war."

10) He is the son of Hideo Hatoyama, who was molded by his father Kazuo to be an Imperial University Professor.

11) There are other similar descriptions, and some differences can be seen (Taketani 1951, p. 161; *Yomiuri Shimbun* 1988, pp. 186–187).

12) The possibility of the existence of the atomic bomb and other radioactive weapons in general was mentioned in magazines before this time. (Nakao 2008, 2009; Ezawa 2010).

13) There is an article by the same author in *Kodomo no kagaku* (Science for children, Yukawa 1944b). This does not appear to be a pseudonym. Documents from after World War II note an affiliation with Fuji Industrial Co., Ltd. (Yukawa 1951).

14) As previously described, Nagaoka indicated in published writings that he had severe doubts regarding the military utility of nuclear power; owing to generational or personality differences, he appears to have felt no responsibility.

15) Among leaders of the Allied Powers, Churchill (1874–1965) expected such a response from the Japanese (Churchill 1954, pp. 552–553).

16) This remark is reminiscent of Nishina's idea of gathering all the cutting-edge experimental and observational equipment related to research on the atomic nucleus and cosmic rays. Adams' group also visited RIKEN.

a) As of June 2015, there are nineteen Japanese Nobel Prize winners in the natural sciences, ten of whom have been in physics.

b) The Japanese word "Sensei" (teacher) literally means a "person who was born before." Therefore, it is usually used to describe one's elders.

c) A form of ritual suicide involving slicing open the abdomen with a short sword.

d) Iroha Karuta is a set of picture playing cards. Each card has a proverb or an aphorism.

CHAPTER 2
THE FORMATION OF JAPAN'S TRADITION OF ORGANIC CHEMISTRY RESEARCH WITH RIKŌ MAJIMA

MASANORI KAJI

Section 1. In the Beginning: The Promise of the History of Scientific Thought in Twentieth Century Japanese Chemistry

It is very difficult to produce a history of scientific thought that examines the history of the natural sciences in the twentieth century.[1] The challenge of this task would not change very much if we were to narrow our focus to discuss the discrete science of chemistry rather than the natural sciences in general. Because of the progress in specialization and refinement made in the twentieth century, simply understanding the subject matter requires specialist knowledge. Moreover, there are reasons specific to chemistry that make it difficult to construct such a history of scientific thought: traditionally, the pursuit of chemistry has been closely linked with the practice of manufacturing, where practical application has been emphasized over theory. There has been a traditional view that experimentation precedes theoretical thinking in chemistry since the late nineteenth century, when the classic basis of contemporary chemistry was established.[2] As will be described later, this traditional perspective also affected the nature of Japanese research in chemistry.[3]

Until the eighteenth century, when the theories of matter that serve as a foundation for the science of chemistry were still unclear, various theories relating to matter had been developed together with the concerns of practical business. Up until that time, theories were closely tied with practical operations, and this was an interesting development from the perspective of the history of thought. Moreover, through the nineteenth century, only chemistry among the natural sciences could connect the microscopic world with the macroscopic manipulation of substances. Until the end of the nineteenth century, chemistry possessed the most advanced theories of matter to explore this invisible, microscopic world. This is strongly related to the fact that, in 1803, John Dalton (1766–1844) assumed that a species of indivisible particle—the "atom"—corresponded to each element. Dalton's contributions included the definition of relative weights (atomic weights) as an important quality of atoms, and the suggestion of a theoretical framework ("chemical atomic theory") for how to combine the concept of atomic weights with macro-scale techniques such as gravimetric analysis of compounds (Rocke 1984, pp. 21–47). Indeed, due to the chemical atomic theory, chemistry was at the forefront of natural science developments in the theory of matter throughout the nineteenth century. Chemists spent the first half of the nineteenth century pondering the issue of how to determine atomic weights, and the second half working on problems relating to the existence of atoms and molecules (Rocke 1984, pp. 86–87, 313–335).

Although the classic foundation of modern chemistry was established in the second half of the nineteenth century, the so-called "physics revolution" of the late nineteenth and early twentieth centuries resulted in physics being able to provide a realistic means of approaching the physical world on a very small scale;[4] and later on physics stood at the cutting edge of research into the nature of matter. Thereafter, chemistry gave up its spot at the forefront of the quest to deepen our understanding of the nature of matter to physics, instead opting for a more practical approach: synthesizing a succession of new compounds and expanding the subjects of its research quantitatively,[5] while compiling discrete data on particular substances.[6] In the twentieth century, among the fields of natural science, it has been physics that has changed our conception of nature and science at the micro-level, while biology took on this role in the macro-world. Accordingly, at the beginning of the twentieth century, when the philosophy of science was established, its main subject of concern was physics. Recently, biology has also been a subject for the philosophy of science; but traditionally, chemistry has not been of much concern.[7]

Reflecting this situation, there were few major chemists in the twentieth century in Europe and the United States who published philosophical writings.[8] Likewise, most of the Japanese chemists in the twentieth century strived more for laborious research, and almost none published any philosophical speculation. How, under such circumstances, could one go about constructing a history of scientific thought concerned with chemistry? In fact, there were some who had received specialized education as chemists but became philosophical thinkers; figures such as Shigetake Sugiura (1855–1924) and Mitsuo Hara (1909–1996) come to mind. It may be possible to try to write a history of scientific thought (history of thought in chemistry) around such individuals. Nevertheless, this chapter is an attempt to write a history of scientific thought that looks at experiment-centered chemical practice through the field of organic chemistry, which was a central concern of chemistry in twentieth century Japan and was even farther removed from philosophical thought. It is almost meaningless to write such a history of thought if one cannot focus on the central core of chemistry rather than its periphery; indeed, if it were possible to focus on this core, I believe that looking at the periphery would be easier, and that is what this collection of essays seeks to do.[9] In fact, there is one person with whom we may be able to effectively try this approach: Rikō Majima[10] (1874–1962), the first chemist to begin full-scale organic chemistry research in Japan. Majima was of the first generation of Japanese organic chemists. As we will discuss in this chapter, he established major organic chemistry research methods that were used in Japan through the 1960s, and his impact is apparent even now.

Section 2. The History of Japanese Chemistry up to Majima

The introduction of modern science into Japan is regarded as having started with the publication of *Anatomische Tabellen*, trans. *Kaitai shinsho* (New book of anatomy), an anatomy text translated from Dutch academic literature by a group of Edo-period physicians, centering on Gempaku Sugita (1733–1817). This marked the onset of Dutch learning, namely the study of Western knowledge through such fields as scholarship, culture, and technology in the Dutch language.[11] One of these scholars of Dutch, Yōan Udagawa (1798–1846), published *Seimi Kaisō* (Introduction of Chemistry), from 1837 to 1847. This can be seen as the beginning of the introduction of modern chemistry to Japan,[12] as through this text, the modern chemistry of Antoine Lavoisier (1743–1794) gained a general introduction.

Udagawa did not fully understand Dalton's chemical atomic theory. However, Kōmin Kawamoto[13] (1810–1871) was a chemist during this flowering of Western science at the close of the Edo Period.[14] Kawamoto was also an instructor at *Bansho Shirabesho* (the Institute for the Study of Barbarian Books),[15] an organization set up by the Shogunate that specialized in the study and teaching of Western learning. Kawamoto, along with others, taught a systematic introduction to chemistry based on Dalton's chemical atomic theory.

After the Meiji Restoration, Bansho Shirabesho's successor institution, Kaiseijo, was seized by the new government. Thereafter, in 1869, it was reopened as the *Kaisei Gakkō* under the auspices of the Ministry of Education, becoming a specialist school where foreign teachers, hired by the Meiji government ("Oyatoi") taught a Western curriculum. In 1877, this school (called Tokyo Kaisei Gakkō at the time) merged with the Tokyo School of Medicine to become the University of Tokyo. The former school provided the faculties of law, science, and literature, and the latter became the Faculty of Medicine (Toshiaki Ōkubo 1997). Ultimately, the University of Tokyo became the center of chemistry education in Japan.

Jōji Sakurai (1858–1939) is representative of the first generation of Japanese chemists who studied at the new Meiji-era educational institutions (Yoshiyuki Kikuchi 2000; 2004; 2006). He was born in Kanazawa as the son of a samurai in the Kaga domain (presently Ishikawa Pref.). Sakurai studied English from an early age, and in 1871 entered a predecessor of Tokyo Kaisei Gakkō called Daigaku Nankō, a secondary education institution that offered instruction in foreign languages. When this school was renamed Tokyo Kaisei Gakkō in 1874, Sakurai enrolled in a specialized course within the department of chemistry. In the chemistry department, Sakurai had the opportunity to learn from Robert Atkinson (1850–1929), a British chemist who came to Japan in September of that same year.[16] Although the regular course was normally three years in length, Sakurai completed the curriculum in two years and was then dispatched to the United Kingdom to study at University College London until 1881 under Atkinson's mentor, Alexander Williamson (1824–1904).

Upon returning to Japan in September 1881, Sakurai became a lecturer in place of Atkinson, who had returned to Britain, in the faculty of science at the newly established University of Tokyo—which, as previously related, had formed in 1877 from the merger of Tokyo Kaisei Gakkō and the Tokyo School of Medicine. Just twenty-three years old at the time, Sakurai was promoted to Full Professor in August the following year. He was the second Japanese professor in the field of chemistry, only after Naokichi Matsui (1857–1911). Matsui, who was initially part of the same class as Sakurai, left to study in the United States a year before Sakurai, and returned a year earlier than him to become a lecturer in the chemistry department. Matsui was promoted to professor in 1881.

When the Imperial University was founded in the year 1886, the chemistry department became the Chemistry Department in the College of Science at the Imperial University, with Sakurai taking a leadership role (Matsui moved to the Applied Chemistry Department at the College of Engineering when the Imperial University was established). Sakurai was initially responsible for analytical chemistry and inorganic chemistry, but later was put in charge of physical chemistry, organic chemistry, and the history of chemistry. His lectures are said to have been sophisticated and refined, and to have strongly impressed students (University of

Tokyo Department of Chemistry 2007, p. 38),[17] one of whom was Rikō Majima.

Section 3. Rikō Majima's Path to Becoming a Chemist

From the 1910s, when the Taisho Period (1912–1926) started, in the area of organic chemistry research, Japan was finally starting to show growth in independent research on the structure of bioactive organic compounds in natural products. Rikō Majima was the first professor of organic chemistry to lead this study at the Department of Chemistry in the College of Science at the Tōhoku Imperial University. Majima lived for eighty-eight years, and led an extremely active life, taking successive positions teaching at the Tōhoku Imperial University, the Tokyo University of Engineering (present Tokyo Institute of Technology), Hokkaido Imperial University, and Osaka Imperial University, and participating in the founding of organic chemistry programs at each institution. Majima had many students and was a significant influence on the establishment of organic chemistry in Japan. In the sections below, we will trace the life and work as well as the philosophical trajectory of this one chemist, trying to analyze the history of scientific thought as it relates to chemistry in Japan from the 1910s through the 1950s.

1. Rikō Majima the Student

Rikō Majima was born on October 13, 1874 as the eldest son of a physician in Kyoto. He had a sister, Umeno, who was nine years older than him, and a brother who was two years younger. The Majima family specialized in ophthalmology from the early Edo period, serving as town doctors or working for feudal landlords in and around the districts surrounding Kyoto.[18] Rikō Majima's grandfather, Toshizumi Majima (1804–1882) had served the Tango-Tanabe "han" (domain ruled by a feudal lord, later called Maizuru han and controlled by the house of Makino) as a physician. His eldest son, Toshitami (1840–1886) spent some time learning at Tekijuku, a school run by Kōan Ogata, a renowned scholar of Dutch learning. In the list of Ogata's students we can still find the signature of Taira Majima.[19] "Toshitami traveled to learn at Nagasaki, where he studied rampō (Dutch style medicine), and also apprenticed himself to a British doctor." (Posthumous collection of Rikō Majima, 1970, p. 378). After returning home from Nagasaki, for a time Toshitami was employed by the neighboring Ayabe han (controlled by the house of Kuki); after the Meiji Restoration, he relocated to Kyoto and successfully established his own private practice. Rikō, Toshitami's oldest son, enjoyed a carefree childhood, although he was sickly and needed to be raised carefully. It was thought that this frail nature might prevent Rikō from surviving to adulthood, so Toshitami decided to leave his medical practice to his son-in-law, Shūzō Inoue (birth year unknown–1936), who would train as a doctor in order to continue the Majima's family medical tradition.

In September 1886, Rikō's father died of a sudden illness. Rikō was twelve years old and had just enrolled in Kyoto Normal Middle School (later Kyoto Prefectural First Junior High School) the previous year. He continued in middle school for two more years, but since "Of course, there was no University in Kyoto—even the Third Higher School hadn't been established" (Posthumous collection, 1970, p. 7),[20] he dropped out of middle school in May 1888 at age 14, and went to Tokyo with his brother-in-law to attend Kyōryū school,[21] a typical prep school for students aiming at admission to First Higher School (which bore the name the "First Advanced Middle School" at the time). This was a distinctive school, at the time headed by Korekiyo Takahashi[22] (1854–1936). Kikunae Ikeda (1864–1936), who later became a professor of chemistry at the Imperial University, was still a graduate student teaching English part-time there. In July of the following year (1889), Rikō took the entrance examination for First Higher School but failed; he took the examination for the second time the year after that and passed with "excellent performance" (Posthumous collection, 1970, p. 8).

Advanced Middle Schools of that time required a total of five years to complete. This consisted of a preparatory course of three years, equivalent to a middle school curriculum, followed by a further two years of regular coursework. Majima failed one year in school due to heavy involvement in physical activities such as rowing. He wrote in his journal that, "My health considerably improved, and my determination and energy became robust" (Posthumous collection, 1970, p. 10). As can be seen from Majima's subsequent journal entries, he remained truly active even in his later years, with stamina and vitality far in excess of an average person. Nevertheless, around this time Rikō discovered that most of his father's assets had been embezzled by the estate administrator. Fortunately, Rikō's brother-in-law had al-

ready become a doctor, and through his assistance it was possible for Rikō to continue attending school.

Experiencing such fraud seemed to have psychologically wounded Rikō to
quite a degree: "It became something truly disagreeable for me to engage at all
with society . . . and I preferred instead to study nature" (Posthumous collection,
1970, p. 10). Thus, Rikō enrolled in a course of study in science rather than in the
humanities. Rikō's mother believed that his father's early death was due to working hard at his medical practice, and she told Rikō to be anything but a doctor.
Although his lack of sociability meant that Rikō had no desire to become a physician, he appears to have aspired instead to basic medical sciences.[23] In terms of
selecting his future career, Majima was torn between medicine, geology, and
chemistry. When Mt. Bandai exploded on July 15, 1888, Majima was thirteen
years old, and he was sixteen when the Nōbi earthquake hit on October 24, 1891;
his love of travel and his interest in fieldwork meant that geology was initially his
first choice. However, Majima was told by the head of the geology department at
his university, Bunjirō Kotō (1856–1936), that Rikō's myopia would be disadvan-
tageous for a career in geology.[24] (Posthumous collection, 1970, pp. 10–11). Eventually, Majima decided to concentrate on chemistry, reasoning that, as the child of
a doctor, he was familiar with medicine, and that, as a student at First Higher
School, he had been deeply impressed by the clarity of Mitsuru Kuhara's (1856–
1919) lectures on organic chemistry. In July 1896, Majima graduated from First
Higher School (which was reorganized from the Advanced Middle School in 1894)
and was admitted to the Department of Chemistry in the Faculty of Science at the
Imperial University without having to take an entrance examination.

Majima was a member of the first generation to be educated right from the
beginning in the modern education system developed in the Meiji Period. At the
time, there was only one Imperial University (founded in 1886), but in 1897, the
second, Kyoto Imperial University, was founded in Majima's hometown. Therefore
the Imperial University was renamed Tokyo Imperial University. Although it was
said that the maximum capacity in the Chemistry Department at the time was 10
people (University of Tokyo Department of Chemistry, 2007, p. 40), that capacity
was not met. Including Majima, there were only seven students enrolled. There
were only three chemistry instructors at that time: the professors Jōji Sakurai, a
foreign instructor Edward Divers[25] (1837–1912), and Divers' student, assistant
professor Tamemasa Haga (1856–1914), a graduate of Kōbu Daigakkō (the Imperial College of Engineering under the Ministry of Public Works, founded by the

Meiji government). When Haga left in 1896 to study abroad for two years, Kikunae Ikeda was appointed assistant professor. In 1899, Haga returned home from his studies abroad and was promoted to professor, and then Ikeda himself left to study abroad in Europe. Ikeda was promoted to professor after returning home in 1901 (Tokyo University Department of Chemistry, 2007, pp. 102–105).

In July 1899, Majima and five others graduated from the Chemistry Department (one transferred to the Applied Chemistry Department in the College of Engineering). While Majima graduated second in his class, he secured a spot as a graduate student and became an assistant in the Chemistry Department. At that time, he was the only assistant in the Chemistry Department, and the first to have a bachelor's degree from the Imperial University. Jōji Sakurai, the chair of the Chemistry Department, became Majima's advisor. Majima did not have to perform clerical work, and he was able to concentrate on research except for assisting some students with guidance. Also, there was no limit to the subject matter he was allowed to research. Majima aspired to carry out research in organic chemistry, but he was not able to get real guidance from Sakurai. Given that there were no experts in organic chemistry in the department, Majima had to develop new research methods himself through trial and error. At that time, Nagayoshi Nagai (1845–1929) was the chair of pharmacology in the College of Medicine at the Imperial University. Nagai had studied organic chemistry under the famous German organic chemist August Wilhelm von Hofmann (1818–1892), but students in the Chemistry Department were practically unable to receive his instruction for political reasons. In Majima's memoirs, this situation is described delicately: "Of course it was not impossible for a graduate from the Chemistry Department in the College of Science to receive guidance from Dr. Nagai, but if one dared to do so, it carried the danger of resulting in an unfortunate and unhappy situation. It might displease both departments; there were real examples of this" (Posthumous collection, 1970, p. 18). Regarding this, it was said that during the preparations for the launch of the new Imperial University, Nagai had moved to Germany in order to marry his German fiancée, and he did not return in time for the inauguration of the new Imperial University—because of this, Jōji Sakurai, who had held a long-standing hatred of Germany, requested that Nagai's name be removed from the list of candidates to become full professors in the College of Science.[26] If there was indeed such an antipathy, Majima, who was Sakurai's student, could not afford to attempt to learn organic chemistry from Nagai.

The year Majima became an assistant in the Department, Kōichi Matsubara

(1872–1955), who was three years Majima's senior (an 1896 chemistry graduate), was appointed assistant professor from a teaching position at First Higher School. Matsubara began studying abroad in 1903, and Majima replaced him as assistant professor. The research methods Majima had formulated around this time consisted of borrowing and reading the Western chemistry literature that was already available in the Department of Chemistry—in particular he read through the basic organic chemistry literature of Germany. According to Majima, the chemistry students had already arranged to get together once a week for a journal club to discuss recent publications from overseas[27] (Posthumous collection, 1970, p. 14). There was at that time from the perspective of a freshman "an amazingly impressive array of innumerable chemistry publications and texts from overseas (Ibid.)." This journal club included instructors, graduate students, and undergraduates in their second year or later and was the nascent form of the type of journal clubs that are present even now in natural science departments. Majima believed he would acquire an understanding through this journal club naturally. Every evening for a few years Majima took home a few copies of chemistry journals. He studied the works and research of the German "organic chemistry masters" such as Adolf von Baeyer's (1835–1917) indigo dyes, which were used for staining items such as blue jeans, Otto Wallach's (1847–1931) research on terpenes, the main component of fragrant essential oils in plants, and Hermann Emil Fischer's (1852–1919) research on sugars and purines (heteroaromatic compounds related to uric acid, also contained in nucleic acids). Specifically, Majima "expeditiously abridged and read" German-language articles (Ibid., p. 194). He called this "research on great research." As a result of such activity, "From the inspiration gleaned from the great masters' methods conceived to overcome experimental difficulties, I even felt as though I had been instructed by the master chemists themselves." (Ibid., pp. 17–18). Majima later wrote in an essay titled "Yūki Kagaku Kenkyū Kokoroe" (Maxims on studies on organic chemistry): "I especially recommend this method to students in places where teachers and peers are lacking" (from *Kagaku jikkengaku*, Study on chemical experiments, 1940, rerecorded in Posthumous collection, 1970, p. 194). The Japan of the late Meiji Period, when Majima was a novice researcher, was definitely "a place where teachers and peers were lacking."

Majima decided to study natural products as his particular field of organic chemistry. This was because his readings of "research on major research" was about natural products, and Majima decided to carry out research into useful natural products that were unique to Asia, in order to compete with and surpass Western researchers. At the time in Japan, "laboratory conditions were not really state-of-the-art, and if we were to begin studying what could be carried out anywhere at the same time, Western researchers would always be ahead of us; therefore I thought that it was better to study compounds that Westerners did not have access to." (Majima 1945a, p. 1). The foreign advisor and teacher Atkinson, who had educated Majima's teacher Sakurai, among others, was also engaged in chemical research on substances such as sake and rice malt, which were related to traditional industries in Japan, and he employed some of his students in this research. Atkinson's approach is somewhat similar to Majima's research strategy in that their subject matter was found locally. It is clear that Atkinson in particular consciously developed a special research interest in Japanese traditional industries. This research strategy was developed as pure chemistry research, but with application to local industry in mind. As we will discover in the next section, Majima's research strategy was not concerned with potential industrial applications, and as such, it should be considered independent from that of Atkinson. Majima chose to concentrate first on chemical research concerning *urushi*—Japanese lacquer.

2. Majima's Research Strategy: The Commencement of Research on Urushiol, the Main Component of Japanese Lacquer

Majima embarked on the chemical study of urushiol, the main component of raw Japanese lacquer,[28] which oozes out from the bark of Japanese lacquer trees. According to Majima's posthumous collection of writings (1970, p. 64),[29] the first chemical studies on Japanese lacquer were conducted by Sadamu Ishimatsu (1857–1943) who was later adopted into his benefactor's family as Yoshimi Hiraga. Ishimatsu liquefied Japanese lacquer through treatment with alcohol, and then produced an organic precipitate using lead acetate. Through chemical analysis of this precipitate, he discovered that the empirical formula of the main urushiol group was $C_{20}H_{30}O_2$. Hikorokurō Yoshida (1859–1929) then conducted a similar experiment, and obtained an empirical formula. He also discovered the acidic nature of the compound and named it urushic acid in 1884.

About ten years later, in 1894–95, French chemist Gabriel Bertrand (1867–1962) studied the main components of the Annam wax tree in the then French colony Vietnam, and Bertrand found that this was similar to Japanese lacquer.

Nevertheless, he concluded that it was not an acid and that it was a kind of poly-hydric phenol, which he named laccol (Bertrand 1894).

Also, Kisaburō Miyama (born in 1873) researched Japanese lacquer in industri-al laboratories from 1902. By 1906, he proceeded with studies on the chemical structure of urushic acid. Miyama believed the name urushic acid was not appro-priate, as the substance possessed chemical properties more consistent with a phenol. Therefore, he renamed the substance urushiol[30] (Kisaburō Miyama 1907). At the same time, Majima aspired to study the components of Japanese lacquer as a research subject worthy of his aforementioned strategy. Around the spring of 1905, Majima "received permission from Miyama to study the chemical compo-nents of urushiol" so long as he "did not touch on anything related to its applica-tion"[31] (Posthumous collection, 1970, p. 64).

Thus did Majima begin studying Japanese lacquer. He spent one year, from 1905 to 1906, as an assistant professor in the Faculty of Science at Tokyo Imperial University, studying Japanese lacquer. He also studied this for about half a year in 1909 while studying abroad at the University of Kiel in Germany, and then anoth-er six and a half years from 1912 to 1918 after taking office as professor in the Faculty of Science at Tōhoku Imperial University—a total of eight years of re-search—before fully elucidating the structure of urushiol.

To procure raw materials, Majima went out in mid-summer, the peak season for Japanese lacquer production, to find lacquer-scrapers in nearby production areas. During his time at Tokyo Imperial University, Majima went to Hadano in Kanagawa Prefecture, and during his tenure at Tōhoku Imperial University, Maji-ma collected urushi near Sannohe in Iwate Prefecture (Posthumous collection, 1970, pp. 65, 73).

Majima set about determining the structure of urushiol, the principle compo-nent of Japanese lacquer. Before studying in Germany, Majima worked in the chemistry laboratory of Tokyo Imperial University. He processed roughly 800 grams of urushiol in various ways and explored its general structure. From the products of decomposition and dry distillation, Majima believed that catechol[32] formed the basic structure of urushiol and that there were fourteen or more total carbons and an unsaturated hydrocarbon side chain. Majima marked his group containing R ($C_6H_3R(OH)_2$). A solution of melted metallic sodium in ethanol (in the solution the hydrogen of the ethanol's hydroxyl group is replaced by a sodium) added to urushiol creates a situation where the replaced sodium can react with methyl iodide to substitute methyl groups in place of the hydrogens in urushiol hydroxyl groups. Hydroxyl groups attached to a benzene ring (phenolic hydroxyl groups) were thereby methylated[33] to comprise the first synthesis of urushiol dimethyl ether ($C_6H_3R(OCH_3)_2$):

$$2CH_3CH_2OH + 2Na \rightarrow 2CH_3CH_2ONa + H_2$$
$$C_6H_3R(OH)_2 + 2CH_3CH_2ONa \rightarrow C_6H_3R(ONa)_2 + 2CH_3CH_2OH$$
$$C_6H_3R(ONa)_2 + 2CH_3I \rightarrow C_6H_3R(OCH_3)_2 + 2NaI$$

When Majima tried to subject urushiol to nitric acid oxidation, the amount of product was too low for further extensive analysis. From the above-mentioned results as well as the elemental analysis of the product, Majima estimated that it was a derivative of catechol with a fairy large, unsaturated hydrocarbon side chain.[34] But there was still a lot that was unclear. To begin with, he did not know whether urushiol was a single compound or a mixture of two or more compounds. Other questions remained: how many side chains were there? Where were they located on the benzene ring? Was the hydrocarbon group a straight chain or branched? If the side chain were unsaturated (i.e. having a double bond), where was the double bond located? To purify the product, Majima wanted to use vacuum distillation rather than distillation at atmospheric pressure,[35] but this was not possible since the laboratories in Japanese universities at that time did not have a powerful-enough vacuum pump. For such a process, Majima would need to conduct further research in Germany.

Section 4. Rikō Majima's Research in Germany

In 1906, after studying with the British chemist William Henry Perkin, Jr. (1860–1929) and with Emil Fischer in Berlin, Kōichi Matsubara returned to Japan and was placed in charge of organic chemistry within the Chemistry Department at Tokyo Imperial University where he was promoted to professor in 1909.[36] That same year, Tamemasa Haga, who was in charge of inorganic chemistry, came down with tuberculosis, and Majima was ordered by Jōji Sakurai to study inorganic chemistry abroad in order to succeed Haga. Majima had already been involved in organic chemistry through his research on urushiol, but he agreed to study inorganic chemistry abroad. He added in his journal: "I said that I would be more than happy to be transferred, even to a regional institution, if I could study organic chemistry" (Posthumous collection, 1970, p. 20. That year, Majima had summoned his mother from Kyoto and set up house in Nishikata-chō Komagome Hongō-ku,[37] near the Tokyo Imperial University, and he married on August 5.[38] His wife, Mieko Shinkai, was an instructor at Tokyo Prefectural First Women's Higher School. Majima was thirty-one years old, and his wife was twenty-nine.[39] Five months after his honeymoon, on January 10th, Majima boarded a cargo-passenger ship of the NYK Line (Japan Mail Shipping Line) called Sadomaru, and departed from Kobe.

Initially, Majima had intended to study under Alfred Werner (1866–1919), one of the founders of coordination chemistry, for the purposes of engaging in inorganic chemistry research. Majima arrived in Zurich in late February. Then, a telegram came from Jōji Sakurai that there were plans to establish Tōhoku Imperial University in Sendai. If Majima agreed to be appointed to the Science Faculty there, he would be able to study organic chemistry[40] (Posthumous collection, 1970, p. 20). Originally, for determining the number and location of double bonds in the side chain of urushiol, Majima considered incorporating the ozonolysis techniques of Carl Harries (1866–1923) (Harries 1904, 1905). Therefore, he moved to Harries' lab at the University of Kiel.[41]

After moving to the University of Kiel, Majima did not immediately begin urushiol research. He received a research task from Harries to determine the structure of terpinene, a kind of terpene and a type of aromatic liquid which was also a plant essential oil. Majima also attended Harries' classes and the special lectures of young assistant professors and other lecturers, and he exchanged ideas with assistants (Posthumous collection, 1970, pp. 21–23). In this way, Majima became accustomed to university life in Germany. The next year, 1908, was challenging for Majima, who was ill for most of that time (Posthumous collection, 1970, pp. 24–25). First, he contracted influenza at the beginning of the year and was admitted to the university's hospital. After recovering, he was readmitted with pneumonia—his entire winter semester collapsed due to his struggle with illness. Finally, at the start of the summer semester, Majima was able to settle down into his terpinene research, and he was able to obtain some results. However, he developed erysipelas then;[42] fortunately he recovered, but this damaged his kidneys. He rested and recovered at a hot spring until the following fall,[43] and he returned to research at the beginning of the winter semester that year.

In fall 1908, after Majima's health was restored, he finally began in-depth research into the chemical structure of urushiol. He was able to easily perform distillation using a powerful vacuum (approximately 0.4–0.6 mmHg),[44] which he had been unable to do at Tokyo Imperial University, on urushiol dimethyl ether and on urushiol itself, although for the latter compound, there was still some degree of polymerization. This high-vacuum distillation method had been developed by Harries when he was at Emil Fischer's laboratory in Berlin.[45] Using this technique, and with a sufficiently pure sample, Majima was able to determine the molecular weights and the molecular formulas for urushiol ($C_{20}H_{30}O_2$) and its corresponding dimethyl ether ($C_{22}H_{34}O_2$). If the side chain of urushiol were indeed comprised of a single catechol derivative, its rational chemical formula[46] would be $(HO)_2C_6H_3 \cdot C_{14}H_{25}$. Since this side chain ($C_{14}H_{25}$) contained four fewer hydrogens than there would be in a saturated hydrocarbon group, there must have been either two double bonds or one triple bond. Majima intended to use ozonolysis to determine the position of these double bonds. Ozonolysis is a reaction that uses ozone to oxidize and cut carbon-carbon double bonds (Harries 1904, 1905). Majima first rehearsed his techniques with ozonolysis on a more simple compound (eleostearic acid in wood oil), which he ordered from Japan in addition to Japanese lacquer: he treated this eleostearic acid with ozone and estimated the position of its double bonds. Then he commenced the ozonolysis of urushiol. Because the products of this ozonolysis were not simple, Majima hypothesized that "urushiol was composed of a mixture of several kinds of similar compounds, for example, those with different numbers or locations of the double bonds in side chains or those with slightly different numbers of carbons in side chains." (Posthumous collection, 1970, pp. 71–72).

In summer 1909 Majima left Kiel, staying for a while in Berlin for summer vacation, before moving to Zurich in the fall that year, where he continued his research at the Swiss Federal Institute of Technology[47] under Richard Willstätter (1872–1942). Since Majima's original planned period of study abroad was three years, and since he wanted to study dye chemistry with Willstätter for his last six months, he gained approval of Willstätter with the help of Harries and researched methods for quantitative determinations of quinone, a research subject given by Willstätter. Nevertheless, the establishment of Tōhoku Imperial University was delayed by another year, and Majima received permission to extend his study abroad accordingly. This let him continue research on aniline oxidation under Willstätter for another semester. Just around that time, Willstätter had begun to directly reduce unsaturated organic compounds at room temperature using hydrogen with platinum black (platinum in a black powder form) as a catalyst (Willstätter and Mayer 1908a, 1908b). Although Majima wanted to reduce the double bonds of the urushiol side chains using this method, he had no time left, and decided that this would be a project to take up after returning to Japan (Posthumous collection, 1970, pp. 27–28, 72–73).

When the 1910 summer semester was finished, Majima headed to London and spent his last six months in Europe studying there. He continued his work on aniline oxidation at the Davy-Faraday Research Laboratory of the Royal Institution, having received the permission of director James Dewar (1842–1923). In London, Majima met Edward Divers, who had taught in Japan for nearly thirty years, and who had worked in the Chemistry Department at Tokyo Imperial University, before returning to England to retire (Posthumous collection, 1970, pp. 29–30).

Majima departed London at the end of January 1911, crossed the Atlantic, and, after landing in New York and traveling across the United States, departed from Vancouver Canada back to Japan. Getting on the cargo-passenger ship of the NYK Line called Tanbamaru, Majima landed in Yokohama on March 3 (Posthumous collection, 1970, p. 30).

Section 5. Rikō Majima's Arrival at Tōhoku Imperial University and the Completion of His Research on Urushiol

Majima was appointed professor at the Tōhoku Imperial University the day he returned to Japan, and he moved to Sendai, where he spent a busy first year occupied with the launch of the new university. He resumed research on urushiol in the beginning of 1912, the year after his return. At that time there was no water service in Sendai, so in order to supply water with sufficient pressure to his laboratory, Majima installed his own water pump within the university, which made it easy to implement vacuum distillation (Posthumous collection, 1970, pp. 31–32). Because of this, substances such as urushiol could be easily purified by distillation. Then Majima tried a hydrogen reduction of urushiol dissolved in anhydrous alcohol using Willstätter's platinum black catalyst. When he did this, he discovered a substance with a melting point of 58 to 59 degrees Celsius and obtained crystals with the molecular formula $C_{20}H_{34}O_2$. He named this product hydrourushiol. Ma jima also reduced urushiol dimethyl ether with hydrogen, obtaining colorless crystals with the molecular formula $C_{22}H_{38}O_2$, and a melting point of 36 to 37 degrees Celsius. These were the first crystalline compounds obtained from urushiol. The ability to crystallize a compound makes working with it much easier, since recrystallization[48] can be used as a convenient and reliable method for purification. This is because whether a substance is a pure substance or a mixture cannot really be determined by its appearance, but when a material is a crystal, it can be easily purified by recrystallization, and purity can be confirmed easily by measuring the melting point. The ability to "crystallize" is an indicator of progress in the study of new organic compounds; this is what everyone aimed for in structural studies. Majima also wrote: "This has put my study of urushiol on the right track. I won't forget this joy for the rest of my life" (Posthumous collection, 1970, p. 74). Majima's joy at successful crystallization is very much understandable.

For about seven years thereafter, until 1918, during which time Majima aged from 38 to 45 years old, he experienced his finest years of research. During these years he was engaged in the structural study of urushiol alongside students who came to his laboratory at the Tōhoku Imperial University. Specifically, Majima performed a variety of reactions which converted crystalline hydrourushiol and hydrourushiol dimethyl ether as starting materials into other compounds (derivatives); and he made efforts to synthesize the structures of related compounds, intending to compare their nature with hydrourushiol and derivatives thereof. This shows that Majima began to expand his research in accordance with the normal practice of using chemical reactions for structural studies.

Majima's urushiol research as described above later became the model for Japanese research into the organic chemistry of natural products up until the 1950s. All of Majima's experimental techniques for urushiol research were the latest from Europe, which had been published only recently. These included:

(1) Harries' vacuum distillation methods, published in 1902.
(2) Harries' ozonolysis techniques, published in 1904.
(3) Willstätter's normal temperature and pressure catalytic reduction methods, published in 1908.

Majima applied these cutting edge techniques from Europe to urushiol, "a special local product in the East" (Posthumous collection, 1970, p. 18) that could not be easily obtained by Westerners. He wrote that "I believe I was able to finish the task

without much competition because urushiol was not easily available to Westerners" (Ibid., p. 74).[49]

This research into the organic chemistry of natural products—where such cutting edge techniques from Europe were utilized to study the structures and properties of the organic compounds contained within the natural products found in
Japan and its surrounding environment—was the main methodology employed
in organic chemistry research in Japan until the 1950s.

Majima was deeply involved in the creation of organic chemistry programs
throughout Japan, modeled after the program at Tōhoku Imperial University. With
Majima's leadership, organic chemistry chairs were established in the Tōhoku Imperial University (1911, Faculty of Science), Tokyo University of Engineering
(after 1946, renamed Tokyo Institute of Technology, 1929, Dye Chemistry Department), Hokkaidō Imperial University (1930, Faculty of Science), and the Osaka
Imperial University (1932, Faculty of Science). Additionally, to regress in time
slightly, Majima had a laboratory at RIKEN, where he was named a researcher in
1917 and a senior research fellow in 1922, guiding younger researchers. As already
described, prewar research in organic chemistry at the Tokyo Imperial University
was considered subpar. At that time in Japan, pharmaceutical chemistry within
the pharmaceutical departments of faculties of medicine at various Imperial Universities—which focused on organic compounds and natural products research—
were the centers of organic chemistry research in Japan; the research methods
used at such locations were similar to Majima's approach. Therefore, one might go
so far as to say that Majima's approach to organic chemistry could be considered
mainstream in Japan.

Section 6. The Further Development of Organic Chemistry Research on Natural Products by Majima's Students in Japan: Expansion and Limitations

In order to see how, and in what direction Majima's students developed his research, we should look at the life of one of those students, Tetsuo Nozoe[50] (1902–
1994), who was one of the representative organic chemists of Japan in the
twentieth century, and see how his research developed. Nozoe established a new
field of nonbenzoid aromatic chemistry, and almost exhausted the entire field

during his long life. Nozoe's starting point was the era of research conducted during the twenty-two years he spent in Taiwan from 1926 onward. There, Nozoe isolated the compound hinokitiol from a special variety of Taiwan cypress. While it had an unsaturated, seven-membered ring that was different from the usual aromatic compounds, it was discovered to have aromatic properties. Nozoe began his research in the exact same fashion as Majima. From there, he was able to take organic chemistry research on Japan's natural products great distances.

1. The Education of Tetsuo Nozoe

Tetsuo Nozoe was born in Sendai on May 16, 1902. Tetsuo's father, Jūichi (1865–1927), originally carried the name Kinoshita, and was born in Nagasaki Prefecture. In 1882, at the age of seventeen, Jūichi was adopted by the Nozoe family, who lived near the home of his birth parents, and he enrolled in the Faculty of Law at the Tokyo Imperial University. Jūichi married Toyo, the sixth daughter of his adopted father, Yasozaemon Nozoe, became a lawyer when he graduated from the Faculty of Law, and moved to Sendai. Tetsuo was the sixth of eight sons of Jūichi and Toyo, and he also had three sisters.

Having been inspired by a chemistry teacher at Sendai's First Middle School, Tetsuo was interested in chemistry. The Christian church that his mother was a member of also counted among its congregants Masao Katayama (1877–1961), a professor of chemistry at the Tōhoku Imperial University, which was also in Sendai. Through that connection, Tetsuo was able to discuss his future with Katayama. Katayama strongly encouraged Tetsuo to attend Tōhoku Imperial University. In 1920, Tetsuo continued on to the local Second Higher School, a privileged liberal arts college, where he took the course for prospective science majors, and he studied German as his first foreign language. After graduating in 1923, Tetsuo Nozoe matriculated in the Chemistry Department of the Faculty of Science at the Tōhoku Imperial University, in accordance with Katayama's recommendations. There Nozoe met Rikō Majima, who would play a decisive role in Tetsuo's life. Nozoe concentrated in organic chemistry under Majima and continued on to graduate research at Majima's laboratory.

2. Tetsuo Nozoe's Trip to Taiwan

In March 1926, Nozoe graduated from Tōhoku Imperial University and remained as a paid research assistant in Majima's laboratory. Nevertheless, he was to leave for Taiwan on Majima's recommendation. Nozoe departed Sendai on May 28, then boarded a ship in Kobe, arriving in Taipei on June 2. Nozoe was dispatched in a fairly high-handed way, which was determined without his approval. In the prewar era, whatever one's mentor commanded was absolute, yet Nozoe himself remained unhappy with the decision that had been made.[51]

Nevertheless, there was a reason for Majima's somewhat forcible decision to dispatch Nozoe. Following the founding of Keijō Imperial University in 1926, the establishment of the second colonial imperial university, Taihoku Imperial University, was imminent (in fact, this occurred two years after Nozoe arrived in Taipei). Majima wanted Nozoe to become a staff member in the department of chemistry at the new university.

It seems that there were also reasons related to the Nozoe family that entered into the decision. Tetsuo Nozoe's father, Jūichi, ran for representative of the third district of Miyagi Prefecture in the 14th House of Representatives election in 1920. He soundly defeated the influential local politician Ikunosuke Fujisawa (1859–1940), who had held that position for 13 terms since the 1892 election.[52] After that, Fujisawa became Minister of Commerce and Industry, Chairman of the House of Representatives, and Imperial appointee to the House of Peers. He was sixty-one when he lost to Jūichi. Jūichi was six years younger, and this was the first House of Representatives election in which he participated. This election had significant local effects. In the 1924 campaign four years later, Fujisawa's camp waged a desperate campaign. This election occurred just before the General Election Law came into existence, and Fujisawa sought revenge against Nozoe. The campaign became heated against a backdrop of confrontation between the ruling Seiyū Hontō Party and the opposition Kensei Kai Party, which aimed at the legislation of the General Election Law (for Universal Suffrage). Jūichi was affiliated with the Seiyū Hontō Party and lost in the election. He died three years later, perhaps from the stress of the election on which the family had spent a great deal of money. In fact, Tetsuo's brothers were not all in Sendai, but were working outside Japan, in places such as Manchuria and Taiwan. In a sense, they felt as if they had been exiled, no longer able to live in Sendai. This was also the case for Tetsuo. The following year, there were additional potential problems generated by his younger brother's political actions, which Nozoe described as the "political movements of my brother, who then studied at Tōhoku University's Law Department" (Tetsuo Nozoe 1966, p. 4). Majima's parental attitude probably developed in consideration of such circumstances, and he rather forcibly sent Tetsuo to Taiwan.

3. Encounters with the Taiwan Cypress

As a result of the Sino-Japanese War, Taiwan was ceded from the Qing Dynasty to Japan in 1895, becoming Japan's first colony.[53] There was initial frequent armed resistance from the Han Taiwanese, therefore the Governors-General of Taiwan at the time were all military personnel, who thoroughly suppressed the armed resistance with force. Resistance continued until roughly 1915, at which time the eyes of the security and administration network had been spread around the entire island. At the same time, infrastructure such as railways, ports, roads, and telegraphs were developed. The census carried out in 1903 showed 3,040,000 people (57,000 Japanese). In 1930, four years after Nozoe arrived, there were 4,600,000 people, with the Japanese population having reached 229,000. After World War I, civilians began to be appointed Governor-General. The wartime economic boom prompted major investment in infrastructure during WWI, together with the upgrading and expansion of Taiwan's educational institutions.

Eighty percent of Taiwanese spoke Fulaohua (also called Hokkien in English, a southern Chinese dialect of Fujian Province), which is commonly called Taiwanese.[54] Nevertheless, the common language of colonial Taiwan was Japanese, with all education being conducted in this language. Therefore, Nozoe could expect no language difficulties with his appointment.

In Nozoe's first year, he worked at the Nammon Factory of the Monopoly Bureau of the Governor-General of Taiwan. There he was engaged primarily in research on the by-products of camphor oil, an indigenous product in Taiwan. In Taiwan at that time, there were only a few Imperial University chemistry graduates throughout the island, and research was nonexistent. Under such circumstances, Nozoe had to initiate the expansion of a laboratory for serious research with the procurement of equipment and chemicals, along with the collection of books and literature. The training that Nozoe received under Majima at the Tōhoku Imperial University was by no means spoon-feeding. He had been trained to develop a research program from scratch, skills which proved useful in Taiwan. When the Nozoe family had been beset by crisis with the election defeat of Tetsuo's father, he was in his second year at university. Perhaps Majima had trained Nozoe to build a research operation from scratch, already intending that he would go to Taiwan.

In June 1927, during Nozoe's second year in Taiwan, the Organic Chemical Industry Division was established at the Central Research Institute of Taiwan's Governor-General, to which Nozoe was transferred in June. The research subject which Nozoe was assigned there brought his first acquaintance with the Taiwan cypress. In Taiwan's Central Mountain Range, above an altitude of 3,000 meters, the mountains are covered with numerous kinds of plants ranging from tropical to temperate forest according to elevation. The evergreen arbor locally called biǎnbǎi was also called the Taiwan cypress because it was similar to the Japanese cypress. There is another tree in Taiwan called the Formosan cypress. This has a similar appearance to the Taiwan cypress but its wood is redder. In order to investigate the essential oils contained within the Taiwan cypress, Nozoe needed to be able to differentiate between these two trees. He collected wood and leaves of the Taiwan cypress himself from locations in the high mountain regions of central Taiwan, such as Alishan range, and he sent these samples to the laboratory where they were processed into small pieces. Essential oils were collected through steam distillation. Regarding essential oils, there is a great difference between the Taiwan cypress and the Formosan cypress, and even within the same tree, essential oils from leaves and those from wood and roots differed significantly in nature. Additionally, researchers on the Japanese mainland were developing research on the Japanese cypress, since a substance in its essential oils was thought to foster resistance to wood-decaying fungi, and thereby could prevent wood rot. Previous studies had discovered that dark red crystals with a melting point of 251 degrees Celsius precipitated when essential oils from the wood of the Taiwanese cypress were isolated through a process consisting of separation and extraction of essential oil constituents with phenols in acidic solution and subsequent treatment with iron chloride. These crystals were called "hinokichin." Nozoe confirmed this result, and further found that crystals produced from this separation method did not seem to be sufficiently pure. He discontinued his research at this time due to a shortage of raw materials.

Nozoe's supervisor at the Central Research Institute was Kinzō Kafuku (who died in 1948), a 1909 chemistry graduate from the Tokyo Imperial University (Tokyo Imperial University ed., 1926, p. 293), who had been in Taiwan since 1912. Kafuku did not have much to say on the details of particular research projects; he had a habit of saying that researchers should think on their own and develop original projects. In 1927, Nozoe married Kyōko Horiuchi (1908–2006), the niece of Kafuku's wife. Her father Seiichi Horiuchi was an 1898 graduate of the Agricultural Chemistry Department of the Faculty of Agriculture at the Tokyo Imperial University, and he served as the head of agricultural research for the Governor-General of Taiwan.

4. Taihoku Imperial University

Around this time, Nozoe was provided with a stable home when the Taihoku Imperial University was founded. He was appointed Associate Professor of Chemistry in 1929 under Professor Kafuku.

Taihoku Imperial University was the seventh Japanese Imperial University overall, founded before both Osaka Imperial University and Nagoya Imperial University. It was the second Imperial University founded in a Japanese colony, after the Keijō Imperial University. At Taihoku Imperial University's founding, it consisted of two Faculties: Humanities-Law and Science-Agriculture. Within the Faculty of Science and Agriculture, four departments of biology, chemistry, agriculture, and agricultural chemistry were formed. Costs of construction and research expenses were covered by the budget of Taiwan's Governor-General rather than by that of the Ministry of Education of Japan, and the University was under the jurisdiction of the Governor of Taiwan, not the Minister of Education. Therefore, since funding was at the discretion of the Governor, the university enjoyed facilities and ample research funds that compared favorably to mainland universities. In 1933, the Faculty of Science and Agriculture was divided into the Faculty of Science and the Faculty of Agriculture.

5. The Discovery of Hinokitiol

In 1935, six years after Nozoe moved to the Taihoku Imperial University, he resumed his research on hinokichin obtained from the Taiwan cypress. He discovered that hinokichin is an iron-containing complex, and named the organic component of this complex, which had the chemical formula $C_{10}H_{12}O_2$, hinokitiol.[55] However, he was able to obtain only trace amounts of hinokitiol from the Taiwan cypress—on the order of 0.1 to 0.2 percent. This raw materials problem had been a big obstacle to Nozoe's research, but circumstances unexpectedly enabled him to procure such raw materials in abundance.

In 1936, the Faculty of Medicine was established at the Taihoku Imperial University. Shigehiro Katsura (1895–1989) was sent to this Faculty of Medicine from the Tōhoku Imperial University to conduct research on chemotherapy for tuberculosis. In 1938, wartime restrictions meant that the organic acid Katsura was investigating at that time became less available, and he consulted with Nozoe to see if there was any alternative. Nozoe proposed rosin acid, obtained from cypress oil. Katsura immediately tested this and found it superior even to the organic acid that he was previously testing. With the collaboration of the Taipei factory of the Takasago Chemical Corporation, a local chemical enterprise,[56] Katsura began extracting large amounts of oil from the Taiwan cypress, and he extracted rosin acid. As a result of that process, as much as several dozen grams of hinokitiol were also obtained.

Nozoe proceeded with structural studies of hinokitiol using ten grams of materials that he had obtained. He then confirmed hinokitiol's primary structure as a seven-membered ring. In April 1940, just before the war with the United States began, Nozoe presented his results at the Pharmaceutical Society of Japan in Tokyo. Because products of oxidized products in structural studies could not be fully explained by the formula $C_{10}H_{12}O_2$, which Nozoe had initially proposed, he went instead with $C_{10}H_{14}O_2$ as the formula, even though this seemed rather unreasonable. Nozoe returned to Taiwan and re-examined the structure of hinokitiol by conducting various experiments. Through that process, Nozoe returned to $C_{10}H_{12}O_2$ as the chemical formula. One distinctive property of hinokitiol was that its structure was extremely stable in either acidic solution or basic solution. Nozoe described this stability using the concept of resonance developed by American chemist Linus Pauling (1901–1994) (see figure). As a result of the war, obtaining Western journals and literature in Taiwan had become difficult. However, Nozoe was able to learn about resonance and reaction mechanisms from Pauling's work, *The Nature of the Chemical Bond*. This book had just been published in 1939, and had arrived in Taiwan as part of the very last shipment from the United States. From this resulted Nozoe's description of hinokitiol's stability.[57]

When the war with the United States began on December 7, 1941, research

Figure: The structural formula of hinokitiol

began to concentrate on war-related topics. From 1943, air raids by US forces became more severe, and this kind of research could no longer be conducted. Therefore, Nozoe independently decided to evacuate his laboratory. Nozoe took advantage of the evacuation of the Kao Soap's Taiwan factory, and used the vehicles dedicated to that purpose to evacuate his own laboratory to the Sanxia suburbs located in the valley to the southeast of Taipei.[58] Nozoe and his students traveled the roughly twenty-kilometer road from the university to the evacuation site every day thereafter by truck or bicycle. Nevertheless, shortly after the evacuation was complete, the war ended, and the laboratory at the evacuation site went largely unused.

6. Postwar Days in Taiwan as Retained Japanese and Its Consequences

On August 15, 1945, Japan accepted the Potsdam Declaration of the Allies which sought unconditional surrender. This included a provision under which Taiwan was to be returned to the Republic of China. On October 17, two divisions of the Chinese army—roughly 12,000 Chinese Kuomintang (Nationalist) military personnel—along with 200 government officials, landed in Taiwan to take over and immediately occupied Taipei. At the time of the defeat, about 488,000 Japanese, including 166,000 military personnel, lived in Taiwan. As of April 20, 1946, roughly 460,000 had been repatriated back to Japan by a special organization instituted by the Governor-General of Taiwan specifically for that purpose. Nevertheless, 28,000 Japanese specialists and their families were retained by the government of the Republic of China. Tetsuo Nozoe was able to return his eldest son to Japan on an evacuation ship but he himself remained in Taiwan with his wife and three daughters by the order of the Chinese Kuomintang government.

After the war, the Taihoku Imperial University became the Republic of China's National Taiwan University. Many of the Chinese teachers who joined the University from the continent had experience studying in Japan and were able to speak Japanese, and thus were friendly to the retained Japanese specialists who remained at the university. Many of the students who enrolled in the University after the war had been initially educated in Japanese before the war, and so there were no language difficulties.

Immediately after the defeat, Nozoe began the work of returning his scattered laboratory to the university. Thanks to his Taiwanese friends and the other Japanese staff who had remained in Taiwan with him, Nozoe was able to restore his laboratory over the course of approximately one year, albeit in a different building from the pre-war facility.

There was one serendipitous event for Nozoe: during the war, mainly at the Takasago Chemical Industry's factory, cypress oil was produced in large quantities as a substitute for gasoline and beneficiation oil. Although these products were made, they were not fully used. Much had been placed in drums piled at the back of the facility. By reacting with the iron drum, this cypress oil had produced large amounts of hinokichin crystals, which were comprised of hinokitiol complexed with iron. These became rich sources of raw hinokitiol. Thus from Taiwan, Nozoe was able to fully research hinokitiol without having to worry about securing raw materials.

Nozoe had hinokitiol undergo various reactions, confirming its nature as a new species of aromatic compound. These results were all published between 1949 and 1951, after Nozoe had returned to Japan.

In May 1948, Nozoe returned to the Japanese mainland, along with his family, on a repatriation ship. It was said that one of the reasons the Taiwanese government finally gave the authorization for Nozoe to return to Japan is that there was a solid offer from Nozoe's alma mater, Tōhoku University, for him to return as an instructor. However, it is also possible that the worsening political and social situation in Taiwan may have played a role. The 228 Incident that occurred at the end of February 1947 was symbolic of this. On the evening of February 27, a regulatory officer physically assaulted a Taiwanese widow dealing in black-market tobacco, triggering a collision between the authorities and the Taiwanese people that evolved into city-wide riots the next day. The populace occupied the city of Taipei's broadcasting stations and called for the uprising of the entire island in the cause of political reform. The Nationalist Party administration of Chen Yi in Taiwan bought time by offering gestures of conciliation to the people, and appealed to Chiang Kai-shek in Nanjing for troops. The reinforcements that arrived from the mainland soon engaged in an armed crackdown that slaughtered people almost indiscriminately. Furthermore, the Chen Yi government began a systematic purge of the intellectuals and the elites who had been educated by the Japanese. Large numbers of people were arrested without warrant, executed without trial, or went missing. Fortunately, this hand of repression was not extended to the Taiwan National University, which was host to some Japanese nationals. Nozoe also wrote about these events: "Due to the unfortunate incident on February 28, 1947, for a while the university suspended all teaching and research. Fortunately, the 228 incident was resolved and peace soon returned ... at last we made a firm determination to return to Japan" (Tetsuo Nozoe 1966, p. 26). Some Taiwan history researchers claim that this incident caused the Taiwanese to favor Japanese rule, and there were fears that the Japanese would incite the Taiwanese people, which is why the Taiwanese government returned nearly all the retained Japanese wards to Japan during the following year (Ng Chiau-tong 1985, p. 271). Thanks to the 228 incident, long considered a taboo topic until the democratization of Taiwan, Nozoe's stay in Taiwan was over.

After returning home, in July 1948 Nozoe was first appointed to his alma mater Tōhoku University as a part-time lecturer. After being cleared by the occupation's review of repatriates, he was appointed professor on December 1st. At the end of December, Nozoe conducted a seminar for the Chemistry Department at Osaka University and then in February the following year, gave a lecture in a large auditorium in the Faculty of Medicine at the University of Tokyo. This was his first presentation on the study of hinokitiol that he had conducted in Taiwan. The contents were published that year in *Kikan yakugaku* (Quarterly journal of pharmacology, Nozoe 1966, pp. 39–63). It is obvious from reading this that within six months of returning home, Nozoe had already become familiar with the development of this field of research abroad and in Japan during the war through the postwar period, and it is clear that he did a great deal of planning for future research.

In the study of hinokitiol, Nozoe proposed an unsaturated seven-membered ring structure, and in research conducted in Taiwan from 1942 to 1948, he clarified that hinokitiol's various reactivity properties were similar to those of aromatic compounds. Independently, in 1945, the theoretical chemist Michael Dewar (1918–1997) working in England considered the same unsaturated seven-membered ring structure as the basic form of compounds he was studying (the mold metabolite stipitatic acid and the alkaloid colchicine). He had named this structure tropolone.

Towards the end of 1948, a pharmacology professor Shigehiko Sugasawa (1898–1991) in the Faculty of Medicine at the University of Tokyo sent Nozoe a letter from Swedish natural products chemist Holger Erdtman (1902–1989) along with a copy of Erdtman's publication in *Nature* that year that focused on the thujaplicin class of organic molecules.[59] Erdtman had isolated certain antimicrobial substances contained in the western red cedar that he named thujaplicin, and he had distinguished three isomers: α, β, and γ. Erdtman and Nozoe began corresponding, and they confirmed that hinokitiol was the equivalent of β-thujaplicin and based on the tropolone structure proposed by Dewar.

In January 1950, in London, a symposium "Tropolone and Related Compounds" was sponsored by the British Royal Society of Chemistry. There, Erdtman introduced Nozoe's study of hinokitiol as pioneering research on tropolone. With the assistance of symposium chair James W. Cook (1900–1975), in 1951, Nozoe was able to publish a paper on hinokitiol in *Nature* (Nozoe 1951), which brought his research to the world's notice.

At Tōhoku University, Nozoe resumed all aspects of his research on the reactions of hinokitiol and related compounds, and he was able to successfully synthesize tropolone and hinokitiol in 1951. The results of this research were announced in an oral presentation by his former teacher Majima, who was a member of the Japan Academy, and then successively published in English in the academy's journal, *Proceedings of the Japan Academy*, one of few English-language magazines in Japan at this time. Thanks to this powerful boost from Majima, Nozoe's research became well known at home and abroad. This led to Nozoe receiving various awards early on, including first the Majima Award, which started in 1944, the 1953 Academy Prize, and the Order of Cultural Merit in 1958. He won the Order of

Cultural Merit at a time when he was fifty-six years old and still active as a Tōhoku University professor. Such awards would have been unthinkable without the powerful support and influence of Rikō Majima.[60]

Nozoe himself pursued tropolone research exhaustively throughout his long life, but research on tropolone never widely took hold beyond his research group. Nevertheless, Nozoe certainly opened the way forward for organic chemistry to progress from simple research into the chemistry of natural products. Nozoe was able to study the components of products specific to Taiwan, and to procure a large amount of research material during the special conditions of wartime. He was also able to extrapolate from Pauling's novel resonance theories to develop new areas of organic chemistry. The starting point and foundation for this were found in Nozoe's research in Taiwan in line with the tradition of organic chemistry research that began with Nozoe's mentor, Rikō Majima; that is, an approach to natural products chemistry where the latest techniques from Europe were employed to investigate the nature and structure of organic compounds contained in natural substances found within and in the vicinity of Japan.

7. The Extent and Limits of Majima's Methods for Natural Products Chemistry

In 2008, Osamu Shimomura[61] (born 1928) was awarded the Nobel Prize in Chemistry. His research can be considered an extension of the Majima tradition of natural products chemical research. Shimomura graduated from the Pharmaceutical special division, attached to Nagasaki School of Medicine in 1951, which was thereafter reorganized as the Department of Pharmaceutical Sciences at Nagasaki University. After graduation Shimomura was employed as an assistant in the analytical chemistry laboratory for students of the Department. In 1955, Shimomura had a chance to conduct research under Professor Yoshimasa Hirata[62] (1915–2000) of the Chemistry Department in the Faculty of Science at Nagoya University, thanks to his mentor in Nagasaki, Professor Shungo Yasunaga (1911–1959). After ten months of effort there, Shimomura had successfully crystallized cypridina luciferin, a light-emitting substance of *Vargula hilgendorfii* (the sea-firefly), which no one had successfully crystallized before. *Vargula hilgendorfii* is a light-emitting animal that lives only on Japan's Pacific coast. According to Shimomura's Nobel Prize lecture, the crystallization of the light-emitting substance of *Vargula hilgen-*

dorfii began with 500 grams of raw material, which had been obtained from 2.5 kilograms of dried animal (Osamu Shimomura 2008, p. 117). Such a large quantity could have been obtained only in Japan;[63] this is a typical example of research into regionally specific natural products. In 1960, invited by American researchers who paid attention to Shimomura's success, he visited America as a Fulbright Scholar to study the light emission of the bioluminescent hydrozoan jellyfish (*Aequorea victoria*) at Princeton University. In 1962, he discovered the luminescent proteins aequorin and green fluorescent protein (GFP).[64] Shimomura continued his research on GFP until 1979, when he published a model for its mechanism of light-emission. After that, he conducted research on aequorin and the emission mechanisms of other light-emitting organisms. In the 1990s, Shimomura's research on GFP was used in techniques developed by other researchers to label specific locations in living cells. In 2008, Shimomura was awarded the Nobel Prize in Chemistry for his discovery of GFP. Throughout this time, Shimomura continued researching natural products.

Majima's approach to research was designed so that Japanese researchers working in poor conditions could compete with researchers in advanced Western nations; it was at heart a strategy for research in a country where academic infrastructure was underdeveloped. Experimental procedures and theoretical frameworks were to be received from the West, and then research was focused on experiments on local natural products. In recalling his teacher, Majima's student Shirō Akahori said: "Our teacher said that in terms of research it was important to engage in thorough experimentation; he was very cautious and cool towards theory and hypothesis." (Posthumous collection, 1970, p. 501). To put it more bluntly, it was possible that Majima's doctrine was extremely focused on experimentation, valuing moving hands over thinking heads.[65] Although Majima's approach to research was valuable as a starting point, it was left to the next generation to break through its limitations, and the few people who were able to do this successfully produced world-leading research. Nozoe could be said to have been one of the first to do so.

Ken'ichi Fukui (1918–1998) was the first in a series of Japanese winners of the Nobel Prize in chemistry who won their awards for the development of new theoretical frameworks and new experimental techniques.[66] On the other hand, Shimomura's Nobel Prize was for his own discoveries, which other researchers could develop further. In general, however, Japanese chemistry from the 1950s or 60s gradually developed new experimental techniques that can be said to have allowed for the transition to a stage of developing new theoretical frameworks.

Section 7. Rikō Majima's Subsequent Research and Accomplishments, or His Philosophical Pathway as Seen from His Journal

For a considerable period of time in Majima's long life, he kept a regular journal. His original journal was inherited by his second son Yukio after Majima's death, and later passed on to Yukio's wife Hiroko, a resident of Kyoto, when her husband passed away. In 2007, microfilms were taken of the journal and stored in the Tōhoku University archives, and it is now possible for researchers to view these microfilms, which have been made open to the public.[67]

The preserved elements of the journal begin in 1914, when Majima was thirty-nine years old, three years after he arrived in Sendai in 1911 and was appointed professor of chemistry in the Faculty of Science at the newly established Tōhoku Imperial University. The only segment from this first year with continuous entries is from January, followed by entries afterwards on only February 1, August 23, and October 3. After this, there are no entries from 1915 or 1916. However, from 1917, with the exception of the year 1920, entries continue regularly until the first half of 1944. Most was written in commercially-available single year, templated journals for daily use. Nothing remains from the journal for the period at the end of and immediately after World War II, from August 1944 to September 1948. After the war, there is material from October 1948 which was not recorded in a commercially-available daily use journal; instead Majima dated blank pages and wrote freely in commercially-available college notebooks, leaving a record of almost every day through May 1959. From here the journal jumps to an entry from September 3 of that same year, the last entry made by Majima's hand. Majima was eighty-four years old at that time and would die three years later, on August 19, 1962. In summary, Majima left a journal covering a time period of over forty years, from the time he was thirty-nine years old until he was eighty-four.[68] The descriptions in this daily journal, although sometimes consisting of just a single line, were often fairly detailed. Thus, Majima's remaining journal can be said to essentially comprise a primary historical source for any analysis of the life and achievements of Rikō Majima, and it offers an insight into the daily lives of Japan's first-generation of organic chemists.

In preparing to write this chapter, I duplicated the microfilm version of Majima's journal stored in the Tōhoku University archives, prepared printouts from these microfilms, and deciphered many of the pre-war sections of the journal myself. Only once has an attempt been made to decipher and publish Majima's journal. This was related to an Osaka University compilation on that institution's own history. The deciphered print publication involved only Majima's description of the university, as he was Osaka Imperial University's third president.[69] At that time, the journal was borrowed from Majima's son Yukio, who was still alive.

The prewar entries remaining from Rikō Majima's journal can be divided at April 1933, when he relocated to Osaka with his family; the period prior to this can be referred to as the Sendai era, and the period after it can be referred to as the Osaka era.

From this, focusing primarily on Majima's Sendai-era journal, let us discuss the following five themes based on what we can gather from reading in relation to Majima's thought: (1) Rikō Majima the Christian; (2) Rikō Majima and Family; (3) the Death of Majima's Family Members; (4) Rikō Majima the Administrator; (5) Rikō Majima and the Emperor System

1. Rikō Majima the Christian

Considering the events that took place in the second half of Majima's life, it is important that he had converted to Christianity in the middle of his life. Although four children were born to Majima and his wife,[70] his eldest daughter Kimiko died at age two, and his first son, Minoru, died at age seven. Majima's second son, Yukio, and his third son, Toshimitsu, lived to adulthood. The death of Majima's first-born son, Minoru, was a significant blow to the family, and this brought Christianity into the Majima household. This became a major turning point in Majima's life. Minoru had a mild hernia which Majima thought should be surgically repaired prior to elementary school. This was in January 1919. Because the family had already lost a child, they wanted to carefully guard the health of their oldest son. They had put their trust in a professor of the Medical Faculty at Tōhoku Imperial University[71] and were waiting for the professor's return from a business trip abroad (Posthumous collection, 1970, p. 406). Nevertheless, while the surgery itself was successful, Minoru passed away without waking up from the anesthesia

(Ibid., p. 35). It is possible to believe that this death occurred because Minoru was subjected to unnecessary surgery. This brought severe grief to Majima's wife. As he recalled in later years: "Of the sorrows that afflicted my family, especially biting was that of the boy's mother. There was no way to comfort her." If there was something at this time that brought great comfort to the family, it was the staff of The Anglican Church of Japan's Aoba Kindergarten, which their son had been attending. Majima said: "Finally at the end of deep meditation, my family determined to be baptized in March that same year, and to become Christians. We were greatly comforted by such beliefs, and my wife also was able finally to calm her soul" (Ibid., p. 36).

During this period, Rikō Majima's journal entries were extremely simple—at most a few lines every day—and without feeling. Nevertheless, because of this very style, perhaps Majima's feelings are all the more clear: on January 20, 1919: "Minoru admitted, took a bath in the evening"; 21st: "Minoru in the hospital"; 23rd: "Minoru had surgery"; 24th: "Minoru's death, oh, today's emotions!!!"; 27th: "Two o'clock this afternoon: Minoru's funeral. Cremation afterwards."; 28th: "We went to pick up the bones and deposited them at the church."; February 1: "Minoru's memorial service." After this, on February 2 and 3, Majima visited those involved with the funeral to express his gratitude, and returned to work at the university on the 4th. The first time he went to church was Sunday the following week, February 9. Majima's journal entry on that day: "Went to the Anglican Church for the first time." Thereafter, he attended Anglican services every Sunday, and also attended an Anglican church in Tsukiji during this period on business trips to Tokyo. On Sunday, March 9, he attended church with his wife. They indicated that they wanted to be baptized and were baptized as a family the following Sunday. In Majima's journal for this day: "The whole family was baptized. From now on we begin a life strengthened and brightened by our faith, and we pray for the divine protection of the Holy Spirit through the aid of Jesus, the Son of God." Because Majima's second son Yukio (born September 18, 1915) and third son Toshimitsu (born April 27, 1918) had already been born at this time, they were probably baptized as children, together with the rest of the family.

Immediately after this, the Majima family had another bad experience: Majima's second son, Yukio, developed dysentery, and came very close to death. Majima's journal entry from July 8, not much more than five months after losing Minoru, reads in large black-ink letters: "Yukio has dysentery." He writes descriptions such as—on the 11th: "I have asked for a nurse"; on the 13th: "Yukio is critically ill from midnight to 2:30. Anointed." Nevertheless, the entry on the 15th: "I asked for another nurse," indicates that Yukio had overcome the worst. Yukio himself wrote about this experience in his own memoirs following the death of Rikō Majima:

"Soon after my brother's death I contracted dysentery. The doctors said they could not cure me and that I would die. In Christianity (Catholicism) it is common to offer the dying an anointment—the last rites—to lead them on the path to a miracle at such times. I am told that I received an anointment from the pastor of the Anglican Church. Once, my breathing and pulse stopped, but I returned. The doctors said, 'We can't believe he came back. He must have a very strong heart.' Perhaps what the doctors said was correct, but my father had just seen his first-born son die, and was stupefied by the repeated shocks. Both my father and my mother believed that I came back because of the anointment. This event may have further deepened my father's faith in Christianity" (Posthumous collection, 1970, p. 381).

Certainly during his Sendai era, Majima went to church eagerly every Sunday, and if for some reason he was unable to attend, he always wrote, "did not attend church" in his journal. After the family moved to Osaka, the church there was far away from their home, and Majima himself attended about once a month.

When Majima converted to Christianity, he chose the Anglican Church perhaps arbitrarily, based on personal experience and relationships. At that time, a nephew close to Majima recalled him having made fun of Christianity, but after he converted to Christianity, his nephew stated, "Once he got religion, he instantly read through the Old Testament and the New Testament, his enthusiastic engagement with church doctrine surprised the pastor." (Posthumous collection, 1970, p. 408). Not only did Majima attend church, but he also participated in the church management committee, and hosted Bible studies and children's Christmas parties at his home, being generally actively involved in the church during his Sendai era. In church, sometimes congregants took turns to deliver sermons in place of the pastor, something in which Majima also participated.

Majima has left behind a few materials pertaining to lectures where he discussed the relationship between religion and science. Two such documents are contained within his posthumously collected memoirs: "Shinkō to Kagaku" (Faith and Science) from 1925, during his Sendai era (Posthumous collection, 1970, pp. 244–249); and, from 1951, after the war, "Kagaku to Shūkyō" (Science and Religion, Ibid., pp. 345–356), given as a commemorative speech during Tōhoku University's graduation that year.

There are no notes on the origins of "Faith and Science," other than the era in which it was written, but from the content it appears to be a lecture meant for an audience of Christian believers. Because 1925 was merely six years after Majima's conversion to Christianity, in places this document also offers descriptions of the circumstances surrounding his conversion. Before becoming a Christian, Majima had a materialist view of nature, not at all unusual for a natural scientist. In his words: "The world is as it appears—everything is made of atoms of all elements. The atoms themselves are all formed from electrons. The mind arises from the physical and chemical changes of cells in the brain. I believed I was philosophical enough to say, 'if we die and are burned, our body will mainly turn into water, carbon and ammonia; apart from these, mere ashes and dust remain.'" (Ibid., p. 246). For that reason, when Majima had a serious illness while studying in Kiel, Germany, he believed that there was nothing to be done about the possibility of him dying there, and says that he did not consider spiritual matters.

However, he also states, "The loss of my most beloved child to a sudden calamity has highlighted the fact that those many things that I had heeded out of a belief in their rightness have all been defeated and are at an end; science alone does not have the power to give meaning to life. This has awakened in me a sense of a God of life, and of death" (Ibid.). Nevertheless, Majima frankly acknowledges that, rather than being satisfied with the particular doctrine of the Anglican Church, his conversion was the result of personal relationships at the time of the death of his beloved child.[72] The conclusion of this lecture, which seems to have been addressed to Christian believers, was that neither admirable sermons nor skillful theological discussion would serve to convert scientists to Christianity; rather, this required interaction with those who embodied the essence of this religion.

What were Majima's views on the relationship between faith and science? He seems to have believed that the study of natural phenomena belonged to the natural sciences, but that religion was: "about conveying belief in God and the personality of God to believers, and teaching them to communicate with the Holy Spirit" (Ibid., p. 248). Religion is not intended for the study of natural phenomena, thus religion and the natural sciences address two completely separate domains and are not contradictory: "Religion and science are separate manifestations of truth, and there is no contradiction in this interval" (Ibid.). In this sense, Majima's views were similar to the dualism popular in the Middle Ages in Europe.

After World War II, when Majima was seventy-six years old, he gave a lecture

called "Science and Religion" as a guest speaker for the Tōhoku University graduation ceremony. In this lecture, he expanded upon his espoused notion of the two
distinct truths. That is to say, the ultimate aim of the natural sciences is "discovery
of the ultimate truths that govern the natural world." The "ultimate truth of the
universe," Majima argued, "is the same as the God in Christianity." Furthermore,
religion extends to areas not addressed by the natural sciences—those of beauty
and goodness. Thinking in this manner implies that there are two aspects of God;
the "God of nature," who overlaps with the ultimate objective of the natural sciences, and the "moral God." In the former aspect, God works through laws. This is the
area of the natural sciences. In the latter aspect, God works through human emotions, the domain of religion. In this way, the natural sciences and religion complement each other.

2. Rikō Majima and Family

Majima got married on August 5, 1906, five months before he left to study abroad.
At the time, Majima was thirty-one years old, and his wife Mieko twenty-nine,
which was a rather late marriage for the end of the Meiji period. They lost their
first two children one after the other, before finally being blessed with sons Yukio
when Majima was forty-one, and Toshimitsu when he was forty-four. At that time,
he may have worried about the age difference between himself and his children.
Majima's youngest child, Toshimitsu, recalled after his father's death: "When I became an elementary school student, I noticed that my parents were somewhat
older than the parents of other children. As I grew older, I felt like there was a large
generation gap between me and my parents. For this reason, I did not really speak
all that much with my father. Conversely, from the perspective of my parents, we
were too young, and it's possible that they weren't sure how to deal with us." (Posthumous collection, 1970, p. 395). Yukio had similar sentiments: "I felt like there
was a generational difference, as I was a child born to older parents" (Ibid., 387).
There are frequent passages in Majima's diary describing his children, until the
time when they graduated from middle school. The children were frequently afflicted by fevers when young (whenever this happened, there was always a journal
entry documenting body temperature), and Majima relates many incidences of
diarrhea, as well as the names of doctors from whom he had requested house calls.
Once the children began to go to school, he wrote frequently of their grades. Maji-

ma seems to have expected quite a lot of Yukio, now his oldest son, and he mentions his class standing for every semester of junior high school. There were frequent laments that, contrary to expectations, Yukio's grades were often poor.[73] As a result of these poor grades, Yukio was severely scolded and given advice on how to study, with his teachers consulted; Majima appears to have been very concerned.

During his Sendai era, Majima often took walks all over the town and in the hills nearby, and he would take his children with him on such excursions. There were also family trips to Matsushima, and in summer, they rented a house in Haragama (now part of Sōma City) in Fukushima Prefecture where his family would enjoy vacation. On these occasions, Majima would remain at home alone and occasionally visit the rest of the family by train for a day-trip. In this era, middle- and upper-class households would often hire a housekeeper; during his family's absence, such a housekeeper would arrange Majima's meals and housework, and this made such separate living arrangements possible. Majima had also often hired young unmarried women in their teens from villages near Sendai to serve as housekeepers.

Majima's journal also gives an indication of an equal marital relationship that was unusual in this era. When Majima's wife went out and came home late, he would complain, lamenting, "My wife travels all over the place and comes home very late, sometimes after nine. This bothers me."[74] One such incident bothered him particularly: "My wife went out with her friend Ms. Iwaki in the early afternoon and didn't come back until after eight. How many times do I need to tell her to come back early? She is so disobedient! Even though she's responsible for the home, she loses track of time and neglects her responsibilities. She is too impudent." Although Majima did write such words in anger towards his wife at times,[75] such instances are rare. He sometimes sent his wife alone to distant locations in the Kansai region, near Kyoto and Osaka, in order to participate in meetings related to Christianity, or to reunions, and the couple would go for a walk or shopping together, or they would take part in events. They also often attended church in Sendai as a couple, together with their children. Majima would also take his wife and children on outings relatively frequently and today would be viewed as quite a family man. In Majima's recollection of that, he described his first-born son's death and his subsequent conversion to Christianity as the turning point of his life, up until which he had been "completely dedicated to his research laboratory, intent solely on pushing forward," and "separated from the world."[76] (Ibid., p. 36).

Indeed, when the children grew up to some extent, the couple would travel together without them.[77] In the journal entry of August 13, 1931: "Our marriage was twenty-five years ago on August 5, so I gave a prayer of thanks because we could celebrate our silver wedding anniversary."

According to Yukio, Majima had an introverted personality; in contrast, his wife Mieko was outgoing and considerate. Mieko would routinely take care of any illnesses of the boarding students of Majima's laboratory. She was intimately knowledgeable of the students' familial circumstances, and there were countless instances where she introduced them to their future spouses (Ibid., p. 390); she consequently had a wide circle of acquaintances among the students' wives. Mieko played a role in planning reunions for her alma mater Kyoto Women's Normal School and Tokyo Women's Higher Normal School, and also kept in touch with her former students at Mie Women's Normal School and Tokyo Prefectural Women's First Middle School for a long time, where she taught. It is said that she was also actively involved in a woman's society at a church and in the YWCA (Young Women's Christian Association). For a husband of the time, Majima was unusually supportive of his wife's activities.

Majima's wife succumbed to sudden cardiac death at age sixty-seven, on January 4, 1944. It must have been a great shock. Yukio wrote: "My father's grief at the death of my mother was very severe" (Ibid., p. 385). Although Yukio mentions that his father records the state of his emotions in his own journal (Ibid.), as has already been mentioned, nothing of the journal from this period remains.

3. The Death of Majima's Family Members

It can be understood that Majima was in shock following the deaths of his son and wife. In fact, in his journal, he touched on the deaths of those around him, centering on the deaths in his immediate family. Describing the inner path of his father, Yukio describes five turning points—the death of Majima's father, the choosing of his life's work, the death of his eldest son Minoru, the foundation of the Faculty of Science of Osaka Imperial University, and the death of Mieko (Posthumous collection, 1970, pp. 376–388). Of the five turning points, three are deaths.

In Majima's journal, a detailed description is left of his sister's February 1922 death. On February 15, Majima was on a business trip in Tokyo when news of his sister's death arrived from Sendai. Majima left for Kyoto immediately that night to attend the funeral. He gives a detailed description of the circumstances of her sudden death in particular in the form of a supplement at the end of his journal. His sister had been making preparations to travel at the time, and was scheduled to leave in the evening. However, she died on the morning of that day. The sentences at the end of his journal begin with: "When I was thirteen my father died; when I was forty-two years old I lost my mother, and when I was forty-nine, my sister." His writing is composed as a dispassionate record of the days leading up to his sister's passing, which he learned from his relatives during the subsequent funeral service.

Throughout his life, Majima was concerned about the progress of his orphaned nephew Susumu, whom his sister had left behind, and Susumu makes regular appearances in Majima's journal. Susumu was never able to decide on a course in life, which was a cause of considerable worry to Majima. Majima or his wife would frequently encourage Susumu, at other times reprimanding him and endeavoring to put him on an upright path. Nevertheless, for the next fourteen years—until the day of May 29, 1936, when Majima records in his journal, "Susumu Majima has passed away"—despite the earnest efforts of the couple, Susumu never lived up to their expectations.

It seems that death In the Taisho Period (1912–1926) was seen as something that came more suddenly than it does now. Reading Majima's journal, we find people are described as alive and well until their sudden deaths. For example, Majima's colleague Keiichi Aichi (1880–1923), came down with food poisoning on the evening of June 20, 1923 and was in critical condition by the 22nd. He died at dawn on the following day. Furthermore, Junjirō Kushibiki (died 1926), an assistant whose efforts focused on editing the journal *Nihon kagaku sōran* (Complete abstracts of Japanese chemical literature) described in the next section, collapsed from a cerebral hemorrhage and died on January 5, 1926.

Of course, the turning point, and the most significant blow of all for Majima, was the death of his son Minoru. Majima was unable to overcome the grief for a long time. Every year, on January 24, the anniversary of Minoru's death, Majima held a gathering in memorial of his son's passing. For example, the day of January 24, 1925 was the seventh anniversary of Minoru's death: "Evening. We had Minoru's anniversary. About twenty-six people came. Among the guests—Satō and Tōyama made a speech. Conversation between me and my wife. After that the gramophone was played." In a January 24, 1927 entry: "It's Minoru's anniversary. We invited people from Aoba kindergarten and some women; my wife hosted the reunion." These commemorations eventually became for the family only. The last one Majima mentions was on January 24, 1933, the fifteenth anniversary of Minoru's death: "On Minoru's anniversary we displayed his photos. The family was all there and prayed. My wife and Yukio cried and prayed." This was possibly the last commemoration. After that, there are no more such descriptions in Majima's journal.

4. Rikō Majima the Administrator

Majima's conversion in the wake of Minoru's death became the turning point in a life that had been devoted to research. After the "baptism-induced middle-age mental remodeling" (Posthumous collection, 1970, p. 36) that Majima experienced in his mid-forties, he began to become more involved in university administration in addition to research. He became a member of the Imperial Japan Academy and the Dean of the Faculty of Science of the Tōhoku Imperial University in 1926, when he was fifty-one years old; he was appointed to an additional professorship at the Tokyo University of Engineering in 1929, at age fifty-four; Dean of the Faculty of Science of the Hokkaidō Imperial University in 1930, at age fifty-five (This included a one-year additional professorship); and Dean of the Faculty of Science of the Osaka Imperial University in 1932, at age fifty-seven (This also included an additional professorship). In 1933, Majima was transferred to the Osaka Imperial University from Tōhoku Imperial University. In this way he acquired a series of positions of increasing academic administrative responsibility. Of course, Majima had reached an appropriate age for such appointments; plus, at this era of transition from the Taisho to the Showa Period, institutions of higher education were entering a period of expansion; Majima described this himself:"If I had not been baptized and undergone such personal change, probably I would not have been called on for such responsibilities. And even if I had been called on for them, I would not have wanted to take them on" (Ibid.).

These jobs were geographically distant from each other. One might think that such part-time professorships would have been only honorific, but Majima's journal indicates that he traveled from location to location to give lectures and host conferences in a manner appropriate for such appointments. Among these was a regular monthly trip to Tokyo. In particular, Majima eagerly gave lectures at the Tokyo University of Engineering[78] early in each month. In some cases he would proceed to Tokyo twice a month to give lectures. He called this trip "easting." In those days, Majima could board the night express train in Sendai at ten or eleven in the evening and arrive at Ueno in Tokyo, at around seven o'clock the next morning. Sometimes he would stay in Tokyo for a few days. Other times, he would return the same night. All of this travel could be accomplished even from Sendai thanks to the recently developed rail networks.[79]

In April 1927, Majima was appointed a member of the founding committee of the Faculty of Science at the Hokkaidō Imperial University (Yoshio Sakudō, Taketo Etō 1976, pp. 503–504). In March 1930, the Faculty of Science rules were established, and Majima was appointed Dean of the Faculty of Science on April 1.[80] His tenure as Dean lasted only one year, until the following March, and he visited Sapporo six times during that twelve-month period—in March just before his term of office began, then in April, May, September, December, and the following March during his term. Looking at his journal, Majima departed by train at seven in the morning and then reached Hokkaidō via the Seikan ferry. The journey was about twenty-four hours, and he would arrive in Sapporo the next morning around eight.

During the period when Majima was Dean of the Faculty of Science at Hokkaidō Imperial University, he embarked on an effort to invite the physicist Yoshio Nishina (1890–1951), who worked at RIKEN (Institute of Physical and Chemical Research, a semi-governmental research institute), to become a professor of theoretical physics at the Faculty of Science. According to Majima's journal from December 9, 1930, when he asked the members of the physics department at the Faculty of Science whom one should appoint professor of theoretical physics, everyone suggested Yoshio Nishina. There was no post for a professor of physics any more, but Majima had borrowed a post of a professor from the chemistry department to invite Nishina. Majima went immediately to Tokyo to meet with him at RIKEN on December 12. When Majima offered the position at Hokkaidō Imperial University, Nishina's reply was that he would "leave his career decision to Nagaoka." That afternoon Majima met with Hantarō Nagaoka (1865–1950), one of most influential academic physicists in Japan, at the Japan Academy, but when Majima requested Nishina, Nagaoka quickly replied that "under no circumstances" would he let him go. In the end, Nishina was only to give an intensive course of lectures at the Hokkaidō Imperial University.[81]

In April 1933, Majima moved his base to Osaka. He served as president of Osaka Imperial University during the difficult period extending from wartime in January 1943 to February 1946, in the postwar era.

Majima's activities as a RIKEN researcher were also important. Majima was employed as a RIKEN staff scientist from September 1, 1917, only a short while after that institution's establishment on March 20, 1917. In January 1921 he became a senior researcher and presided over his own laboratory. Thereafter, until he retired on June 30, 1945, Majima retained his own laboratory in RIKEN.[82] As his journal shows, whenever Majima travelled to Tokyo, he would always stop at RIKEN and meet with staff members attached to his laboratory.

As part of Majima's vigorous activities he would also make trips overseas. For example, he was ordered to travel to Europe and America to attend the fifth general assembly of the International Union of Pure and Applied Chemistry (IUPAC) in 1924 as a representative of Japan. That same year on April 19, he left Sendai and sailed from Yokohama on May 2 on the Shin'yō Maru, a ship of the Oriental Steamship Company managed by Sōichirō Asano. Majima arrived in San Francisco on May 19 via Hawaii and traveled across the United States, visiting many university laboratories on the west coast, in the Midwest, and in the east. On June 4, he crossed the Atlantic from New York on the ship Berengaria, a famous luxurious ocean liner, arriving in the United Kingdom on June 10. During the European leg of this trip, he was in Copenhagen from June 25 to July 1 in order to attend the fifth general assembly of IUPAC. Other than this, during the three-month period before he was to depart Marseille on September 7 to return home, he energetically visited other parts of Europe, including Germany, Switzerland, Italy, the United Kingdom, and France. On his return leg, Majima passed through the Mediterranean Sea on the ship Hakone Maru owned by NYK Line, then through the Suez Canal, arriving at the port of Kobe via the Indian Ocean on October 15. Majima's journal describes daily activities that would put any backpacker to shame.[83] It was precisely because of this energy that Majima was able to become a central figure in the expansion of Japanese chemistry between the Taisho and Showa Periods (1910s–1930s).

Along with activities related to academic administration, Rikō Majima also had a significant achievement with the publication of the *Complete Abstracts of Japanese Chemical Literature*. This collection of chemistry research abstracts covered the years 1877 to 1963. The year 1877 was when the University of Tokyo was established from Tokyo Kaisei School and the Tokyo School of Medicine and the first chemistry graduates[84] of the Faculty of Science were produced. The Chemical Society was formed one year after. After 1963 successor journals have been published.[85] This publication has made it possible to gain a quick understanding of the

contents and bibliographic data of chemistry publications in Japanese from the
Meiji Period down to the present. The origins of its publication were in fact rooted
in Majima's policies for natural products research.[86] In 1918, Tōhoku Imperial University chair of clinical pharmacology Masazō Okuno (born c. 1858) proposed the
creation of paper abstracts on the Japanese production of plant and animal components. Majima agreed to help, believing that this would contribute to research
on Japanese natural products,[87] and this project thus began with the cooperation
of many people. Nevertheless, Majima was busy with other work and couldn't
make much progress, so his project came to a natural end. However, in 1920, one
of the students planning to perform his graduation research in Majima's lab was
injured such that he could no longer conduct experiments. Instead of engaging in
experiments, this student was put in charge of creating abstracts from *Kōgyō-kagaku zasshi* (The journal of chemical industry)[88] related to production of Japanese
plant and animal components.

From this teaching experience, and in light of an increasing volume of research
related to plant and animal components, "since in the end this mostly promoted
pure science research" (Kubota 2005, p. 52), it was difficult to limit the range of
abstracts to only research on plant and animal components, and Majima began to
think it would be better to produce a comprehensive volume containing abstracts
of all chemical papers. Chemistry departmental assistant Junjirō Kushibiki had
expressed interest in such a venture, was able to receive a grant from *Keimeikai*, an
incorporated foundation from his hometown of Sendai, and began collecting Japanese language abstracts of chemistry literature. They had completed most of the
abstracting from the period from 1877 to 1925. The group had been planning on
publishing these abstracts, but due to the effect of the Great Kantō Earthquake in
1923, none of the major publishing houses in Tokyo were able to take on the task.
Therefore, the organization began soliciting donations from corporations and other benefactors. On July 15, 1926, these donations were used to establish the Foundation for Japanese Chemical Research with the aim of publishing abstracts using
donations, with Majima appointed as the chairman. The death of Emperor Taisho
on December 25 of that year brought with it the arrival of the Showa Period, and
thus the first anthology was published containing the chemistry literature up to
1926, under the title *Complete Abstracts of Japanese Chemical Literature*. It was
decided to begin publishing the second compilation the following year, 1927, under the same name, containing the latest Japanese chemistry research papers. Although this endeavor began from Majima's own interests, Majima's ability as an

administrator is evident in how he involved students and colleagues in his initiative, and in how he was able to establish the foundation as a matter of course using public support and other donations thereafter in order to publish the abstracts.

5. Rikō Majima and the Emperor System

Reading Majima's journal raises another point, in that it offers an understanding of Japanese scientists from before World War II, an understanding that is difficult to notice from simply reading articles: the relationship at that time between the Japanese people and the emperor system. Majima's journal contains entries related to the imperial family that use extremely honorific and deferential language.

Imperial births and deaths are always noted in the journal,[89] and, whenever there was a special occasion, such as the Emperor's birthday or Kigensetsu (February 11, the day commemorating the enthronement of the first emperor, Jimmu), or the coronation of Emperor Hirohito, there was always a celebration and ceremony at the university, which faculty and students attended. Various kinds of ceremonies, such as an imperial visit to the university, or the reception of an imperial decoration,[90] or even an audience with the Emperor himself,[91] gave opportunities for university professors to be aware of the presence of imperial system on a daily basis.

Born in 1874, Rikō Majima belonged to the first generation educated entirely in the completed Meiji-era modern education system, as has already been described. This also meant that Majima's education occurred under a modern constitutional monarchy. In this sense, he took for granted the emperor system that had been created and which was reinforced in the Meiji Period. Looking at journal entries from before the war, one finds no remark critical of the emperor system.

Majima's journal lacks passages from the period around the end of the war and the immediate postwar period. Nevertheless, contained within his posthumously-assembled collection of materials is an address that Majima gave as president of Osaka Imperial University ("Imperial" was officially dropped from the university name after September 1947) on October 3, 1945, immediately after the defeat. From that it may be possible to grasp what sort of perspective Majima may have had during the period, from which there are no remaining journal entries (Posthumous collection, 1970, pp. 339–345). During the war there had been an attempt at mobilization called "the movement to protect and enlighten military personnel." As part of this, on October 3, the Emperor's address regarding the backing of military personnel was read (Miyaura 2004, pp. 118–119). Majima's speech was delivered together with the Emperor's address concerning the backing of military personnel on October, 3 1945, just after the war ended. Initially, a memorial service for people affiliated with Tōhoku Imperial University who had died during the war was planned for the same time, but because of the uncertain state of transportation immediately after the war, the memorial service was postponed. However, the Emperor's address regarding support for military personnel went ahead, followed by a reading of an imperial rescript on the termination of the war. The address was of a nature suited to a postwar speech. It included a reflection on the war, and it also covered issues related to academia, including the cultivation of character, as well as future educational goals such as the restoration of academic capabilities, research into thought and principles, cultivation of foreign language abilities, popularization of science, and improvements in efficiency. At the same time, the address stated that this defeat came as a result of the military becoming "a type of Shogunate" overly focused on military glory, which "eventually distorted our peaceful and benevolent imperial rule, forming instead a military rule." The address then concluded by expressing "the Emperor's best wishes for the health of everyone present," indicating that Majima harbored no doubts whatsoever about the emperor system.

Majima was one of the most eminent prewar Japanese chemists. He was deeply involved in academic administration, and it seems that as a Christian he had a greater sensitivity to society at large than his peers did. Still, Majima had no doubts about the emperor system, and for scientists in the prewar period, as least for the majority of them, the emperor system was a social premise that was unquestionable.

6. Conclusion—A "Typical" Exemplar of the Scientific Thought of a Chemist

Rikō Majima was a top-level chemist produced by the modernization of Japan during the Meiji Restoration. This chapter has examined what such a chemist may have been thinking. Although Majima was a superlative chemist, we find that he did not really engage in any special sort of scientific thought. Nevertheless, this "typical" chemist had an influence on colleagues and students, peers and successors. This influence developed into a type of "thought," one characteristic of the population of chemists as a whole. Therefore, from an analysis of Majima's thought, I thought it might be possible to envision the "typical" thought of chemists. There are many chemists who leave behind no personal writings besides papers, textbooks, or abstracts. Fortunately, Majima was a chemist who left behind not only autobiographical texts but also a voluminous personal journal collection. Through these, it is possible to follow Majima's philosophical trajectory in considerable detail. I have written this chapter with the belief that it is possible to go through Majima's voluminous journals and come to see an analysis of the thought of chemists who were active during the formation of scientific research in Japan in the Taisho and Showa Periods. Nevertheless, the only journal entries that could be closely-read were those of the prewar era. I hope it is possible in the future to analyze these postwar installments.

Section 8. In Conclusion—Remaining Challenges Facing a History of Thought in Chemistry

In this chapter, we looked at the achievements of Rikō Majima that led to the rise of organic chemistry research in Japan, analyzed the trajectory of his thought, and considered his influence. This paper is only the first step in a description of a history of thought in Japanese chemistry. Nevertheless, although Majima was a leading chemist in prewar Japan and responsible for determining the direction of research, he was an "ordinary" chemist, not a philosopher. I believe that in the analyses of this chapter I was able to reveal to some degree how he thought when engaging in research and what his everyday experiences were like.

As a concluding remark, I would like to briefly touch on some of the challenges to be considered when developing further histories of scientific thought in chemistry in the future.

(1) The examination of natural products as a research subject—We described in detail Rikō Majima's research, based upon the strategy of applying new Western techniques to local products in Japan in order to compete with research in the West. In 1964, the Third International Symposium on the Chemistry of Natural Products took place in Kyoto, from April 12 to 18, and the main thrust of organic

chemistry research up until this point had progressed through Majima's strategy. Other than urushiol and hinokitiol, as this chapter has discussed, we could examine what other natural products have been investigated, and we could further pursue how research subjects have changed. If we were to include not only the Japanese mainland, but also former colonies such as Taiwan, Korea, and Manchuria, we might also be able to explore a "colonial science."

(2) Study of theoretical aspects—Even while looking at just organic chemistry, it may be necessary to consider theoretical organic chemistry separately. For example, electronic theories in organic chemistry led to major changes in organic chemistry research, and the question remains how these theories have been incorporated into Japanese chemistry, and how they have changed organic chemistry research in Japan. Additionally, it is worth considering the impact of the quantum chemistry research of, for example, Ken'ichi Fukui (1918–1998) on organic chemistry in Japan.

(3) Investigating laboratory instruments and equipment for analysis—It is in particular worth considering the effects of analytical instruments that have fundamentally changed structural research in natural products chemistry since the 1950s. Their philosophical and ideological considerations are just beginning to be realized. For example, pioneering work such as Davis Baird's "thing knowledge" (Baird 2004) would be useful for further development.

(4) Investigation of unique chemists and historians of chemistry—It is an interesting fact that the extreme nationalists Michimasa Miyazaki (1852–1916) and Jūgō Sugiura (1855–1924) were initially chemistry majors. I wonder if there is a relationship between their ideologies and their chemical research. There is probably also value in considering those who majored in chemistry, but became historians of chemistry,[92] as well as researchers who wrote philosophical texts.

Further analysis of each of these points raised above would offer a different viewpoint on Japan's modern history of scientific thought in chemistry, and would allow us to understand aspects different from what we have explored in this essay.

Notes:

1) The editor of this volume, Osamu Kanamori, describes events outside Japan in his recent work *Kagaku shisō shi* (History of scientific thought). Kanamori describes the difficulties in discussing the history of scientific thought throughout the twentieth century (Kanamori 2010, pp. 45–46). His work in fact only extends as far as the early twentieth century.

2) What I have in mind here are the atomic weights, molecular weights, and structural organic chemistry based on the chemical atomic theory developed in the 1860s. For more information refer to, for example, American historian of chemistry Alan Rocke's *Chemical Atomism in the Nineteenth Century* (Rocke 1984). The basic concepts of physical chemistry were developed from the 1880s onwards.

3) Dmitrii I. Mendeleev (1834–1907) was the first to publish on the periodic table of elements (March 1869). When he began making this work public (the second half of that same year), Mendeleev was advised by the first president of the Russian chemical society (which had just been founded) and a leading chemist of that time, Nikolai N. Zinin (c. 1812–1880) to "get going on some 'serious' work." What he meant by "work" was experimental research, and in particular experimental organic chemistry, which was mainstream at that time (Kaji 1997, pp. 223–227).

4) X-rays were discovered through the application of electric technology and vacuum technology in 1895. From there, radioactivity was discovered. The means to explore atomic structure were obtained from research on radioactivity—see, for instance, Segre's *From X-rays to Quarks* (Segre 1982).

5) The journal of literature abstracts *Chemical Abstracts*, published by the American Chemical Society (first issued in 1907), issues single CAS (Chemical Abstracts Service) registration numbers assigned to a single substance. The number of registrations is approximately equivalent to that of the chemical substances known today. The number of registered organic and inorganic chemicals in this registry as of February 4, 2016 is more than 106 million. Every day on average, more than 30,000 new substances are registered. On the organization's website—http://www.cas.org—it is possible to see a counter of registered substances that is constantly updated.

6) Because of this, some historians of science even opine that in the twentieth century chemistry became a service science in support of other fields (Knight 1992).

7) The full-scale expansion of the philosophy of chemistry began in the 1990s, though there are earlier exceptions, for instance, the French philosopher of science Gaston Bachelard (1884–1962) and the chemist Friedrich Paneth (1887–1958) from Austria. For more information, see the writings of an American theoretical chemist Eric R. Scerri and his journal *Foundations of Chemistry* (Dordrecht, Kluwer Academic, from 1999) as well as the writings of German philosopher Joachim Schummer and his journal *Hyle* (*Hyle*, international journal for philosophy of chemistry, Karlsruhe, Germany: University of Karlsruhe, Institute of Philosophy, from 1995).

8) We can look at chemists who did work on philosophy or the history of science, including Friedrich Ostwald (1853–1932) and Michael Polanyi (1891–1976), who studied physical chemistry, an interdisciplinary field between chemistry and physics, and a physical chemist James Partington (1886–1965). Partington wrote a voluminous and comprehensive history of chemistry. However, such chemists are a minority. Ostwald's student Kikunae Ikeda (1864–1936), who played a role in the introduction of physical chemistry to Japan, also engaged in some writing on the history of chemistry.

9) Osamu Kanamori defines the history of scientific thought as "an attempt to capture, in a fashion as dense and multi-layered as possible, the way that the human mind investigates nature—that is, observation, concept building, and the configuration of theories." (Osamu Kanamori 2010, p. 36). This chapter attempts to follow this definition by focusing on Rikō Majima, a typical Taisho and early-Showa organic chemist.

10) For information on Rikō Majima, a good place to start may be with: *Nihon no yūki kagaku no kaitaku-sha: Majima Rikō* (The Pioneer of Japanese Organic Chemistry, Rikō Majima, Kubota 2005), *Majima*

Rikō sensei: Ikō to tsuioku (Posthumous collection, 1970), or *Waga shōgai no kaiko* (Reflection of my life, Majima 1954). It should be noted that Majima's first name was originally read "Toshiyuki," but when he was young he developed a dislike for this because, in spite of his youth, his name could also mean elderliness. When writing his name in Roman letters on his articles, Majima always wrote it as Rikō, which is another way to read the Chinese characters which comprise his name. This continued for the duration of his life (Kubota 2005, pp. 3–4). See also my paper on Rikō Majima's achievements in chemistry in *Kagakushi kenkyū* (Journal of the Japanese Society for the History of Chemistry) (Kaji 2011). It should be noted that there are some duplications in the description in this chapter.

11) For more information, see, for example, *Yōgaku* (Western learning, Numata 1989).

12) The textbook was based on a Dutch translation of a German translation of William Henry's *Elements of Experimental Chemistry*. Henry's book was translated by J. B. Trommsdorff (1770–1837) into German. This was then translated into Dutch in 1808 by A. Ypey (1749–1820). However, Udagawa expanded the Japanese translation substantially by adding various relevant information and arguments, which included his own opinions and comments with some original analysis of hot spring waters in Japan. The modern translation of that, along with a reprint of the original, has been published as *Seimi Kaisō: Fukkoku to gendaigo yaku/chū* (*Seimi Kaisō*: Reprint and Modern Translation/Annotation, Udagawa 1975). *Seimi Kaisō kenkyū* (Study on *Seimi Kaisō*), a separate volume of the same, can be a starting point for research. *Nippon no kagaku no yoake* (Dawn of Japanese science, Dōke 1979) is also a good introduction of Yōan research.

13) *Kawamoto Kōmin den* (Biography of Kōmin Kawamoto, Kawamoto and Nakatani, 1971). Kōmin's main work, *Kagaku shinsho* (A new book on chemistry) has been republished (Translation by Kawamoto, 1998). This is a retranslation of the Dutch translation by J. W. Gunning (1827–1900) of the renowned chemistry textbook, *Die Schule der Chemie* (School of chemistry, Stöckhardt 1846), written by J. A. Stöckhardt (1809–1886).

14) In the closing days of the Edo period, in addition to Dutch, English, French, German, and Russian were also learned, and because the academic and cultural traditions of those countries were also studied, the phrase *Rangaku* (Dutch learning) came to be replaced by the phrase *Yōgaku* (Western learning). Moreover, in addition to the natural sciences, medicine, and technology, the humanities and the social sciences also came to be studied. See *Yōgaku* (Western learning, Numata 1989).

15) The Institute for the Study of Barbarian Books founded by the Edo Shogunate was established in the year 1856 and lasted until 1868. The Institute had tentatively been called Yōgakusho (Institute for Western Learning), but soon it was officially rendered Bansho shirabejo. It was renamed Yōgaku shirabejo (Institute for the Study of Western Learning) in 1862, and the next year, in 1863, it was renamed Kaiseijo. See *Nihon no daigaku* (Japanese universities, Ōkubo 1997).

16) Atkinson was a student of Alexander Williamson (1824–1904), who was famous for the eponymous ether synthesis (Tokyo University Department of Chemistry, 2007, pp. 25–28).

17) Rikō Majima described the way Sakurai conducted his lectures as "well-reasoned" (Posthumous collection, 1970, p. 13).

18) Yukio Majima, "Chichi Majima Rikō: Aru kagakusha no shōgai" (My father Rikō Majima: Life of a chemist, Posthumous collection, 1970, pp. 371–395). Yukio was Rikō's second son. He became a businessperson after graduating from Kyoto Imperial University's Asian History Department (Kubota 2005, p. 5). He was born September 18, 1915. According to my personal correspondence with his widow Hiroko, he died on September 17, 1992.

19) See "Tekijuku monkasei shimei (todōfuken betsu)" (The names of students at Tekijuku [sorted by prefecture], Noboru Umetani 1996, annex [iv], p. 157). "Seimeiroku" (a log book containing names of students) of Tekijuku for the years 1844 to 1864 still remains today. This contains names, years of enrollment, and hometowns of 636 people. Taira Majima's name appears in the 548th "Seimeiroku."

20) Because the so-called the Third Higher School had been established as the Third Higher Middle School

in 1886, Majima's words are not correct. However, Kyoto Imperial University was not yet in existence; it was finally established in 1897. This was one year after Majima enrolled in Tokyo Imperial University. This is probably why he leaves us with the words, "Of course, there was no University in Kyoto—even the Third Higher School hadn't been established." He is referring to the fact that at the time it was not possible to attend an institution of highest learning in Kyoto.

21) The predecessor to the private Tokyo Kaisei Middle School (a name which came into being in 1901). After World War II, this became Kaisei Junior and Senior High School. Initially, this facility was located at Kanda Aioibashi (now Kanda Awajichō), but the school buildings were destroyed in the Great Kantō Earthquake, and it was moved to its current location in Nippori.

22) Korekiyo Takahashi was a well-known man who was active as a financier and a politician, and later took on successive roles as Minister of Finance and Prime Minister, before finally being shot to death by an insurgent officer in the February 26th uprisings. He mastered English at a young age, and had traveled to the USA as a student sponsored by his "han." So skilled was his English that he was appointed as English teacher at the Kyōryū school at the age of sixteen.

23) From the account of Rikō Majima's second son, Yukio (Posthumous collection, 1970, p. 379), Majima apparently wanted Yukio to become a doctor.

24) Although Majima himself attributed this to myopia in his journal, according to the accounts of Majima's son Yukio, this was nothing more than a pretext. Rikō had apparently relayed to his son verbally that Doctor Kotō had experienced some difficulties with one particularly wild student from Kyoto, and became prejudiced against all students from Kyoto as a result (Posthumous collection, 1970, p. 379–380).

25) Edward Divers came to Japan in 1873 as a teacher at the Kōgakuryō (Imperial College of Engineering). When Imperial University was founded, he joined the Faculty of Science there as an instructor and remained there for the duration of his stay in Japan until 1899, a total of twenty-six years (Tokyo University Department of Chemistry, 2007, pp. 33–35).

26) In the last days of the Taisho Period, Majima wrote an essay titled "Nihon kagaku shi" (The history of chemistry in Japan) in which he mentioned Nagai: "(Nagai) entered University East School (precursor to the Faculty of Medicine at the University of Tokyo) in 1869. In 1871 he left quickly to study in Europe. After thirteen years in Germany, he finally became an assistant to Hofmann, and conducted a great deal of research. In 1884, he returned to Japan and became the chief engineer at the Nagakane Pharmaceutical Company and the director of the Ministry of Home Affairs' Institute of Public Health. He also maintained a relationship with the Imperial University of Tokyo, where he participated in discussions on the construction of the new Chemistry Department in the Faculty of Science. However, the following year, his marriage prompted him to return to Europe, and during his visit in Europe there was an imperial edict issued from the Imperial University (issued in March 1886), and for a time he cut his relationship with the University" (Posthumous collection, 1970, p. 141). Regarding the interpretation of this last sentence, a student of Majima at Tōhoku Imperial University who married Majima's niece (Kazuko Okada) and later became president of Osaka University, Shirō Akahori (1900–1992), reminisced that he heard the following story about Nagai from Majima: Nagai had unofficially been offered an appointment as a professor of organic chemistry at the Imperial University, but during preparations for this he traveled to Germany to get married. His return to Japan was delayed, and he did not make it back in time for the Imperial University inauguration. Jōji Sakurai, who was famous for "a huge hatred of Germany," eliminated Nagai from consideration for the professorship, citing his delayed return as the reason. Nagai returned to Japan with his new German wife, but because he was not able to become a professor at the Faculty of Science, he was reluctantly forced to appeal to the Ministry of Education and university authorities, who set up a Pharmaceutical Department, where he began teaching and researching organic chemistry" (Posthumous collection, 1970, p. 492–493).

27) Journal club meetings in the Chemistry Department of the Faculty of Science at the Imperial University are said to have begun in 1890 (Tokyo University Department of Chemistry, 2007, p. 58).

28) According to *Urushi no hanashi* (Stories of Japanese lacquer, Matsuda 2001, p. 37), the distribution of *urushi* lacquer trees is limited to Japan, China, the Korean peninsula, Taiwan, Burma, Vietnam, Thailand, and to India. The trees do not grow further west. There is evidence that Japanese lacquer was already used in the Jōmon period of prehistoric Japan (Ibid., pp. 13–14).
29) This first appearance is in "Urushi shuseibun kenkyū no kaiko" (Reminiscence of the main components of Japanese lacquer, Majima 1945b), which was dated "August 1943" and showed his home at that time (Takarazuka Jurakusō) as the place where he wrote at the end the article.
30) Scientific research was conducted in 1906, and the proposal to name this compound urushiol came in 1907. Miyama concluded in his paper: "It is legitimate to give this compound the name urushiol in place of urushic acid" (Miyama 1907, p. 117).
31) Miyama was born in 1873. In 1898, he received a degree in applied chemistry from the Faculty of Engineering at the Tokyo Imperial University. Majima was born in 1874. In July 1899, he received a degree in chemistry from the Faculty of Science of the Tokyo Imperial University. It is natural to suppose that they may have been acquainted from their university days (Tokyo Imperial University ed., 1926, pp. 203, 292). In fact, Majima refers to Miyama as "my friend, the engineer Kisaburō Miyama (Posthumous collection 1970, p. 64).
32) $C_6H_4(OH)_2$, a compound in which two hydroxyl groups (-OH) are attached to a benzene ring (C_6H_4).
33) In this case, the chemical reaction involves a hydrogen of a hydroxyl group (-OH) being replaced by a methyl group ($-CH_3$) to form ($-OCH_3$).
34) This is referred to as a "derivative," as it is derived from certain starting material.
35) If the pressure can be decreased, it can be distilled at a lower temperature, and thus degradation by heat of the distilled component (fraction) should be reduced.
36) Matsubara learned under Europe's leading chemists. During his time abroad he produced a decent amount of research, but his research output after returning to Japan was unremarkable. He was known for his encyclopedic knowledge and strong memory, an ability that he demonstrated in the running of the Tokyo Chemistry Society and in educational administration (University of Tokyo Department of Chemistry, 2007, pp. 107–108). Bennosuke Kubota (1885–1962), who took over after Matsubara, was engaged in research on hydrogenation (catalytic reduction) using nickel and copper as catalysts, and on the synthesis of sugars, but he published few of his results (Tokyo University Department of Chemistry, 2007, p. 114). Kubota graduated from Tokyo Imperial University, and was admitted to RIKEN in September 1917, where he immediately began serving as a research assistant in Majima's lab. He went on to become a researcher in October 1921 and a senior researcher in April 1923, after which he presided over his own laboratory (Riken Memorial Office). In this way, Kubota can be said to have been a student of Majima in a sense.

    In this manner, organic chemistry research in the Faculty of Science at Tokyo Imperial University during the prewar era was not particularly productive. On the contrary, organic chemistry research within the pharmacology department at the Faculty of Medicine gave birth to the achievements of such talents as Nagayoshi Nagai, Yasuhiko Asahina (1881–1975), Heizaburō Kondō (1877–1963), Eiji Ochiai (1898–1974), and Kyōsuke Tsuda (1907–1999). The feud between Sakurai and Nagai seems to have cast a large shadow on the prewar development of the Department of Chemistry at Tokyo Imperial University.
37) This was the location of one of the Edo (Tokyo) residences of the Abe family of Bingo Fukuyama feudal domain. The residence was rented out by the Abe family in the Meiji period, and it became home to many students and civil servants. These included anthropologist Shōgorō Tsuboi (1863–1913), author Sōseki Natsume (1867–1916), and dean of the Tokyo Higher Technical School (later Tokyo Institute of Technology) Seiichi Tejima (1849–1918) ("Komagome Nishigata-machi," *Tokyo-to no chimei* (The place names of Tokyo Prefecture), Kōta Kojima 2002).
38) We can see this description in Rikō Majima's journal from August 13, 1931: "This year is our twen-

ty-fifth wedding anniversary. This means it is our silver wedding anniversary, so I offered a prayer of thanksgiving."

39) Mieko Shinkai was born as the fourth daughter of Heikaku Shinkai, a samurai at Tanabe domain, on June 28, 1877. Mieko's family is said to have had enough status to be eligible for chief retainer of a feudal lord during the Edo period, but her father died young, and her mother struggled to raise her children. After elementary school, Mieko immediately entered Kyoto Women's Normal School, a special teacher's school. After graduation, she served an obligatory term as an elementary school teacher in Kyoto before being admitted to Tokyo Women's Higher Normal School. After this, she served another obligatory term as a teacher at Mie Prefectural Women's Normal School and became an instructor at Tokyo Prefectural First Women's Higher School. As mentioned earlier, because Majima's grandfather was a physician who belonged to the Tanabe domain, there may have been some mutual family connection who arranged this marriage. In contrast to Majima, his wife Mieko was outgoing and considerate. She was sixty-seven years old when she suddenly died from a heart attack in 1944. This was written about by Majima's second son Yukio (Posthumous collection, 1970, pp. 385, 388–391).

40) In a cabinet meeting on December 4, 1906, it was determined that Tōhoku Imperial University would be created. Founding costs for Colleges of Science and Agriculture (the latter of which would be achieved through the reclassification in status of Sapporo Agricultural School) would be incorporated into the following fiscal year's government budget. In 1907 this budget made it through the House of Representatives and the House of Peers. On March 9 of the same year, the fiscal year's budget was put in place, thereby establishing the budget for Tōhoku Imperial University (Tōhoku University Hundred Year History Compilation Committee, 2007, pp. 33–37). Sakurai's telegram was probably dispatched in response to this. Since Majima's memoir was published in 1954, it was referred to as the Faculty of Science, but that at the time in 1907, when this telegram was received, it was called the College of Science.

41) Because Tamemasa Haga was studying with Harries, who was still in Berlin, for two years from 1889 (Tokyo University Department of Chemistry, 2007, pp. 102–103), Majima could take advantage of this connection to procure an acceptance from Harries.

42) This is mainly purulent inflammation caused by streptococcus. Although this can now be treated effectively with antibiotics, before the discovery of such medication it caused serious symptoms and was life-threatening.

43) Since Majima stayed in Germany as a student at the University of Kiel, he also enrolled in the *Krankenkasse* medical insurance program. Because of this, the university hospital was almost free (Majima was thus aided by the social security program that Otto von Bismarck [1815–1898] had engineered). Nevertheless, since the spa treatment had to be paid at one's own expense, Majima had to borrow 800 yen from relatives in Japan at that time (Posthumous collection, 1970, p. 25). It is difficult to imagine what the present value of that 800 yen is. The Bank of Japan's website features corporate goods prices index (the price of goods traded between companies) tables that show price changes based on average values from the years 1934 to 1936 (http://www.boj.or.jp/oshiete/history/11100021.htm). These charts run continuously from 1904 to 2006, and thus we can use them to check to see approximately how much 800 yen in 1908 would be worth today. The numbers for the 1908 and 2006 corporate goods price indices are 0.569 and 664.6 respectively. Therefore, the price value from this period will have increased 1,168 fold (664.6/0.569), meaning that 800 yen in 1908 would be worth about 930,000 yen today. In today's prices, Majima's debt to his relatives for his spa treatment would be about 1 million yen (10,000 dollars).

44) The vacuum at Tokyo Imperial University before Majima studied abroad could not produce pressures any lower than about 50 mmHg (Kubota 2005, p. 19).

45) See also Fischer and Harries 1902; Kubota 2005, pp. 19–20.

46) A convention for structural formulas to indicate an entire functional group.

47) In 1908 this institution attained the same rank as a university, and earned the right to confer degrees (conveying its first degrees in 1909), and in 1911 it was renamed with its current title, Eidgenössische

Technische Hochschule (the Swiss Federal Institute of Technology) (http://www.ethistory.ethz.ch/ besichtigungen/epochen/debatte2/index_EN). It should be noted that the University of Zurich is another prestigious university also found in the same canton. Albert Einstein (1879–1955) was enrolled at the Swiss Federal Institute of Technology from 1896 to 1900, and graduated from that institution, but his degree was acquired from the University of Zurich.

48) After dissolving a crystal in a suitable solvent, using appropriate methods one should expel the solvent to crystallize the dissolved substance again from solution. This is the recrystallization, a traditional and reliable way to purify a compound.

49) Majima seems to have said the same thing to his students. According to Harusada Suginome (1892–1972), who would later become a professor at Hokkaidō Imperial University and serve as president of that University from 1954 to 1966: "The professor always gave priority to Japanese-specific products when selecting topics for research, and if raw materials were available, he also selected natural products from elsewhere in Asia. He thought it quite natural and desirable that such Japanese natural products should be studied with Japanese hands. Furthermore he felt that for Japan, which already appeared to be lagging in the field of information, there was no benefit in competing with researchers from Western countries [on equally available subject matter]" (Posthumous collection, 1970, p. 447).

50) Tetsuo Nozoe left a great deal of writing about his life. Of particular importance are *Kagaku o kokorozashite 40 nen* (Forty years of my devotion to chemistry, Tetsuo Nozoe 1966) and *Seventy Years in Organic Chemistry* (Nozoe 1991). See also my own work "Nozoe Tetsuo" (Kaji 2008) and "Taiwan jidai no Nozoe Tetsuo to hinokichiōru: Tennenbutsu kagaku toshite no yūki kagaku" (Tetsuo Nozoe in Taiwan and Hinokitiol: Organic Chemistry as Natural Chemistry, Kaji 2008). As a part of my research on Tetsuo Nozoe, I interviewed his eldest son, Shigeo Nozoe, his student Toyonobu Asao, and one of his last students from his period in Taiwan, Lo Tung Tung-Bin, in 2006.

51) Regarding Majima's decision of the time, Nozoe recalled later that "the decision was made by Majima single-handedly" (Tetsuo Nozoe 1966, p. 4), and reflects that "it was both funny and surprising to see this dogmatic side to the Professor" (Tetsuo Nozoe 1999, p. 89).

52) The results of elections to the House of Representatives can be obtained from the table of general election results of members of the House of Representatives, issued within a few years of each election by the office of the House of Representatives.

53) Many books on the history of Taiwan have been published in Japanese. At present I would recommend the concise and balanced Taiwan: yonhyakunen no rekishi to tembō (Taiwan: 400 years of history and future prospects, Kiyoshi Itō 1993).

54) According to the 1943 Taiwan Governor-General statistics, of a total population of 6,580,000, Hoklo people (the descendants of immigrants from Southern Fujian Province on the mainland) numbered 4,997,000, or 75.9% (81.5% if Japanese people are excluded), the Hakka people (Han Chinese from northern Guangdong who are native speakers of their own dialect) comprised 913,000, or 13.9% (14.9% if Japanese people are excluded), the "Takasago" tribes (Taiwanese aborigines who mostly lived in the mountains) numbered 162,000, or 2.5% (2.6% if Japanese people are excluded), and the Heiho tribe (also an aboriginal group that mostly lived in the northern plains) numbered 62,000, or 0.9% (1.0% excluding Japanese). Likewise, Japanese comprised 397,000, or 6.0% (Masahiro Wakabayashi 2001, p. 49–50).

55) Just as Nozoe was conducting this research in 1937, Majima made a short visit—his travels took five days and he was in Taiwan for seven days—at the invitation of a professor of agricultural chemistry at the Taihoku Imperial University, Kinzō Kafuku, and others. At that time Majima was already living in Takarazuka, Hyogo Prefecture during his tenure at the Osaka Imperial University. He made a round trip from Osaka, heading west to Shimonoseki, Yamaguchi Prefecture and then traveling to and from Taiwan by ship. In Majima's journal, which will be described later, this visit to Taiwan is also described in detail. During Majima's visit, Nozoe spent almost two days with him on travels through the southern-

most part of the island. Additionally, just before returning to Japan, Majima visited Nozoe's laboratory in the Chemistry Department at the Taihoku Imperial University. In his journal entry for March 12, 1937, he wrote: "I'm delighted to see quite excellent research undertakings in Mr. Nozoe's laboratory." Majima's later strong support of Nozoe may be rooted in the impression that Majima formed at that time.

56) In 1920, Tadaka Kainoshō (1880–1938) founded the perfume manufacturer Takasago Perfumery Company Limited. Kainoshō was a 1904 graduate of the Chemistry Department of the Kyoto Imperial University. In 1938, this company relocated its head office to Taipei. From 1938 to 1945, the company's name was Takasago Chemical Industry Company Limited (Eighty-Years Chronicle Editing Committee [ed.] 2003, pp. 7–14, 30–32). This company became the main organization separating rosin acid and hinokitiol from cypress oil thanks to the founder's second son, Masayasu Kainosho (1917–1999). He studied under Nozoe at the Taihoku Imperial University and joined the Takasago Chemical Industry afterwards (Nozoe 1991, p. 38).

Because Takasago Chemical Industry had its headquarters in Taipei, from 1945 to 1951, it was under the control of GHQ. On August 1, 1951, when the Allies' occupation of Japan was nearly over, this company was able to restart as Takasago Perfumery Industry Company Limited (The eighty years of chronicle editing committee [ed.] 2003, pp. 38–41). This company (now called Takasago International Corporation) is currently the largest perfume manufacturer in Japan.

57) At present it is believed that hinokitiol is not a resonant hybrid but rather is a mixture of structures that tautomerize at high speed.

58) Even now, there remains a tea field in the town of Sanxia. It is owned by a tea shop "Tianfang Chaxing" located at No. 175–3, Chengfu Rd, Sanxia District, Taihoku prefecture. I visited this area with personnel from the National Taiwan University on March 1, 2007, and was guided around the site by the current proprietor, Mr. Huang Zheng-zhong. It was the editor of *EPTA*, the public relations magazine for Hinoki Clinical, the company that commoditized hinokitiol after World War II, who discovered this for the first time; this discovery is featured in a travel article on Taiwan in this sample publication, related to hinokitiol (EPTA editorial office [ed.] 2006, pp. 53–54).

59) Shigehiko Sugasawa graduated from the Faculty of Medicine at the Tokyo Imperial University in 1922 having studied pharmacology. From 1929 to 1932 he studied at Oxford in the United Kingdom under Robert Robinson (1886–1975) (The entry of "Shigehiko Sugasawa" in *Nihon dai hyakka zensho* [Encyclopedia Nipponica], written by Soyoko Nemoto); moreover, Erdtman came from Sweden to study under Robinson as a Ramsay Fellow at exactly the same time (1929–1931). This fellowship was started in 1920 to commemorate the famous Nobel Prize winner, William Ramsay (1852–1916), who discovered the noble gases. This scholarship was founded by the Ramsay Memorial Fellowships Trust established in University College London, as a system of incentives intended to encourage young foreign-born chemists to study in the UK (A brief biographical sketch by Torbjörn Norn on KTN Royal Institute of Technology in Stockholm, accessed September 13, 2015, http://www.kth.se/che/divisions/orgkem/2.12715/holger-erdtman-1902-1989-1.33364?l=en_UK). In other words, Sugasawa and Erdtman were old acquaintances.

60) Rikō Majima himself was awarded the Order of Cultural Merit in 1949.

61) Regarding the career of Osamu Shimomura, an English autobiography is posted on the Nobel site: accessed September 13, 2015, http://nobelprize.org/nobel_prizes/chemistry/laureates/2008/shimomura. html.

62) Hirata, a native of Yamaguchi Prefecture, graduated from the Chemistry Department of the Tokyo Imperial University in 1941. His advisor at the university was Bennosuke Kubota. Kubota, as described in note 36, studied under Majima's research organization at RIKEN. In that sense, Hirata was Majima's second-generation student. In fact, Hirata's research, starting with *fugu* poison (tetrodotoxin), is part of Majima's research tradition in structural determinations of natural products.

63) Shimomura looked at large quantities of dried sea-fireflies when he first studied at Princeton University after moving to the United States. This was collected by the Japanese military during the war; it was confiscated by the US Navy during the postwar occupation of Japan and donated to researchers at Princeton University (from Shimomura's autobiography at the Nobel site: accessed September 13, 2015, http://nobelprize.org/nobel_prizes/chemistry/laureates/2008/shimomura.html).

64) Shimomura originally named this simply "green protein," but another researcher renamed it GFP in 1969. To describe studies on fluorescent proteins as well as Shimomura's research, a group of graduate students has put together the reference *Hikaru kurage ga nōberu shō o totta riyū* (Reasons why the luminous jellyfish won a nobel prize, Association of Young Biochemistry Researchers, 2009). This text is detailed, yet easy to understand.

65) While studying chemistry at the Tokyo Institute of Technology in the 1970s, I remember hearing such words.

66) Japan's Nobel Prize-winning chemists and what they won for are listed here: Ken'ichi Fukui, 1981, "for (his theory) concerning the course of chemical reactions;" Hideki Shirakawa, 2000, "for the discovery and development of conductive polymers;" Ryōji Noyori, 2001, "for (his) work on chirally catalysed hydrogenation reactions;" Kōichi Tanaka, 2002, "for (his) development of soft desorption ionisation methods for mass spectrometric analyses of biological macromolecules;" Osamu Shimomura, 2008, "for the discovery and development of the green fluorescent protein, GFP;" and Akira Suzuki, Eiichi Negishi, 2010, "for palladium-catalyzed cross couplings in organic synthesis."

67) This is stored in the Tōhoku University archives: http://www2.archives.tohoku.ac.jp/. It is classified under "documents pertaining to Rikō Majima" in the catalogue of individuals and related organizations (related to Tōhoku University).

68) In his later years, in 1952, Majima visited Sendai, and he stayed at Aone hot springs in southern Miyagi Prefecture, where a student saw him write in his journal before turning in for the night. "Even now, I still remember him writing in his journal before he went to sleep" (Posthumous collection 1970, p. 485).

69) "Majima Rikō nikki shō: Showa 5 nen—Showa 19 nen (Excerpts from the journal of Rikō Majima: from 1931–1944)" (Shiba 1987). However, it should be noted that Tetsuo Shiba, who deciphered the journal, guessed that the reason journal entries from the second half of 1944 to the first half of 1948 were missing as "it may be due to circumstances surrounding the war when he was the university's President." Certainly, it is unlikely that Majima did not write in his journal during that entire time. It is more reasonable to think that this may have been lost due to some circumstances. In fact, Yukio recalled that the death of his mother, Majima's wife Mieko, on October 4, 1944, struck a particular blow to his father: "*My father at that time was writing in his journal* and also writing *tanka* poetry [a genre of classical Japanese poetry], through which it was possible to understand my father's feelings towards his deceased wife" (Posthumous collection, 1970, p. 385) (*emphasis mine*). Here the journal is specifically mentioned, suggesting that it did in fact exist.

70) According to the recollections of Majima's nephew, soon after they married, Majima's wife became pregnant, but had a miscarriage while Majima was studying abroad (Posthumous collection, 1970, p. 406).

71) According to a nephew who happened to be living with Rikō Majima's family at the time, he was called "Professor Sekiguchi from the Faculty of Medicine" (Posthumous collection, 1970, p. 406). I believe this refers to Shigeki Sekiguchi (1880–1942), the first Surgery Chair of the College of Medicine at the Tōhoku Imperial University. At that time, from April 1, 1919, the College of Medicine began to be called the Faculty of Medicine. Sekiguchi became a professor of the College of Medicine at the Tōhoku Imperial University in May 1917, and in that same year, studied in the United States from July, returning to Japan in December (The Editorial Committee for a Hundred Years History of Tōhoku University [ed.] 2005, p. 672).

72) Majima said: "I still don't believe that I understand all of the Anglican Church's doctrine, but I have converted to Christianity because I was influenced by the noble personalities of Christians, not by the

doctrine. Therefore, I would like to learn it little by little going forward" (Posthumous collection, 1970, p. 246).

73) Statements such as that of December 12, 1929: "I have learned Yukio's grades. His class standing has plummeted to 130. He is a miserable fool," are typical.

74) From the entry on April 11, 1929.

75) From the entry on July 21, 1931.

76) He was criticized by his wife for "not caring enough about the world" (Posthumous collection, 1970, p. 36).

77) From October 3 to 5 in 1932, they left Sendai as a couple and visited Towada, Akita, and Shōnai.

78) "Ōokayama," the name of the location of the Tokyo University of Engineering made its first appearance in February 1925, prior to the institute's elevation to university status, and frequently appears in Majima's journal in the early Showa period. It should be noted that this was the university's official English name before the war and only soon after the war its official English name was changed to its present name, the Tokyo Institute of Technology, as part of official reform.

79) During his days at First Higher School, Majima was interested in swordsmanship, boating, travel, climbing, swimming, and "modifying body" (Posthumous collection, 1970, pp. 9–10). It is clear from his journal that he was imbued with physical strength and energy.

80) According to Majima's journal, the first Faculty of Science meeting took place on March 13.

81) The journal entry from May 1, 1931 reads, "I telegrammed Professor Nagaoka in Osaka for approval for Nishina to give three weeks of lectures in September this year at Hokkaidō University. Obtained permission immediately." Here he received the approval by Hantarō Nagaoka again. According to South Korean historian of science Kim Dong-Won's biography of Yoshio Nishina, Nishina was already thirty-eight years old when he returned from Europe in late 1928. Because he was not from the physics department of the Tokyo Imperial University, he was not invited to be a professor there. Dong-Won argues that Nishina could not even acquire a post in any Imperial Universities even with the influence of Nagaoka (Kim Dong-Won 2007, p. 55). Nevertheless, looking at Majima's journal, this seems wrong: in reality, there was an opportunity for Nishina to become an Imperial University Professor, but it can be understood that Nagaoka did not allow this. It seems that Nagaoka did not want Nishina to leave RIKEN.

82) According to the RIKEN memorial room.

83) Since Majima wrote of his travels in his journal in detail, it may be possible to complete an analysis of "Majima the traveler."

84) These graduates, Mitsuru Kuhara (1856–1919), Rokurō Takasu, and Michimasa Miyazaki (1852–1909) formed the Chemical Society in April 1878. The Chemical Society was renamed the Tokyo Chemical Society in November 1879 (University of Tokyo Chemistry Department 2007, pp. 29, 185).

85) The first collection of *Complete abstracts of Japanese chemical literature* consisted of seven volumes; the second collection had thirty-seven volumes; and the index consisted of fifteen volumes. The first collection consisted of the abstracts of chemistry papers from 1877 to 1926; the second collection was from 1927 to 1963 (issued by the Foundation for Japanese Chemical Research). Later, the publisher was changed to Nihon Kagaku Gijutsu Center. The various titles up to the present have included: *Kagaku gijutsu bunken sokuhō kokunai kagaku hen: Nihon kagaku sōran (The chemical abstracts of Japan*, 1964 to 1974); *Kagaku gijutsu bunken sokuhō. Kokunai, kagaku/kagaku kōgyō hen* (1974 to 1975), and *Kagaku gijutsu bunken sokuhō kagaku/kagaku kōgyō hen* (*kokunai hen*) (Current bibliography on science and technology: Chemistry and chemical engineering [Japanese] 1975–).

86) Regarding the history of the issues surrounding *Complete abstracts of Japanese chemical* literature, Majima himself wrote in detail in the introduction to volume one, issue one (quoted in Kubota 2005, pp. 52–54).

87) Majima said, "This satisfied part of my desires, so I immediately agreed." (Kubota 2005, p. 52).

88) *Kōgyō-kagaku zasshi* is an academic journal that has been issued from the year 1898 by the Society of

Chemical Industry. The Society merged with the Chemical Society of Japan in 1948.

89) For example, on December 6, 1925: "At 8:30 pm, the imperial princess was born." This referred to Emperor Showa's first daughter Shigeko Higashikuni (1925–1961). On March 6, 1928: "Naishinnō Yūko Hisanomiya—born September 10th last year—passed away at three o'clock this morning. We will mourn her death." This referred to Emperor Showa's second daughter, who died prematurely of sepsis at six months of age. On December 23, 1933: "This morning at 6:39, Emperor Showa's son was born. The whole nation celebrates." This referred to Emperor Showa's first prince, Akihito. Majima dutifully recorded imperial events in this fashion in his journal.

90) During his Tōhoku Imperial University era in Sendai, Majima was decorated with: Order of the Sacred Treasure, fifth class on January 1, 1918; Order of the Sacred Treasure, third class on January 8, 1923; and Order of the Sacred Treasure, second class on May 16, 1930. Masataka Ogawa (1865–1930), who served as president of Tōhoku Imperial University, was decorated with the Order of the Rising Sun, second class on July 20, 1930, immediately after his death, following application from Tōhoku Imperial University which was spearheaded by Majima.

91) On November 8, 1932, Majima and his wife met with the Emperor at Shinjuku Gyoen, an imperial garden. It is unknown what kind of event took place.

92) For example, Nozomu Yamaoka (1892–1978), Mitsuo Hara (1909–1996), and Nagayasu Shimao (1920–2015).

CHAPTER 3

THE FORMATION AND DEVELOPMENT OF THE SELF-IMAGE OF KAMPŌ MEDICINE IN JAPAN: THE RELATIONSHIP BETWEEN SHOWA-PERIOD KAMPŌ AND SCIENCE

SHIN CHANG-GEON

Section 1. Situating the Issue

How would the development of scientific thought in Japan appear, not from the perspective of scientists or other supporters of scientism, but rather from the viewpoint of what has been labeled the unscientific, the irrational, and the superstitious?[1] This approach may be unorthodox; however, kampō [Editor's note: kampō is an abbreviated form of *kampō igaku*, meaning (traditional) Chinese medicine] medicine represents the sole surviving discipline in what could be called the field of traditional science and forms the subject of this chapter, which focuses on the historical evolution of the self-image of kampō vis-a-vis scientific medicine after continued exposure to science, particularly since the Meiji Period (1868–1912). As such, kampō continues to this day to maintain a character distinct from Western medicine. By discussing the medical philosophy of kampō practitioners and examining how they depicted the self-image of kampō and the reference image of Western medicine, I believe that, by reflection, we can cast new light on modern Japanese scientific philosophy in general.

So, how does kampō envision itself in the present day? Table 1 shows a comparative chart featured in an introductory text edited by The Japan Society for Oriental Medicine. We can see here a degree of difference in viewpoints among the various scholars making comparisons. However, it is reasonable to assume that

Table 1: Comparison of Western medicine and kampō (modern)

Western medicine	Kampō
Scientific (modern rationale)	Philosophic (Traditional Chinese medical rationale)
Rationalist	Empiricist
Analytic (specialized)	Synthetic (holistic)
Mechanistic (local)	Humanistic (systemic)
Seeks to treat symptoms	Seeks to restore state of health
Universalist	Personalized
Objective	Subjective
Synthetic products	Natural products
Simple products	Compound products

Source: Japan Society for Oriental Medicine Committee on Academic Education 2002:3.

whereas the image of Western medicine is that of a scientific, logical, and analytical discipline, most kampō practitioners share a self-image of their discipline as philosophical, experiential, and integral. Still, during the development of the self-conception of modern Japanese kampō, claims were made to its being more scientific than earlier forms of the discipline. Kazuo Tatsuno, (1902–1976), a doctor and a central figure in The Association of East Asian Medicine (founded in 1938), makes the following remarks on that subject:

> Because kampō is structured around the ideal of Yin and Yang [Editor's note: Yin is the dark, mysterious half, while Yang denotes the light, positive half of the traditional Taoist Yin/Yang cosmology, a key concept in East Asian philosophy], it possesses an aspect of being shrouded in a veil of mysticism. This is true not only for kampō itself, but those practicing kampō medicine may tend to indulge in and appreciate this mysticism. . . . In the past, that may have been acceptable, or indeed we might rather say that in the past society reveled in imposing that character on kampō. However, in the present Showa Period, we must begin to recognize kampō as a scientific discipline, and that imbuing its methodology with scientific rigor is an indispensable task in its development.[2]

Here, imparting Western medicine with a scientific character and associating Showa with scientism for his professional audience, Tatsuno imbued the discipline with a powerful new self-consciousness. To quote Yoshinori Ōtsuka (1900–1980), a figure of note in Showa kampō, this marked the entrance into the field of kampō practitioners who had undergone baptism in the ways of science.[3] The primary issue addressed by this chapter is not a medical assessment of the therapeutic and prescriptive policies of those practitioners who underwent baptism in the ways of science, but rather an examination of how figures such as Yoshinori Ōtsuka, who had a huge influence on modern kampō medicine, shaped the modern self-image of the profession.

To date, most research on the history of Japanese kampō has been insider work undertaken by professionals already working in the kampō community. The author of this chapter, however, seeks to conduct a study of kampō history from a research standpoint differing from that kind of insider perspective—a research stance, in other words, different from the usual kampō insider focus on topics such as succession and lineages of different kampō schools. Focusing on the history of kampō in the Showa Period, I will trace the evolution of the self-image of Japanese kampō medicine up to the present day.[4] While a tremendous volume of work has been done on pre-modern kampō-related medical literature, such as the evolution and historical development of Chinese medicine; the creation of the oldest surviving Japanese medical text, the *Ishimpō* (Prescriptions from the heart of medicine, AD 984); the influence of the father of the revival of Japanese medicine, Manase Dōsan (1507–1594); and the birth of Japanese kampō during the Edo Period, very little research has been done on the history of kampō medicine since the Meiji Period. While it has been generally noted that, after a period of decline in the Meiji Period, a revival of interest in kampō can be credited to the publication of Keijūrō Wada's *Ikai no tettsui* (The iron hammer of the medical world, 1910), with Tadanao Nakayama's *Kampō igaku fukkō ron* (An essay on the renaissance of kampō medicine, 1926) and Kyūshin Yumoto's *Kōkan igaku* (Sino-Japanese medicine, 1927) inspiring the Kampō Revival Movement of the 1930s and, more specifically, leading to the formation of the Japan Kampō Medicine Association and the Association of East Asian Medicine, there is a lacuna in the literature regarding any kind of study of the thought of these organizations or analysis of their discursive activities during wartime before research picks up again with studies on postwar history.[5] That said, Terutane Yamada and Hiromichi Yasui have called attention to *Kampō shinryō no jissai* (The practice of kampō care, 1941), co-authored by Yoshinori Ōtsuka, Dōmei Yakazu (1905–2002), Chōkyū Kimura (1910–1945), and Fujitarō Shimizu (1886–1976), with Yamada citing the book as the origin of kampō practice incorporating modern medical disease names.[6] Ultimately, we can recognize that the inflection point for the modern incarnation of Japanese kampō medicine can be found in its formative experiences during Japan's full mobilization for the war effort during World War II.

In my view, examination of the period starting from the 1930s, which saw the Kohō, Gosei and Setchū schools overcome their factional differences and begin cooperating, the holding of workshops at Takushoku University, the formation of the Association of East Asian Medicine, and the co-authoring of *The practice of kampō care* highlights the self-awareness that emerged in the discipline during this period, which laid the foundation of kampō medicine's self-image today. Using the *Shanghan Lun* (*Shōkan ron* in Japanese; "*Treatise on Cold Damage Disorders*," hereafter abbreviated "*On Cold Damage*") as their theoretical base, the Kohō, Gosei, and Setchū schools came to focus less on their differences with each other, and to place emphasis instead on making contributions to the cause of medical care in Imperial Japan, differentiating their discipline from both Western medicine and (pre-Showa Period) kampō medicine, and through differentiation from Chinese and Korean traditional medicine. In this manner, they firmly established a unique identity for Japanese kampō.

This chapter begins with an overview of the main trends in the Kampō Medicine Revival Movement since the Meiji Period and, examining the comparative study of West and East medicines by Keijūrō Wada (1872–1916) and Tadanao Nakayama (1895–1957), which laid the intellectual foundation for Showa kampō, sheds light on the characteristics of their outlook on medicine. I next examine how the self-image of Japanese kampō (manifesting the differences between Western medicine and the uniqueness of Japanese kampō medicine, etc.) took shape during the Showa Period beginning in the second half of the 1920s, by focusing on Yoshinori Ōtsuka and Dōmei Yakazu and analyzing and accumulating the medical discussion of the various figures who rallied around the East Asian Medicine Movement. Finally, in order to approach the subject of the symbolic 'othering' of Korea that was the decisive moment in the formation of the self-identity of this East Asian Medicine Movement, I address the East Asian medicine theory and views on Korea espoused by Keijō Imperial University professor Tokuyuki Sugihara, who became an academic champion and leader of Manchurian and Korean traditional medicine to analyze the relationship between kampō and Western medicine.

Section 2. The Historical Foundation of Showa Kampō Medicine

1. A Critical Theory of Kampō Medicine

According to records from the period, there were 5,274 practitioners of Western medicine and 23,015 practitioners of kampō medicine in Japan in 1874, when the nation's official medical policy was promulgated. But as is well known, all the would-be medical practitioners had to pass the examinations of Western medicine after the Ministry of Education's medical licensing examination was instituted in 1875. Shortly thereafter, the Japanese medical profession plunged into the so-called era of kampō vs. Western medicine debate, which saw the establishment in 1879 of the Onchisha schools. After repeated entreaties and legislative debate, in 1883, government regulations were established regarding criteria for the awarding of licenses to practice medicine and examinations with regard to the establishment of medical businesses. Under the new rules, doctors were not permitted to practice kampō medicine without being licensed in Western medicine. There was a sustained political movement pushing for the amendment of these regulations in favor of kampō practitioners, but a bill to amend the criteria for the awarding of licenses to practice medicine, which was submitted by kampō practitioners, was rejected by the Imperial Diet in 1895. This saw the effective end of the movement.[7]

The leading figure in the fight against kampō medicine at the time was Tai Hasegawa (1842–1912), a medical educator, politician, and medical bureaucrat who vigorously promoted Western medicine. In 1876, Hasegawa established a private medical school "Saisei-Gakusha." While educating new doctors there, Hasegawa set forth the following three reasons to justify his belief that the continued existence of kampō medicine was no longer warranted. First, in Hasegawa's view, a medical doctor was "a weapon against disease," and thus the quality of the weapon was a valid subject of critique. In short, a sharp weapon was preferable to a dull one. Whereas a kampō practitioner might be likened to a bow and arrow, a practitioner of progressive Western medicine would be a gun—kampō practitioners were thus ill-suited to the nineteenth century. Hasegawa's second position was that kampō practitioners were unsuited to taking a hand in national governance. In his view, doctors were indispensable in administrative agencies, responsible as they were for national hygiene, forensic medicine and military medical services. For example, while local doctors could be expected to perform the ultimate national hygiene function of helping to inoculate the populace against infectious disease, kampō practitioners who had not studied progressive Western medicine could not perform such work. When acting in a forensic capacity as officers of the court, professionals with specialized medical knowledge were needed to perform duties such as autopsies, whereas kampō practitioners were not legally eligible to offer medical testimony in court. Moreover, kampō practitioners were of no utility in attending to matters of military surgery or hygiene, or to the health preservation of any Imperial military personnel. Hasegawa's third main criticism of kampō medicine was that, as it was the professional responsibility of doctors to reduce deaths and time lost to medical treatment, their efforts influenced the national economy, albeit indirectly. If the people's medical needs were attended to by kampō practitioners in lieu of Western medicine practitioners, there would be an increase in the number of people suffering from and dying of disease, and people would need to remain under care for longer periods of time due to the slow-acting nature of kampō treatment. Therefore, the logic went, compared with Western medicine, kampō medicine was detrimental to the national economy.[8]

Another figure who, along with Hasegawa, also devoted his efforts to the introduction of Western medicine during the Meiji Period, and who also criticized kampō medicine, although from a different angle, was Sensai Nagayo (1838–1902). Nagayo laid out the following conditions for the practice of medicine.[9]

(1) A foundation in medical theoretical knowledge is a prerequisite for the practice of medicine.

(2) This foundation in theoretical knowledge should be in line with reality, such as the study of anatomy.

In his examination of this issue, Sugiyama calls the first condition an issue of systematicity, in which medical training begins with anatomy and ends with therapeutic techniques, and the second condition an issue of validity.[10] According to Nagayo, kampō medicine did not qualify as legitimate medical practice, as it was unable to fulfill the prerequisite conditions and standards of real medicine.

Hasegawa's and Nagayo's arguments have been introduced here to give some idea of the kind of criticism the followers of the Kampō Revival Movement had to overcome, and the scale and scope of the task they faced in trying to do so. At the heart of this criticism was Hasegawa's viewpoint of "medicine useful for the nation" and Nagayo's argument for "systematicity and professional validity." That said, neither Hasegawa nor Nagayo completely rejected the efficacy of kampō medicine; it was rather the case that both men judged the profession as yet inadequate from the perspectives they set forth. How then did kampō practitioners respond to this challenge? Before moving on to a discussion of scientific kampō practitioners of the Showa Period, I will examine two key figures in the construction of the ideological foundation that paved the way for kampō medicine's scientific foundation, and see what we can discern about their outlook on kampō medicine by looking at the East-West comparative medicine theories they espoused.

2. Kampō as Causal Treatment

In research on kampō medical history to date, Keijūrō Wada, the author of *The iron hammer of the medical world* (1910), is credited as having saved kampō from extinction[11] and paving the way toward the Kampō Revival.[12] Wada was born in Nagano Prefecture in 1872. After his graduation from Nagano Prefectural Normal Middle School, he entered Saisei Gakusha medical school in 1892, which had been established by the leading critic of kampō medicine at the time, Tai Hasegawa. According to Wada's recollection, he bought a book by the leader of the Kohō school of kampō, Tōdō Yoshimasu (1702–1773) in a Tokyo bookstore. After reading it cover to cover several times, he decided to become a disciple of Tōdō.[13]

In developing his East-West comparative medicine theory, Wada presented counterarguments against the main points of anti-kampō criticism as follows:

(1) Kampō is old-fashioned medicine.
(2) Kampō literature is groundless talk.
(3) Are herbal roots and tree bark medicinally effective?
(4) Kampō medicine has no basic medicine.
(5) Kampō treatment only addresses the symptoms of a disease, not its causes.
(6) Kampō is roundabout.
(7) Kampō pharmacists, who refer to dire side-effects as a "healing crisis" (*menken*), cause their patients unnecessary pain.

Speaking as a doctor, Wada's own position is clear. In his own words, "Kampō may not be able to match Western medicine's systematized methodology, but Western medicine cannot match the meticulous prescriptions of the kampō medical arts. This is why I depend on the Western theories while favoring the practice of kampō."[14] Conceptually, he viewed the uniting of the two great medical traditions, that is, functional, comprehensive kampō medicine and instrumental, discriminative Western medicine, as the true fulfillment of the academic approach. However, in terms of actual medical examination and treatment, from a certain eclectic standpoint, he suggests that theory is something for Western medicine, and thus, outside of the purview of surgery, while other treatment needs could be attended to using kampō medicine. Wada considered Western theories in disciplines such as physiology, anatomy, pathology, and etiology superior to those of kampō. However, these theory-intensive disciplines, in his words, appear to possess a penetrating logic, but provide little in terms of effective results in actual medical practice; therefore, in terms of treatment, he regards kampō medicine as something that can complement the areas in which Western medicine is weak. Accordingly, Wada attempts to head off criticism that kampō medicine has no basic medicine (see item 4 above), by responding that the fundamental work of doctors was treatment, that is, the healing of disease.[15]

Why then does Western basic medicine not lead to cures? Here, Wada establishes two categories for the causes of illness: internal (or indirect) causes, and external (or direct) causes. He regarded the internal as the more profound form of pathogenesis, and saw both individual and general predispositions (with variables such as physical constitution, gender, age, etc.) at work in the progression of illness. On the other hand, external causes can be powerful enough to directly cause disease—an idea that was the theoretical basis for the modern medical practice, looking for the causes of diseases in specific areas of the body or in invasive germs. But in Wada's etiological theory, Western medicine only focuses on external causes, thus missing half of the etiological picture. In other words, because Western etiology was incomplete in this regard, it could not offer effective treatments against illnesses in which both types of causes were involved. Wada noted that, according to the modern medical standards of the time, etiological discovery and therapeutic discovery were treated as separate matters, and the discovery of the cause of a disease did not necessarily directly lead to the establishment of an effective treatment of that disease.[16] In the obvious context of the famous battle of treatment between kampō and Western medicine,[17] criticism of Western medicine as not having established treatment methodology, especially in comparison with kampō medicine, was not without grounds.

Here, Wada turned the tables on critics of kampō by asserting that kampō treatment was symptomatic, whereas Western medicine practiced causal treatment:

> Although Western medicine claims that germs cause disease, if the cells that make up the body are in optimal condition, they will certainly be strong enough to withstand germs. Western medicine's so-called causal treatment is really nothing more than a method for killing germs . . . kampō treatment does not necessarily concern itself with germs. Instead, it increases cell vitality and improves blood circulation with the aim of preventing the body from

becoming a host to germs in the first place. This is practical, a treatment of root causes.[18]

As outlined above, Wada acknowledged that kampō had no foundation in medical scientific areas such as physiology or anatomy, and he was in favor of the use of Western medicine as a theory. According to him, "there is no other reasonable alternative to a basis in Western medical theory. Moreover, the more we borrow from such theory in our explanations, the more we can discover about the true value of kampō."[19] This marked the beginning of modern kampō medicine's self-image while using Western medical/biological terms such as cell and germ.

3. Creating Nihompō (Japanese Medicine): Abandoning the Theory of Yin/Yang and the Five Elements

The new self-image Wada was carving out for his discipline became increasingly detailed in terms of counterarguments being developed against the criticisms of kampō listed above as (1), (2), and (6). Wada did not present kampō medicine monolithically. Instead, he attempted to depict it as an up-to-date scholarly discipline shaped by a long history of advances and branched out into various schools. According to Wada, the discipline experienced a Golden Age with the compiling of *On Cold Damage* in the third-century China. The branch of kampō medicine which came to be known as the Kohō school based its practice upon the treatments prescribed in *On Cold Damage*, which the school regarded as perfect and faultless. However, in time, kampō began to enter a period of decline. Wada explained that, during this period, which he termed the Era of Yin/Yang and the Five Elements Philosophy, kampō practitioners relied on this philosophy to explain illness and obtain medical effects. This branch of kampō using the Yin/Yang and the Five Elements as the basis of its practice came to be known as the Gosei school.

We can see Wada emphasizing the salience of these two schools as a means of evading criticism of kampō medicine. Against item (2) in the list of anti-kampō critiques, i.e., the argument that kampō literature was so much groundless talk, Wada claimed that all the books containing groundless treatment came from the Gosei school. There may have been some minor anatomical errors in the Kohō school's books, but they never contain groundless descriptions.[20] Moreover, he also defended kampō medicine against item (6) in the list of critiques, namely, the charge that kampō is roundabout, by blaming the Gosei school for this reputation:

> In Kohō school practice, careful effort is devoted to ascertaining the charac-
> teristics of an illness, strong medication is generally used, and the main aim
> of treatment is to kill the pathogen. In Gosei school practice, treatment is
> based on the Yin/Yang and the Five Elements philosophy, weak medication
> tends to be used, and the main aim of the treatment is to augment the body's
> own healing ability. Consequently, the Kohō school's practice of careful diag-
> nosis and the specific prescription of medication appropriate for the illness
> results in speedy healing that is beyond the capability of Western medicine
> today. However, the treatment of the Gosei school seems quite reliable,
> though it was given by a master in this field.[21]

By distancing the discipline from the Yin/Yang and the Five Elements philoso-
phy-based Gosei school, Wada sought to make kampō medicine the exclusive purview of the Kohō school. He expressed the opinion that "this is in actuality not
even kampō anymore. It has become 'Nihompō'—Japan's own unique medicine.
This line of logic rejected Yin/Yang and the Five Elements principles and instead
espoused the theory of Tōdō Yoshimasu (1702–1773), which held that all diseases
come from one pathogen. Wada said, "I regard the discourse of Mr. Tōdō Yoshimasu as the most reliable, unerring kampō literature."[22] According to Yoshimasu,
all illnesses originated from a single pathogen. The differing symptoms of diseases
were no more than the result of this pathogen being centered on different areas of
the anatomy. Moreover, he explained, as all medications were themselves toxic,
effective treatment entailed a "fight fire with fire" method of using one toxin to
fight another. Accordingly, he insisted that treatment involved a physician going
after the illness aggressively, and whether the patient lived or died was a matter of
his or her own fate.[23]

While this can be viewed in actuality as a rejection of Yin-Yang/Five Elements
principles, it can be pointed out that there was a subtle difference between Wada
and Yoshimasu in terms of Wada bringing back some aspects of Yin-Yang philosophy in his restructuring of kampō medicine theory.[24] Indeed, where Wada explains
Yin/Yang and the Five Elements principles, he limits criticism to the Five Elements
viewpoint: "The Five Elements principles categorize human organs according to
the Five Elements, and the Five Flavors correspond to the Five Elements. By analogy of the harmony or rivalry of the Five Elements, they judge whether a flavor is

appropriate or not, or whether the disease is curable or not. The logic of the Five Elements principles is invoked to underlie and explain everything.[25]

Kyūshin Yumoto (1876–1941), who went on to write *Sino-Japanese medicine* after graduating from Kanazawa Medical School, reported having been initially inspired to study Imperial kampō medicine on reading Wada's work.[26] Declaring his support for the Kohō school, the self-proclaimed kampō/Western eclecticist Yumoto claimed "The majority of the Western medical practitioners are believers in scientism, led by an obsession that they can solve anything with the power of science. They think of human bodies as akin to test tubes and believe blindly in animal experimentation."[27] In other words, he was critical of putting too much faith in the power of science. This certainly did not imply a rejection of science; rather, his objective of clarifying the advantages of East Asian medicine by making use of Western medical theory was one that was held in highest esteem by the Kohō school. Here we see the birth of Showa kampō's strong sense of self-respect. "I do not disregard Western medicine because I am versed with kampō medicine. Also, I do not bypass scientific knowledge in favor of respect empirical knowledge."[28]

Yasuo Ōtsuka (1930–2009) credits Keijūrō Wada's and Kyūshin Yumoto's restructuring of traditional thought, such as Yin-Yang teachings and six stages of disease, as the most important factor in laying the groundwork for such thought to form a theoretical *raison d'être* within a historical context of near-total belief in the superiority of Western medicine. However, for Wada, who declared Western physiology and anatomy to be the foundation of medical research, what relationship could there be between modern anatomical thought and restructured Yin-Yang philosophy? Wada's explanation of the value of kampō medicine employs Western medical knowledge as its basis, and one wonders if his references to physiology and anatomy were made primarily in the instrumental context of boosting the persuasiveness of the argument. A key figure of Showa Kohō school, Kenzō Okuda, approached the matter differently; unlike Wada's and Yumoto's stance, he makes no appeal to modern medicine in his explanation of kampō.[29] If the modern medical disciplines of physiology and anatomy with Yin-Yang principles are compatible in the works of Wada and Yumoto, did they not discover any problems there? As far as I know, no mention of, or attempt to, address this issue appears in any of their publications.

4. Kampō's Theoretical Basis: Symptomatic Theory

Criticism of Wada's and Yumoto's "Western theory, kampō treatment" approach as being intellectually contradictory appeared in 1926 with the publication of *Kampō igaku fukko ron* (An essay on reestablishment of Chinese medicine) by poet and writer Tadanao Nakayama (1895–1957). In the journal *Nihon oyobi nihonjin* (Japan and Japanese), Nakayama made a famous binominal diagram in which he outlines the differences between Western medicine and kampō medicine (see table 2).

However, this is not Nakayama's true contribution. While he was an inheritor of Keijūrō Wada's theory, it is the very closeness in which his own argument clearly adheres to Wada's thought that deserves attention. In short, his argument is that the theoretical basis of kampō medicine lies not in physiology or anatomy, but rather, in what could be termed symptomatic theory. In his book's third chapter, titled "The Relative Merits of Western and Kampō Practice," Nakayama lays out his main argument, beginning with a section titled "The theoretical advantages and disadvantages of Western medicine." In this section, he criticizes the two leading figures in kampō medicine at the time, saying, "Even those who have been disappointed in the clinical results of Western medicine and feel that treatment must follow kampō methods still make the mistake of believing that Western

Table 2: Comparison of Western medicine and kampō (Tadanao Nakayama)

Western medicine	Kampō
Deductive	Inductive
Theoretical basis in physiology, anatomy	Theoretical basis in disease states (yin/yang, exterior/interior, deficiency/excess, etc.)
Emphasis on external causes of disease	Emphasis on internal causes of disease
Focus on the disease (treating the specific disease)	Focus on the state of health (treating the overall condition)
Body = test tube	Bodily = organic
Treatment of symptoms ('leaves')	Treatment of causes ('roots')
Local treatments	Systemic treatments
Purity principle (use of purified extracts)	Herbal principle
Monotonic, 'single-flavor' (treatment using single components)	Complex (treatment using compounds)

medicine is superior in terms of basic theory. For example, even Hakushō Kimura said 'we should rely on Western medical theory and follow kampō treatment methods,' and Keijūrō Wada said kampō 'may not be able to match Western medicine's systematized methodology, but Western medicine cannot match the meticulous prescriptions of the kampō medical arts.'"[30] However, the contradiction of believing a basic theory to be correct, but at the same time ineffective in actual practice, did not stand to reason. Today's kampō medicine, Nakayama remarked, suffers from the intellectual contradiction of borrowing frequently from Western medicine's basic theory while relying on kampō treatment.[31]

According to Nakayama, while it was beyond doubt that Western medicine was superior in terms of its fundamental theories, such as physiology and anatomy, and Western medical terminology was useful for explaining physiological and pathological phenomena, this did not mean that kampō theory had to rely upon Western medicine. Kampō possessed its own unique areas of theoretical knowledge different from physiology and anatomy. Nakayama used the following line of argument in his claim that this theoretical knowledge, that is to say, kampō clinical theory, was in fact more scientific than Western medicine: "The origins of kampō are not in theory but in fact. Theory should be based on facts. Science does not exist separately from reality. Thus I can state without hesitation that kampō clinical theory is more scientific than that of Western medicine."[32]

If this was the case, then what exactly was this so-called kampō medicine scientific theory? Nakayama termed it Disease Condition (or Symptomatic) Theory, explaining it as being structured around Yin-Yang and related classical Chinese philosophical concepts such as *hyōri* (exterior and interior) and *kyojitsu* (deficiency and excess).

Western medical treatment involves identifying and destroying a pathogen through anatomical research. In the Western method, therefore, they conduct extremely detailed research in identifying the disease, that is, in determining the conditions of the illness. Kampō treatment, on the other hand, prioritizes the patient's internal condition and extremely detailed discussion of symptoms. This is because Western medicine prescribes medication once the illness has been identified, whereas kampō prescribes medication against symptoms.[33]

Nakayama inherited the self-image of kampō medicine reworked by Wada, and as already shown in table 2, he developed a much more dichotomous schematization of the issue, reacting angrily to the idea of basing the theoretical foundation of Western medicine on kampō theory. As a result, he highlighted an area previously left vague by Wada, i.e., locating Yin-Yang philosophy at the center of the theoretical foundation of kampō medicine while, like Wada, distancing kampō theory from the Five Natural Elements theory. Nakayama saw no intellectual contradiction in using Western medical vocabulary to explain kampō medicine in modern, clear terms to people who otherwise had trouble understanding it.

Section 3. The Origin and Self-Image of the "East Asian Medicine" Movement

1. The Development of the 1930s Kampō Medicine Revival Movement

While kampō medicine in Japan saw a period of decline during the Meiji Era, the publication in 1910 of Keijūrō Wada's *The iron hammer of the medical world* reversed this trend. The dawn of the Showa Period in the 1920s saw the publication of Tadanao Nakayama's *An essay on the renaissance of kampō medicine* (1926) and Kyūshin Yumoto's *Sino-Japanese medicine* (1927).

However, kampō revivalist thought did not develop into a full-fledged movement until the middle of the 1930s. In 1934, the Kohō, Setchū, and Gosei schools broke with long-held tradition by cooperating to establish the Japan Kampō Medicine Association and began publishing the professional journal *Kampō to Kan'yaku* (kampō and herbal medicine).[34]

Moreover, in October 1935, the core members of the movement established a kampō workshop called Kaikō Gakuen, and in April 1937, they held the first Takushoku University Kampō Symposium. This symposium was the most successful event of the Kampō Medicine Revival Movement, reportedly hosting over 700 attendees.[35] In 1941, the core participants in the symposium co-authored and published *The practice of kampō care*. One of the co-authors was Yumoto school product and Kohō school member Yoshinori Ōtsuka. Another co-author was Setchū school member Chōkyū Kimura, the heir of Hakushō Kimura (1866–1931), who had studied under Sōhaku Asada (1812–1894). Others included: Gosei school member Dōmei Yakazu, the younger brother of Kaku Yakazu (1893–1960), who had studied under Dōhaku Mori (1867–1931); and Tōtarō Shimizu, who, although a pharmacologist, had studied Kohō kampō under Yumoto.

In November 1938, the Association of East Asian Medicine was formed to further the cause of cultural cooperation between Japan, China, and Manchukuo. As is evident through the twenty-six issues of journal *Tōa igaku* (East Asian medicine) published between February 1929 and March 1941, the article submissions during this time were dominated by major Showa kampō figures Yoshinori Ōtsuka and Dōmei Yakazu.

2. The Role of Japanese Kampō in Imperial Medicine

Now, what were the factors and circumstances behind Japanese kampō practitioners forming the Association of East Asian Medicine and developing the East Asian Medicine Movement in the historical context of Japan's ongoing invasion of China and the rationalization of the idtweeals of the East Asian Collective by many of Japan's intellectuals? In a previous section, we recounted Tai Hasegawa's earlier opposition to the continued practice of kampō medicine in terms of the medical needs of the nation. At this point in the Showa Period, Japanese kampō practitioners were aware that they were being presented with a wonderful opportunity to overturn Hasegawa's criticism and boost the kampō revival.

The leaders of this movement had no grounds for doubting the importance of cultural cooperation between Japan, China, and Manchukuo, and they placed the practice and art of medical science firmly at the core of this cultural alliance: "Medicine is the discipline best positioned to oversee the immediate concrete realization of cultural cooperation. The benevolent art of medicine knows no national borders, and in time of war, it knows neither friend nor foe."[36] However, it was impossible to accomplish this cultural cooperation through Western medicine alone. This is because there were some one million kampō practitioners active in China enjoying popular support, and even if several thousand medical doctors were sent to the Asian continent, there was no guarantee that the common people would seek treatment from them. Kampō medicine was the key to cultural cooperation in this context.

As the first step in this campaign, Japanese kampō practitioners who had undergone scientific training would be dispatched to the Asian continent. "These kampō practitioners 'baptized in science' would be sent to the continent, where they would cooperate with local kampō practitioners who had not yet undergone this baptism. The Japanese personnel would organize a professional development course to provide their Chinese counterparts with needed guidance. This represented an effort to establish educational institutions for them."[37] We can see awareness on the part of Japanese kampō practitioners, who endorsed the construction of an East Asian Community under Japanese leadership, that this campaign represented an Imperial tool capable of breaking through the formerly impregnable Chinese wall of cultural resistance to Western medicine.

Concurrently, there was an additional area in which Japanese kampō could be of service to the cause of Imperial medicine: it could provide countermeasures against the epidemic disease and malaria, which would be indispensable for the Japanese military's plans for the invasion of the Asian continent. In fact, the third issue of East Asian medicine focused on malaria. The lead article was titled "Use Kampō Methods to Treat Malaria." Other articles included: Yoshinori Ōtsuka's "Malaria as Seen and Treated by a Kampō Practitioner"; Kazuo Tatsuno's "Proof of the Effectiveness of Hachimigan (a traditional Chinese herbal medicine) Against Malaria"; and Sorei Yanagiya's "Acupunctural Treatment of Malaria." The authors continued to dig through kampō literature, searching for and publishing findings about malarial cures that could be used in place of quinine. Since the Meiji Period, kampō had been considered inadequate in the fields of military and group preventative medicine. Nevertheless, by this time, kampō practitioners could claim military medical utility for their discipline, such as Yanagiya's entreaty to the Japanese military's medical services to adopt these very simple treatment methods to relieve the suffering of malaria patients among Imperial military personnel.

3. Japanese Kampō Medicine's Self-Image Reaches Completion

East Asian Medicine Movement ideologues Ōtsuka and Yakazu were both medical doctors trained in Western techniques. Both men were full of confidence in themselves as individuals who first qualified as doctors in Western medicine and trained in scientific techniques before taking up the study of kampō, and they made numerous repeated references to their own qualifications in their East Asian medicine submissions: "Kampō practitioners in Japan today have studied Western medicine before taking up the study of kampō. You could say that we have received our baptism in the ways of science."[38]

However, we will see that this science was not something that sprang from baptism in Western medicine that happened in the Meiji Period, but rather had its origins in the historical characteristics of kampō of the Tokugawa Period.

In the text *On Cold Damage*, which can be considered kampō medicine's Bible, there is a passage that we should attack the disease . . . however, kampō treatment at one time depended mainly on nourishment and temperature regulation, without resort to medication to attack the illness. Today, most practitioners in China do not resort to aggressive medication, only prescribing mild-acting medication instead. However, there is a group in our profession, deserving of our attention, who are calling for progressive innovation in kampō using aggressive medications conforming with *On Cold Damage*. With the onset of the Tokugawa Period, kampō in our nation underwent a dramatic process of Japanization. . . . Paralleling our own Japanese national character, kampō medicine in Japan has developed a personality with both peaceful and aggressive aspects.[39]

The reliance of Japanese kampō medicine on *On Cold Damage*-sanctioned aggressive treatment was seen as something distinguishing it from Chinese medicine, and even as comprising a historical basis for a claim of the Japanese kampō being more scientific than Chinese medicine.

Facing domestic criticism from Western medicine as being unscientific, Japanese kampō medicine used its *On Cold Damage*-based position to claim scientific superiority over Chinese medicine. This was one way that Japan sought to secure a leadership role in East Asian medicine. However, as Tatsuno's remark about the need to tear the veil of mysticism away from kampō[40] may have suggested, the word "scientific" had no concrete substance in a kampō context. In any case, the word "scientific" was enlisted as a way of othering Chinese medicine, and both Japanese kampō and Western medicine, which otherwise shared an antagonistic relationship with one another in Japan, share responsibility for thereby imposing a lowly status rank on the reputation of traditional Chinese medicine. While criticizing Western medicine, claims were made for the scientific superiority of Japanese kampō over traditional Chinese medicine. Such thought was revealing of the split personality in Japan's overarching self-image vis-à-vis the West.

What sort of overall relationship within the East Asian Medicine Movement did kampō medicine have with Western medicine? In East Asian medical discourse,

Western medicine and kampō were reconciled as existing in a parallel and mutually beneficial relationship, with each seen as complementing the strong points and compensating for the weak points, of the other. From an extremely abstract perspective, both fields were represented as following courses that would eventually lead to the perfection of a true Oriental Medicine.[41]

This call for a new Oriental medicine, i.e., a true Oriental Medicine, was trumpeted by many in the field in the historical context of Japan's mass mobilization for war. The prerequisite groundwork for this discourse was based upon discussion of comparisons of the strong and weak points of Eastern versus Western medicine. Keijūrō Wada, Kyūshin Yumoto, and Tadanao Nakayama had already broached this topic. For example, according to Wada, kampō medicine was functional and comprehensive, whereas Western medicine was instrumental and discriminative. Nakayama saw Western practice as symptomatic and local, whereas kampō was overall, fundamental, holistic, and organic. However, it was ultimately up to Dōmei Yakazu to bring all of this thought together and map it out clearly as a polished thesis. Table 3 shows a chart of his analysis of the respective characters of Eastern and Western medicine, taken from his article "Kampō no Gainen to Gendaiteki Shimei" (*Tōa igaku*, Volume 20).[42]

Of particular importance in this classification is Yakazu's comparison of what he called evidence-based treatment versus symptomatic treatment. Ever since

Table 3: Comparison of Western medicine and kampō (Dōmei Yakazu)

Characteristics of Western medicine	Characteristics of Kampō
Analytic	Synthetic
Surgical	Medical (internal medicine)
Basic	Clinical
Seeks to restore balance	Seeks to treat symptoms
Mechanical	Functional
Precise	Unrefined
Theoretical	Actual
Scientific	Philosophical
Peripheral	Fundamental
Prophylaxis against germ infection	Preservation of bodily state
Artificial	Natural
Practical application of animal and in vitro experiments	Relies on human experimentation

Wada's framing of Western medicine as employing symptomatic treatment in contrast to the causal approach to treatment in kampō, Nakayama had also stressed this difference in treatment methods, but up to this point he had yet to make the claim, as in table 1, of kampō medicine as employing *sho* (diagnostic pattern) -based treatment. Yakazu was the successor to Wada's comparative theory of Eastern and Western medicine, but he was the first to introduce the term "diagnostic pattern" into use in kampō medicine diagnosis and treatment methods:[43]

> I have written that kampō treatment is diagnostic pattern-based, whereas the Western method is symptomatic. While at first glance there may appear to be no difference between the two terms, in fact, the difference between diagnostic pattern and symptoms is a very important one. The term symptom refers to specific signs of illness, such as headache or other pains, etc., which are analytically distinguishable. Kampō's diagnostic pattern, however, refers to a holistic consideration of the combined, interrelated symptoms of an illness of an individual as they are revealed. This is what is meant by diagnostic pattern. Headache, nausea, and diarrhea are regarded as being interrelated, with each of those separate symptoms pointing to separate aspects being regarded together as comprising diagnostic pattern of the same overall illness.[44]

In his discussion of kampō medicine's possession of this characteristic, Yakazu refers to two pharmacologists to bolster his claim for the discipline's scientific credibility. These pharmacologists were Tokuyuki Sugihara (1892–1976) of Keijō Imperial University and Tameto Okanishi (1898–1973) of Manchuria Medical College. Yakazu, the guiding physician and theorist behind the East Asian Medicine Movement, praised Western medical scholar Sugihara, who will be introduced in detail in the next section.

In the schematization of his above-described East/West medical theory, Yakazu locates this development within the situation and pace of the times, describing it from the following abstract viewpoint: "the birth of the new Oriental civilization and Oriental medicine will begin with Occidental things being embraced in their entirety by the entirety of Oriental things, swallowed down into the Oriental stomach and digested and absorbed."[45] He saw this as kampō medicine's modern mission, and claimed that Japanese spirit could breathe warm, humanistic life into the coldly analytical character of Western medicine.

Developing this proactive kampō medicine theory, Yakazu, together with East Asian Medical Association chairman Kazuo Tatsuno, were commissioned by the Japanese government in July 1940 to participate in actual governance work as members of the Manchurian Affairs Bureau.

Section 4. Eliminating Korean Influence from the New Oriental Medicine

1. Kampō Pharmacology Research at the Keijō Imperial University Faculty of Medicine

What kind of relationship did Japanese kampō practitioners form with Korea when the East-Asia Medical Association was founded in 1938? At the time, the leading institution of kampō pharmacological research in Imperial Japan was the Second Department of Pharmacology in Keijō Imperial University. Centered around pharmacologist Professor Tokuyuki Sugihara, this research facility's staff of pharmacological chemists and botanists worked in the field of kampō pharmacology, doing chemical analysis and experimenting on the effects of various kampō pharmaceuticals using Korean kampō practitioners as informants.[46]

In ethnic Korean (i.e., Korean language) newspapers at the beginning of the 1930s, there was prominent coverage of the populace's purported state of hygiene as comprising a serious problem. According to recent reports, one article read, economic hardship is causing deterioration in quality of life for most Koreans, with a commensurate extreme deterioration of health conditions and an alarming increase in disease and fatality rates.[47] As an aid measure for rural communities, in 1933 (8th Year of Showa) the Japanese Governor-General of Korea instituted a peninsula-wide campaign promoting the cultivation of medicinal plants.[48] That same year, *Yakusō saibaihō kōwa* (Medicinal plant cultivation), a volume compiled by the Second Department of Pharmacology in Keijō Imperial University, was adopted by the government nationwide as the official textbook for this agricultural campaign.

According to the Governor-General's Office Hygiene Bureau technicians who recommended this agricultural campaign to cultivate medicinal plants, in order to raise the Korean countryside up from its impoverished state, it was prerequisite for the health of its residents to be improved. However, according to one official report, "Korean medical care was insufficient in the extreme in terms of availability. This is especially true for Western medical facilities, which are almost entirely centered in urban areas. In remote areas, one cannot find any doctors, pharmacists or midwives. Moreover, there are not even any drugstores selling cotton gauze or any pharmaceutical retail businesses at all." Accordingly, "the matter of how to improve hygiene in remote areas with no access to medical care is an important one. We think that making the proper application of kampō pharmaceutical treatment widely available may hold one key to solving this problem."[49] In the 1930s, the Government-General officially began to acknowledge the unequal distribution and availability of health care access in Korea, the conditions under which Koreans were being excluded from Western medicine, and the fact that the Governor-General's regulatory policies were exerting negative pressure on Korean traditional medicine. As a result, the Medicinal Plant Cultivation Movement was instituted on the Korean Peninsula with the intention of putting medicinal plants to use toward improving the health of the peninsula's residents.

The Medicinal Plant Cultivation Movement also played a new role in military planning during the Japan's invasion of the Asian continent in the 1930s, with the Korean Peninsula acting as a forward staging area for Japan's continental invasion forces. This can be called the second stage of the movement, during which requests began coming in from the Army of Korea to conduct research and increase cultivation.[50] In 1939, the Keijō Imperial University medicinal herb farm and the Gyeonggi Medicinal Plant Lab and its facilities in Kaesong were integrated, and a special pharmacognosy laboratory was established in the same site "to conduct thorough research on herbal remedies in view of Keijō Imperial University's special mission." This pharmacognosy laboratory was established to:

(1) Expand the research purview of the Second Department of Pharmacology in Keijō Imperial University.
(2) Develop substitutes for Western pharmaceuticals.
(3) Develop medical supply lines that would not depend on resupply from the Japanese Home Islands, making use of Korean and Manchurian resources instead.[51]

Kaesong, where the new pharmacognosy laboratory was located, was a region famous for the production of ginseng. The facility pursued research focusing on the development of ginseng pharmaceuticals and ginseng production, building upon the catalogue of earlier studies of the pharmacological effects of ginseng carried out at Keijō Imperial University. Sugihara was in charge of the facility, holding dual positions of chief administrator and professor in charge of research. Other facility staff included two assistant professors and, at any given time, four or five technicians and research assistants. The budget for operating costs was approximately equal to that of five departments, with the Mitsui & Co. offering financial support for ginseng cultivation.[52] Additionally, the Cheju Island Experimental Facility was established in 1943, with efforts there focusing on the production of insect-repellent pansies and cardiotonic digitalis plants, the cultivation of the latter being prohibited by law in the Japanese Home Islands.[53] Insect-repellent pansy sales were carried out via pharmaceutical firms designated by the Army of Korea.

In this way, the Second Department of Pharmacology in Keijō Imperial University played an important role in kampō pharmaceutical policy on the Korean Peninsula after the 1930s. Japanese kampō practitioners involved in the East Asian Medicine Movement praised clinic chief Tokuyuki Sugihara as the leading medicinal authority among kampō medicine's champions. In discussions of the issue of maintaining kampō in Manchuria, Sugihara and Tokyo Imperial University professor Shōzaemon Keimatsu (1876–1954) supported the kampō cause. Both men journeyed to Hsinking (modern day Changchun) in Manchuria to sing the pharmacological praises of kampō medicine. They undertook this activity along with leading Association of East Asian Medicine figures Dōmei Yakazu and Kazuo Tatsuno.[54]

What then was Tokuyuki Sugihara's kampō philosophy as he coordinated his activities with the kampō practitioners in Japanese Home Islands, who formed the backbone of the East Asian Medicine movement? Let us examine the New Oriental Medicine philosophy Sugihara promulgated, and examine how it dealt with the subject of Korea.

2. Tokuyuki Sugihara's Idea of Constructing a New Oriental Medicine

In 1939, under total war mobilization, Tokuyuki Sugihara, professor of the Second Department of Pharmacology in Keijō Imperial University and chief of the herbal medicine research facility, released a series of studies and books on the subject of kampō medicine. Important publications of his from around this time include:

"Kanpō igaku no kagakuteki kentō" ("A scientific consideration of kampō medicine," *Chōsen oyobi manshū* [Korea and Manchuria], Vol. 374, January 1939); "A Scientific Consideration of Kampō Medicine (Pt. 2)" (ibid., Vol. 375, February 1939); "Chōsen ni okeru kampō igaku to shōkan ron"("Kampō medicine and 'On Cold Damage' in Korea," *Chōsen* [Korea], Vol. 292, September 1939); "Kampō igaku sōnen ni tsuite" ("On Scientific Thought in Kampō Medicine," Keijō Imperial University Continental Culture Research Committee eds., *Tairiku bunka kenkyū* [Study on the continental culture], 1940); *Kampō shohōgaku* (A study of kampō prescription, Vol. 1, 1941), etc.

It should be recognized first that Sugihara was already highly praising certain aspects of kampō medicine as early as 1929, remarking at the time, "I think there is merit in the idea, held by some kampō practitioners, that ginseng has use as a pharmaceutical supplement."[55] At least as far as Korean ginseng was concerned, he could, from a modern scientific perspective, approve of traditional medicine's use of the plant as a supplement. Later, with the outbreak of war, he began developing a line of enthusiastic support for kampō medicine.

We should make clear the reasons behind Sugihara's efforts to construct a New Oriental medicine. First, attention should be given to the fact that Sugihara moved continuously between the realms of medicine and politics. As such, he proclaimed a belief that medical reform would be a prerequisite for building a new social order.

> Medical matters held a high priority in politics in the Orient from ancient times. In ancient China's Fu Xi and Shennong Eras, kings were, by definition, medical doctors. Medicine continued to play an important role every time the organization of governments was reformed thereafter. In Japan as well, we can see great medical reforms as being a significant part of overall programs of reform in periods such as the Taika Reforms or the Meiji Restoration. Medical affairs always play an important role when social systems are reformed, and by some measures, medical reforms are paving the way for the construction of a new order for society.[56]

Sugihara goes on to say that it was time for the Japanese to take up a position of leadership in constructing a new order on the Asian continent, claiming that a "New Oriental Medicine" was an urgently needed prerequisite for this to happen. However, why was the reform necessary for the construction of a new order supposed to take place in Oriental Medicine, not through an internal reform of Western medicine? According to Western pharmacology specialist and Imperial university professor Sugihara, the work on kampō pharmacology being done at Keijō Imperial University's Pharmacognosy Laboratory was not the same thing as kampō medicine research.

> Fortunately, kampō pharmacological research is making steady progress, and an herbal medicine research facility will be established in the next fiscal year. However, I would like to make it clear that kampō pharmacological research is only a part of kampō medicine research. Kampō pharmaceuticals are drugs used in kampō medical practice; however, kampō medicine has unique methods of diagnosis, and also in treatment, it has diverse methods, such as the acupuncturist's arts. Further, it employs unique categorization of illnesses based on this unique philosophy of medicine. Research in kampō medicine is thus not identical to kampō pharmacological research.[57]

Further, he asserts that what is needed is not kampō pharmacological research undertaken from a Western medical standpoint, but rather, research on kampō medicine itself. Sugihara explains the logic behind this while pointing out a flaw in the cultural policy of the Shanghai Science Institute:

> On the occasion of the establishment of the China Cultural Policy Section, it is said the China Organizing Committee gave its wholehearted approval to a suggestion by the late Professor Hattori, following Professor Keimatsu's advice, for the establishment of a kampō pharmacological research facility. This resulted in the creation of a kampō pharmacological research section at the Shanghai Science Institute, which has made many important research findings. However, if I may speak frankly, I suspect that there are some ways in which this kampō pharmacological research section falls short of Chinese expectations. I think the pharmacologists in charge of this research section have carried out research on the ingredients of kampō pharmaceuticals. I dare say that not only Japanese but even Westerners could do that. But is it not our studies into kampō medicine that the Chinese were expecting from us Japanese? This is obviously an area in which we can clearly make more of a contribution than the Westerners. The next time we undertake the establishment of another institution such as this on the Asian continent, we must

include medical doctors in the venture and make research efforts into the area of kampō medicine.[58]

According to Sugihara, the knowledge produced by the Keijō Imperial University Pharmacognosy Laboratory and the Shanghai Scientific Institute was limited to kampō pharmaceuticals, and was no different from the sort of modern scientific knowledge that Westerners produce. Accordingly, the knowledge other Asians were expecting to be produced by Japanese would be new kampō medical knowledge (i.e., New Oriental Medicine) produced by establishing clinical kampō medicine research institutions. Sugihara's thesis is further developed into an assertion that the obtaining of such knowledge would be useful in securing the agreement of the Chinese masses.[59] At the time, the Korean Peninsula served as the forward operating base the dissemination of the knowledge of New Oriental Medicine.

We must create a New Oriental Medicine that combines both Eastern and Western medicine. The Korean Peninsula that is now our forward operating base for the development of the continent must also become our forward operating base for the creation of a new culture. A kampō medicine research institute is needed for this.[60]

The kind of kampō medicine research institute (or an Oriental Medicine Research Institute) proposed by Sugihara expanded to a research network initiative built not only in Korea but spanning the Chinese continent and Manchuria as well. Coordination with the East Asian Medicine Movement toward this end began when Dōmei Yakazu, one of its leading figures, gave his approval to the idea.[61]

3. Under the Spell of Western Medicine and the Expulsion of Korea

However, at this point, there arose a serious problem. While it was simple enough to talk about kampō medicine and Oriental Medicine in the same breath, these disciplines depended on many different texts, and one's perspective could vary dramatically depending on one's choice of diagnostic and therapeutic principles. Sugihara's kampō medicine research related to specific kampō medicine selected by his choice.

Kampō practitioners in Korea at present belong to the so-called Dongui Bogam (Mirror of Eastern Medicine) school, and they study this text as their
Bible. In Japan, however, kampō practitioners belong to the *On Cold Damage*
school. . . . After my many years of study of *On Cold Damage*, I believe this
literature is right on the mark, even when viewed critically from the perspective of modern medicine. . . . (The rest is omitted.)[62]

Sugihara's lumping together here of Korean kampō practitioners in the Dongui
Bogam school and Japanese kampō practitioners in the *On Cold Damage* school
ignores the respective histories of the two kampō disciplines, and imposes upon
them a fabricated tradition. Moreover, denying that there is anything worth learning from Korean traditional medicine, he extols *On Cold Damage* by claiming that
its writings, upon which kampō thought is based, rely not upon the Five Elements
Theory but upon Yin-Yang theory; therefore, its validity is ensured even if one
views it from a Western medical viewpoint.[63]

In Sugihara's kampō medicine thought, he splits the Yin-Yang/Five Elements
philosophy into separate Yin-Yang and Five Elements theories, further dividing
the former into Yin-Yang heat theory and Yin-Yang meridian flow theory, and
assesses their validity from a standpoint of Western medical authority. This is not
discussed at length in this paper, but in terms of Yin-Yang heat theory, Sugihara
believed the theory is well justified from the standpoint of Western medicine, and
indeed that Western medicine should learn from the theory of warm or heat
medicine. He then points out *On Cold Damage* as a kampō medical text is in con-
formity with Yin-Yang heat theory. According to Sugihara, Japanese kampō had
developed with *On Cold Damage* scholarship as its base, whereas kampō every-
where outside of Japan had no basis in *On Cold Damage*. Dismissing Yin-Yang
meridian flow teachings as far-fetched from a Western medical perspective and
discarding the Five Elements theory as groundless, he claims that non-Japanese
kampō medicine tends to depend solely on these scientifically baseless teachings.

In this manner, Sugihara appraised kampō medicine externally, from a Western
medical perspective. Therefore, regardless of how much understanding of kampō
medicine he revealed, his argument leads him to ask, "Shouldn't modern medical
practitioners studying kampō medicine make the choice to offer enlightened
guidance to lead other kampō practitioners to a more academically rigorous
kampō discipline?"

Accordingly, the New Oriental Medicine (i.e., combining Eastern and Western medicine), purportedly differing from Western medicine, is found to be based on Western medical standards after all. And as such, it is assumed that Japan was alone in the Orient in terms of absorbing knowledge from the West and thus qualifies for the leadership of the New Oriental Medicine. With Japanese kampō self-defined as knowledge derived from *On Cold Damage*-derived, Korean kampō medicine was banished from the New Oriental Medicine. Under this configuration, the only role left for Korean kampō practitioners was as people in need of enlightened guidance.

While Sugihara coordinated with the East Asian Medicine Movement and facilitated the enlisting of Japanese kampō medicine in Japan's imperial mission, he was nevertheless unable to come out from under the spell of Western medicine. The kampō practitioners who emerged in the Showa Period, underwent baptism in the ways of science, and joined the East Asian Medicine Movement passionately argued the case for Japanese kampō's uniqueness and constantly emphasized the differences between Japan versus China and Korea. Yet no matter how hard they tried, they were never able to escape the shadow of scientism that hung over the theoretical ropes in which they bound up the self-image of Japanese kampō.

Koreans displayed a rather disdainful attitude toward the efforts of Sugihara, Ōtsuka, and other New East Asian Medicine figures seeking to identify commonalities between Eastern and Western medicine in *On Cold Damage*. Cho Hon-yong (1900–1988), the leader of the Kampō Medicine Revival Movement in 1930s Colonial Korea, sharply criticized Japanese kampō as possessing a character representative of the aggressive aspects of *On Cold Damage*, and rejected it as Westernized kampō treatment.[64]

Section 5. Conclusion

As Nobukuni Koyasu has pointed out, "East Asia" was not initially a naturally self-evident concept of regional identity. Rather, it originated as a cultural construction imposed upon the region by Imperial Japan beginning in the 1920s. Later, as Imperial Japan pursued its China-centered Asian agenda of political, economic, military, and intellectual expansion in the region in the 1930s and 1940s, East Asia became a geopolitical term heavily laden with political meaning.[65]

Although kampō medicine lost its battle for hegemony within Japan, the door to the formation of kampō's self-image was opened by Keijūrō Wada. Wada framed kampō as causal treatment, and Nakayama hammered out a distinct identity for kampō as an academic discipline based on Yin-Yang teachings. By the end of the 1930s, kampō practitioners—under the hyper-politicized banner of "East Asia"—switched their tactics in their hegemonic struggle to encompass the entire Japanese Empire. At the time, they made loud claims regarding the potential utility of kampō medicine in the realms of mass health care and military medicine, even going so far as to claim that kampō was better suited to contribute to the expansion of the Japanese Empire than Western medicine was. In the midst of this discourse, there arose an emphatic consciousness in the profession that Japanese kampō was more scientific than Chinese traditional medicine. This was the critical formative period for the self-image of Japanese kampō that continues to exist, essentially unchanged, to this day.

In some ways, the ideas of the East Asian Medicine Movement resonated in Korea, and it was Keijō Imperial University professor Tokuyuki Sugihara who took action in line with this resonance. As a pharmacologist, Sugihara made clear his position of assessing kampō medicine from the perspective of Western medicine, and in accordance with those standards, he refused to make a place for Korean traditional medicine in his vision of a New Oriental Medicine to be based on *On Cold Damage*. This attitude found unmistakable expression at the deepest levels of the self-image of Japanese kampō.

Notes:

1) For discussion of what exactly constitutes the history of scientific thought, see: Osamu Kanamori, "Kagaku shisō shi no tetsugaku (The philosophy of the history of scientific thought)," in *Kagaku shisō shi* (History of scientific thought, Tokyo, Keiso Shobo, 2010, pp. 1–16 [Chapter 1]).

2) Kazuo Tatsuno, "Kampō to shimpi shugi (Kampō and mysticism)," *Tōa igaku* (East Asian medicine), no. 11, 1939, p. 1).

3) Yoshinori Ōtsuka, "Kagaku no senrei o hetaru kampōi o kyōsei seyo (Foster kampō practitioners who have undergone the baptism of science)," *East Asian medicine*, no. 1, 1939, p. 1.

4) For another argument for revision of the conflict between kampō and Western medicine in the early Meiji Period from an outsider perspective similar to that adopted in this essay, see: Jirō Sugiyama, "Kampō to seiyō igaku (Kampō medicine and Western medicine)," in Ei Shimosaka, Jirō Sugiyama and Kiyoshi Takada (eds.). *Kagaku minaoshi sōsho ichi: Kagaku to hikagaku no aida; kagagu to taishū* (The series of scientific review: The boundary between science and the comparative study; science and the populace), pp. 203–240. Tokyo, Bokutakusha, 1987. While focusing his analysis on the Western medi-

cine/kampō medicine thought of important figures in early Meiji Period government medical policy, Sugiyama traces the development of the discourse by which kampō was branded as quackery. This chapter focuses primarily on the discourse of kampō practitioners during the Showa Period.

5) For example, Hiroshi Kosoto's *Kampō no rekishi: Chūgoku/Nippon no dentō igaku* (The history of kampō: Traditional medicine in China and Japan, Tokyo, Taishūkan, 1999) provides a good compact overview of the history of kampō. But after touching on the founding of the Association of East Asian Medicine in 1938, he moved on to the foundation of the Japan Association of Oriental Medicine in the 1950s.

6) Terutane Yamada, "Nihon kampō igaku no denshō to keifu (Tradition and genealogy of Japanese kampō igaku)," *Nihon tōyō igaku zasshi* (Journal of Oriental medicine in Japan, vol. 46, no. 4, 1996), pp. 505–518.
Hiromichi Yasui, "Nihon kampō shogakuha no nagare (Overview of various schools of Japanese kampō igaku)," *Journal of Oriental medicine in Japan*, vol. 58, no. 2, 2007), pp. 177–202.

7) Shindō Fukagawa, *Kan'yō igaku ronsō shi: Seiji tōsō hen* (The history of controversy between Chinese and Western medicine), Tokyo, Kyūhan to Igakusha, 1934.

8) Tai Hasegawa, *Kampōi keizoku ni tsuite* (On letting kampō practitioners survive), privately published, 1893.

9) Teizō Ogawa and Shizu Sakai (eds.), *Matsumoto Jun jiden/Nagayo Sensai jiden* (Autobiography of Jun Matsumoto/Autobiography of Sensai Nagayo), Tokyo, Heibonsha, 1900, p. 148.

10) Jirō Sugiyama, "Kampō to seiyō igaku (Kampō medicine and Western medicine)," in Ei Shimosaka, Jirō Sugiyama and Kiyoshi Takada (eds.), *Kagaku minaoshi sōsho 1: Kagaku to hikagaku no aida—kagagu to taishū* (The series of scientific review: The boundary between science and the comparative study—science and the populace), 1987, pp. 224–225.

11) Terutane Yamada, "Nihon kampō igaku no denshō to keifu (Tradition and genealogy of Japanese kampō igaku)," *Nihon tōyō igaku zasshi* (Journal of Oriental medicine in Japan), vol. 46, no. 4, 1996, p. 4.

12) Hiroshi Kosoto, *Kampō no rekishi: Chūgoku/Nippon no dentō igaku* (The history of kampō: Traditional medicine in China and Japan), Tokyo, Taishūkan, 1999, p. 177.

13) Keijūrō Wada, *Zōho: Ikai no tettsui* (The iron hammer of the medical world: Augmented edition), Tokyo, Chūgoku kampō, 1974, p. 2.

14) Keijūrō Wada, Ibid., p. 12.

15) Keijūrō Wada, *Kampō to yōhō* (kampō medicine and Western medicine), privately published: 1910, p. 1.

16) Keijūrō Wada, *The iron hammer of the medical world: Augmented edition*, Tokyo, Chūgoku kampō, 1974, pp. 64–71.

17) Christian Oberlander, "The rise of scientific medicine in Japan: Beriberi the driving force in the quest for specific causes and the introduction of bacteriology (Special Issue) History of Medicine and Biology in East Asia." *Historia Scientiarum, Second series: international journal of the History of Science Society of Japan*, vol. 13, no. 3, 2004, pp. 176–199.

18) Keijūrō Wada, *Kampō medicine and Western medicine*, privately published: 1910, pp. 13–14.

19) Keijūrō Wada, *Kampō medicine and Western medicine*, privately published: 1910, pp. 11.

20) Keijūrō Wada, *Kampō medicine and Western medicine*, privately published: 1910, p. 19.

21) Keijūrō Wada, *Kampō medicine and Western medicine*, privately published: 1910, p. 10.

22) Keijūrō Wada, *Kampō medicine and Western medicine*, privately published: 1910, p. 8.

23) Hiroshi Kosoto, *The history of kampō: Traditional medicine in China and Japan*, Tokyo, Taishūkan, 1999, pp. 157–158.

24) Yasuo Ōtsuka, "Edo jidai igaku no shosō (Various aspects of medine in the Edo period)," in Shuntarō Itō and Yōichirō Murakami (eds.) *Kōza kagaku shi 4: Nihon kagaku shi no shatei* (Lectures on scientific history 4: The range capacity of Japanese science), Tokyo, Baifukan, 1989, p. 357.

25) Keijūrō Wada, *The iron hammer of the medical world: Augmented edition*, Tokyo, Chūgoku kampō, 1974, pp. 17–18.

26) Kyūshin Yumoto, *Kōkan igaku* (Sino-Japanese medicine), Tokyo, Ryōgen Shoten, 1927, foreword.

27) Kyūshin Yumoto, *Sino-Japanese medicine*, Tokyo, Ryōgen Shoten, 1927,1.

28) Kyūshin Yumoto, *Sino-Japanese medicine*, Tokyo, Ryōgen Shoten, 1927,2.

29) Yasui, Hiromichi. "Nihon kampō shogakuha no nagare (Overview of various schools of Japanese kampō igaku)," *Journal of Oriental medicine in Japan*, vol. 58, no. 2, 2007, p. 185.

30) Tadanao Nakayama, "Kampō igaku fukkō ron (An Essay on the renaissance of kampō medicine)," *Nihon oyobi Nihonjin* (Japan and Japanese), no. 109, Tokyo, Seikyōsha, 1926, p. 18.

31) Tadanao Nakayama, Ibid., p. 18.

32) Tadanao Nakayama, Ibid., p. 21.

33) Tadanao Nakayama, Ibid., p. 21–11.

34) This type of inter-school cooperation did not always go smoothly. See: Yoshinori Ōtsuka, "Showa no kampō Ikai (The world of Showa kampō)," *Kampō to Kan'yaku* (Kampō and kampō medicine), vol. 10, no. 5, 1943, pp. 1–4.

35) Terutane Yamada, "Nihon kampō igaku no denshō to keifu (Tradition and genealogy of Japanese kampō igaku)," *Journal of Oriental medicine in Japan*, vol. 46, no. 4, 1996, p. 509.

36) Dōmei Yakazu, "Tōa igaku kyōkai hakkai shiki kaikai no ji (Opening speech of the inaugural ceremony of the Association of East Asian Medicine)," *East Asian medicine*, no. 1, 1939, p. 3.

37) Yoshinori Ōtsuka, "Kagaku no senrei o hetaru kampōi o kyōsei seyo (Foster kampō practitioners who have undergone the baptism of science)," *East Asian medicine*, no. 1, 1939a, p. 1.

38) Yoshinori Ōtsuka, "Chūgoku kampō ikai no genkyō to nikka teikei ni tsuite (2) (The present situation of the world of Chinese kampō and the coalition between Japan and China [2])," *East Asian medicine*, no. 2, 1939b, p. 4.

39) Yoshinori Ōtsuka, "Kampō igaku ni okeru wa to kō to no seishin (The ethos of harmony and attach in kampō medicine)," *East Asian medicine*, no. 18, 1940, p. 1.

40) Same as note 2).

41) "Tōa igaku kyōkai no setsuritsu ni tsuite (The establishment of the Association of East Asian Medicine)," *East Asian medicine*, no. 1, 1939, p. 3.

42) Dōmei Yakazu, "Kampō no gainen to gendai teki shimei (The concepts of kampō of its contemporary missions)," *East Asian Medicine*, no. 20, 1940a, pp. 2–3.

43) Yakazu was not the first person to use the term evidence-based in a kampō treatment context. Usage of the term can be found in the journal *Kampō and Kampō Medicine* beginning in the second half of the 1930s. However, Yakazu was the first to use the term in the context of East/West comparative medicine theory discourse.

44) Dōmei Yakazu, "The concepts of kampō of its contemporary missions," *East Asian medicine*, no. 20, 1940a, p. 2.

45) Dōmei Yakazu, "Opening speech of the inaugural ceremony of the Association of East Asian Medicine," *East Asian medicine*, no. 1, 1939, p. 3.

46) Shin Chang-Geon, "Keijō teikoku daigaku ni okeru kan'yaku kenkyū no seiritsu (The establishment of the study on the kampō in Keijō Imperial University)," *Shakai to Rekishi* (Society and History), vol. 76, 2007, pp. 105–139.

47) *Chōsen Nippō*, "Minshū hoken no jūdai kekkan: Haibyō shibōsha no gekizō genjō (Serious defect in national health: Deaths from lung diseases surging)," *Chōsen Tsūshin*, May 26, 1930, p. 2.

48) While the native Korean Kampō Revivalist Movement that began in 1934 came into conflict with the Governor-General Office-instigated kampō movement, upon re-examination, significant differences can be found between the kampō medicine espoused by the two rival movements.

49) Toshikazu Kawaguchi, "Yakusō no saibai to riyō ni tsuite (Culivation and utilization of kampō medicine)," in *Keijō Keizai Kaigijo Keizai Geppō* (Seoul: Keijō Chamber of Commerce Monthly Economic Report), 1934, p. 27.

50) Army of Korea Medical Services Chief Kajitsuka visited Sugihara, offering to assist his research. (Keijō

Teikoku Daigaku Sōritsu Gojūshūnen Kinenshi Henshū Iinkai (ed.), *Kompeki haruka ni* (Deep blue in the distance), Seoul, Keijō Teikoku Daigaku Dōsōkai, 1974, pp. 60–61.

51) Same as note 16).

52) Same as note 48), 61–62.

53) JACAR (Japan Center for Asian Historical Records) Ref. A03010081300, "Keijō Teikoku Daigaku Kanseichu o Kaisei su" (Japan Center for Asian Historical Records *Kōbun ruishu* (Various *Official Records Compilations*), title: 67 (1943), vol. 32, office 26/official 26 (Government-General of Chosen), National Archives of Japan.

54) Kazuo Tatsuno, "Manshū no tabi (Travel in Manchuria)," *East Asian medicine*, no. 19, 1940, p. 7.

55) Tokuyuki Sugihara, "Chōsen ninjin ni tsuite (1) (On Ginseng [1])," *Bunkyō no Chōsen* (Educational Korea), no. 10, 1929, p. 35.

56) Tokuyuki Sugihara, "Kampō igaku sōnen ni tsuite (On the ideas of kanmpō medicine)," in Keijō Teikoku Daigaku Tairiku Bunka Kenkyūkai (eds.), *Tairiku Bunka Kenkyū* (Study of Continental Culture), Tokyo, Iwanami Shoten, 1940, p. 3.

57) Tokuyuki Sugihara, "Kampō igaku no kagakuteki kentō (A scientific consideration of kampō medicine)," *Chōsen oyobi Manshū* (Korea and Manchuria), no. 374, 1939a, p. 42.

58) Tokuyuki Sugihara, Ibid., pp. 391–392.

59) Tokuyuki Sugihara, Ibid., pp. 4–6.

60) Tokuyuki Sugihara, "Chōsen ni okeru kampō igaku to shōkanron (Kampō medicine and 'On Cold Damage' in Korea)," *Chōsen* (Korea), no. 292, 1939c, p. 30.

61) Dōmei Yakazu, "Nihon iji shinpō sha no shasetsu o kentō shi manshūkoku oyobi chūgoku no kan'i mondai ni oyobu (3) (Consideration of the Editorial of Japanese Medical Journal Extended to the Problems of Manchuria and China [3])," *East Asia medicine*, no. 20, 1940b, pp. 6–7.

62) Tokuyuki Sugihara, "Kampō medicine and 'On Cold Damage' in Korea," *Chōsen* (Korea), no. 292, 1939c, p. 31.

63) Shin Chang-Geon, "Cho hon-yong no seijiteki igaku shisō (Political thought of medicine of Cho Honyong)," *Kankokushiron 42: Kankoku Kingendai Kagaku Gijutsushi no Tenkai* (The dicussion on Korean history 42: The development of Korean thought on modern science and technology), edited by Kankoku Kokushi Hensan Iinkai, Seoul, Kankoku Kokushi Hensan Iinkai, 2005, pp. 115–152.

64) Cho Hon-yong, "漢方医学의危機를앞두고 (Future crisis of kampō critical commentary on kampō medicine)," *Kampō igaku no hihanteki kaisesu* (Critical commentary on Chinese medicine), Tokyo, Tōyō Iyakusha, 1942, pp. 132–133.

65) Nobukuni Koyasu, '*Ajia*' *wa dō katararete kitaka: Kindai nihon no orientarizumu* (How Asia has been told: Modern Japan's orientalism), Tokyo, Fujiwara Shoten, 2003.

AFTERWORD

The initial concept of this book was to discuss Japanese case examples of the history of scientific thought in contrast to the approach in *Kagaku shisō shi* (The history of scientific thought), edited by me and published only in the Japanese language by Keiso Shobo Publishing, which mainly focused on Western case examples. *The history of scientific thought* and this book are paired as Western and Japanese counterparts. I would appreciate it if those of you who read the Japanese language would also read *The history of scientific thought*. I was the only person who engaged in both projects, but they will help you to grasp how far our study of scientific history has now come.

We sought to place this book as the Japanese part of the study against the background of the Western part of the study, *The history of scientific thought*. However, we had to limit the historical scope of our examples to contain them in a single volume. Therefore, we set a precondition that this book would be mainly composed of case studies from the early Showa Period. Thus this book was titled *Showa zenki no kagaku shisō shi* (literally, "The history of scientific thought in the early Showa Period"). However, some ambiguity still remains in our limiting the scope to the "early Showa Period." It is apparent that the end of WWII in 1945 marks a great cultural turning point during the Showa Period (1926–1989). However, if one follows the history of individual sciences, their turning point may be less obvious in some subject matters or fields. Therefore, setting a period from 1926 to 1945 may have been too short in some cases. On the other hand, it is naturally reasonable to regard the period from the late 1960s as the late Showa Period. Further, in some realms we can hardly spot any discontinuity between the early Showa Period and the preceding late Meiji and Taisho Periods. Therefore, this book has principally given consideration to the cases that are related to the period from the 1920s to the early 1960s, but there is no rule without exceptions; some chapters go beyond those boundaries. Also, my Introduction does not follow the norm as it simply differs in characteristics from the other chapters.

Based on the time scope, we have covered the histories of physics, chemistry, pharmacology, and other relatively important scientific fields, trying to create a comprehensive perspective.

The following is a more specific elucidation of each essay.

Takuji Okamoto's essay (chapter 1) exceeds the timeframe of this book by mentioning the academic circle of physics from around the late Meiji Period. Especially, he regards Hantrō Nagaoka as representative of the times and emphasizes Nagaoka's academic outlook, especially his acute awareness of the problems of the contemporary Japanese physics community in the world. Then Okamoto grandly encompasses the historical course where Nagaoka's dream has been realized to some extent by world-class achievements in the theory of elementary particles as represented by Hideki Yukawa and Shinichirō Asanaga. Also, he observes calmly how the fields related to physics were forcibly incorporated into wartime science before and after the outbreak of WWII and how the people concerned struggled to deal with the situation.

As chemistry is a practical science that is closely related to industry, which makes it rather incompatible with the approach inherent in the study of scientific thought, the mainstream of the history of chemistry is more closely related to the history of industry rather than the thought of industry. In chapter 2, the author Masanori Kaji mainly discusses studies on organic chemistry with a focus on the work on Japanese lacquer by Rikō Majima and that on Taiwan cypress by Tetsuo Nozoe, based on an important historical record: Rikō Majima's journal. By adopting a non-typical approach to the chemistry of natural products, he specifically and scrupulously traces how Japan, a newcomer in terms of chemistry, tried to establish its position in the world.

Shin Chang-geon (chapter 3) tries to reveal how Kampō medicine after the Meiji Restoration came to occupy a prominent position in society by reviewing the achievements of Kampō practitioners from the late Meiji period to the first twenty years of the Showa Period. The crucial element is how Kampō attempted to establish its own existential value by struggling against or absorbing scientism, which Western medicine is thought to represent. The structural outline of the dichotomy is multilayered and nested: basic structural outlines such as "West vs East" or "China vs Japan" intertwine with branched structures including "basic medicine vs practical medicine," "Japanese Kampō vs Korean Kampō," making the situation more complex. The author also touches on an interesting topic of "science during the wartime system." In a short essay, he develops a highly concentrated discussion.

Lastly, I would like to mention the Introduction of my writing. As you would have noticed instantly, the Introduction is unusually longer than any other chapter. With regard to the time frame, the starting point is almost the same as in the other chapters—around 1920, but the end point is not 1965 but almost our own day. In short, this introduction covers the history of scientific thought in Japan throughout the twentieth century (except for the first twenty-five years) as a quick overview. In other words, it is the "history" of the history of scientific thought. However, it is a truly ultra-rapid overview at low resolution, not so much a broad historic investigation of the history of scientific history as a brief note of the Japanese books in that field. Or rather, it is a reading guide that could be titled, *Introduction to Scientific Thought*. In other words, this Introduction is my version of the "warp of history," a "story" put together and reconstructed to constitute my unique context. On the surface it may look like a biographical dictionary, but this is not the case. The constitution of the context is supported by a sense of the historical, which makes the Introduction different from an enumerative biographical dictionary in that its validity can be subject to discussion though its validity cannot be self-verified. It is true that I could not intensively discuss individual people of thought I took up, for my original purpose was not to analyze individual thinkers as I mentioned at the beginning of the Introduction. However, this ultra-rapid overview can play a role as an introductory guide for culturally-aware laypersons to enable them to become familiar with this ultra-minor area of knowledge, the history of scientific thought. Readers are kindly advised to read the endnotes, which are full of ancillary information, not just the main text. There are more than 650 books in the reference list (the number may differ according to the numeration method) If this Introduction is appropriately utilized, it will be as beneficial to readers as the individual analyses in the other chapters. In short, my objective will be accomplished if readers acquire an interest in the names of people or books they encounter for the first time and they then begin their own investigation.

Not only the Introduction but all the contents of this book are of a considerably high standard not least as reference material. Readers are encouraged to use this work as a toolbox in various ways. If it truly becomes a toolbox and younger researchers begin in-depth study in accordance with their own interest, the role of this book will have been virtually fulfilled. As an editor, I hope there will be a number of such young researchers.

*

The editing of *Episutemoroji no genzai* (Present-day epistemology, Keio University Press, 2008) was a unique opportunity that enabled me to realize how hard this kind of joint intellectual task can be and how overwhelmingly interesting. After that, I proposed several other collections of essays almost concurrently, and this book is one result of such efforts. Some of the other projects were aborted and I could not keep my word with regard to the colleagues I asked to join me. This project, like other projects, also saw several changes midway and involved some risk, but this book has finally come out as you can see (honestly, the final stage of editing was more laborious than expected). It might sound too banal to say that the publication was entirely thanks to the valuable efforts of other contributors. I have to say that I was quite a demanding and stern editor, but all of the writers I chose should have a spirit of extra tenacity to never give in to such pressure.

Let me repeat again: in a sense that the Introduction, where I glanced over the "history of the history of scientific thought" in Japan, is quite different from the other chapters in terms of characteristics, the book in its entirety may indwell strange cracks. The introductory character of my chapter seems all the more prominent because the discussions from Chapter 1 onward are all full-scale specialized treatises. Truth be told, I had intended to discuss a certain topic more professionally in another chapter. However, the "history of the history of scientific thought," which I took on as an introduction to the whole book, became unexpectedly long and I could no longer afford to write my discrete thesis. However, the Introduction should have manifested the academic tradition in which this book ought to be placed. This book is a mixture with a hidden booklet called the Introduction that leads the readers to the other chapters. The book appears to be a bulky, specialized book, but is actually a kind of introductory book to encourage the readers to make contact with a certain academic field. If you fully enjoy serious historical discussion on discrete topics after reading through my chapter and understanding the historical background, you will find yourself in the dual structure of "narrating the history" and "narrating the history of the history," which will directly lead to a glimpse of the complex manifestation of existence inherent in historical recognition.

Mr. Shōzō Miyamoto from Keiso Shobo had charge of all the editorial work of this book. We hereby express gratitude to him. Also, I would like to repeat my acknowledgment to all the contributors of this book. The routine drinking parties after the study sessions during the preliminary phase were always pleasant and inspiring. Among heavy smokers, I, being a non-smoker, always had a sore throat and sore lungs after such parties, but it is happy memory now.

This kind of task may have been too laborious and not particularly rewarding. However, all the contributors should hopefully believe that this travail is nothing for the sake of maintenance and protection of Japan's cultural standards.

In the spring of 2011
Amidst the catastrophic natural and human-made disasters,
wishing for the restoration and revitalization of our country,

Osamu Kanamori

BIBLIOGRAPHY

Introduction

*Although first editions are basically cited here, later editions are cited in cases where collected editions have been subsequently published, as information of such editions are sometimes more useful.

Abe, Makoto et al. 1942. *Nihon kagaku shi* (History of science in Japan). Shinkō dai Nihon shi (New lectures on the grand history of Japan), vol. 19. Tokyo: Yuzankaku.

Aiba, Atsushi. 2009. *Haidegā to Makurūhan* (Heidegger and McLuhan). Tokyo: Serica Shobo.

Aida, Gundayū. 1943. *Kagaku hyōron* (Science review). Tokyo: Hakusuisha.

Aikawa, Haruki. 1935. *Gijutsu ron* (Technology theory). Tokyo: Mikasa Shobo.

Amano, Kiyoshi. 1948. *Ryōshi rikigaku shi* (History of quantum mechanics). Kyoto: Nihon Kagakusha; Tokyo: Chuokoron-sha, 1973.

Aoki, Seizō. 1980. *Garirei no michi* (The way of Galileo). Tokyo: Heibonsha.

Aoki, Tamotsu. 1942. *Sensō to seimitsu kōgyō* (War and the precision machinery industry). Tokyo: Kagakushugi Kougyosha.

Aomi, Jun'ichi et al., eds. 1964. *Kagaku jidai no tetsugaku* (Philosophy in the scientific age). 3 vols. Tokyo: Baifukan.

Araki, Toshima. 1965. *Seiyō tenmongaku shi* (A history of Western astronomy). Tokyo: Kousei-sha Kouseikaku.

Asahi Shimbunsha, ed. 1962. *Nihon kagaku gijutsu shi* (Japanese history of science and technology). Tokyo: Asahi Shimbunsha.

Ayusawa, Shintarō. 1948. *Chirigaku shi no kenkyū* (A study on the history of geography). Tokyo: Ainichi Shoin.

Barrès, Maurice 1925. *Pour la haute intelligence française* (For the high intelligence of the French). Paris: Plon.

Brooke, John Hedley et al. 1974. *The Crises of Evolution. Science and Belief: From Copernicus to Darwin*, units 12–14. Milton Keynes: Open University Press.

Burtt, Edwin A. 1932. *Metaphysical Foundations of Modern Science*. New York: Humanities Press.

Butterfield, Herbert. 1949. *The Origins of Modern Science 1300–1800*. New York: Macmillan.

Canguilhem, Georges. 1983. *Études d'histoire et de philosophie des sciences* (Studies of the histories of philosophy and science). Paris: Vrin.

Collins, H. M., and Trevor Pinch. 1993. *The Golem: What Everyone Should Know about Science*. Cambridge: Cambridge University Press.

Crombie, A. C. 1952. *Augustine to Galileo: The History of Science AD 400–1650*. London: Falcon Press.

Crowther, J. G. 1941. *The Social Relations of Science*. New York: Macmillan.

Dan, Marina. 2008. *Saibou no ishi* (Intention of cells). Tokyo: NHK Publishing.

Dannemann, Friedrich. 1920–23. *Die Naturwissenschaften in ihrer Entwicklung und ihrem Zusammenhange* (The natural sciences in light of their development and connection). Leipzig: W. Engelmann.

Dessauer, Friedrich. 1933. *Philosophie der Technik. Das Problem der Realisierung* (Philosophy of technology, the problem of realization). Bonn: Cohen.

Doi, Toshitsura. 1832. *Sekka zusetsu* (Illustrations of snow flakes). Tokyo: Tsukiji Shokan Publishing, 1968.

Driesch, Hans. 1914. *The History and Theory of Vitalism*. London: Macmillan and Co.

Duhem, Pierre Maurice Marie. 1906. *Théorie physique: son objet et sa structure* (Physical theory: its object and structure). Paris: Chevalier & Rivière.

Enriquès, Federigo. 1934. *La Signification de la pensée scientifique* (The significance of scientific thought). Paris: Hermann.

Farrington, Benjamin. 1936. *Science in Antiquity*. London: Oxford University Press.

Feyerabend, Paul K. 1975. *Against Method*. London: New Left Books.

Fujigaki, Yūko. 2003. *Senmonchi to kōkyōsei* (The public ethic and the spirit of specialism). Tokyo: University of Tokyo Press.

————, ed. 2005. *Kagaku gijutsu shakai ron no gihō* (Techniques of science, technology and society). Tokyo: University of Tokyo Press.

Fujii, Hiroki. 2010. *Doitsu kagaku kyōjugaku no seiritsu ni kansuru kenkyū* (Research on the establishment of chemistry teaching in Germany). Tokyo: Kazamashobo.

Fujikawa,Yū. 1904. *Nihon igaku shi* (A history of Japanese medicine). Tokyo: Shokabo. Definitive edition, Tokyo: Nisshin Shoin, 1941.

Fujimune, Kanji. 1977. *Denki ni kaketa shōgai* (A life's devotion to electricity). Hiratsuka: Tokai University Press.

Fujioka, Yoshio. 1938. *Gendai no butsurigaku* (Modern physics). Tokyo: Iwanami Shoten.

————. 1942. *Butsurigaku nōto* (Notes on physics). 2nd edition, 2 vols, Tokyo: Kawade Shobo, 1947.

————. 1944. *Busshitsu no kyūkyoku* (The extremes of matter). Tokyo: Kawade Shobo.

————. 1964. *Kagakusha to jinsei* (Scientists and life). Tokyo: Kodansha.

Fujita, Motoharu. 1942. *Nihon chirigaku shi* (A history of Japanese geography), revised and enlarged edition. Tokyo: Toko Shoin.

Fujiwara, Sakuhei. 1926. *Kumo o tsukamu hanashi* (A story of grabbing the cloud). Tokyo: Iwanami Shoten.

————. 1929. *Kumo* (Clouds). Tokyo: Iwanami Shoten.

————. 1930. *Kishō to jinsei* (Meteorological phenomena and life). Tokyo: Tetto Shoin.

Fukase, Yasuaki. 2010. *Shōni kagaku no shiteki hensen* (The historical transition of pediatics). Kyoto: Shibunkaku Shuppan.

Fukuda, Mahito. 1995. *Kekkaku no bunka shi* (A cultural history of tuberculosis). Nagoya: The University of Nagoya Press.

Fukui, Ken'ichi. 1984. *Gakumon no sōzō* (Creation of studies). Tokyo: Kosei Shuppan.

Fukuoka, Shin'ichi. 2007. *Seibutsu to museibutsu no aida* (Between living and non-living things). Tokyo: Kodansha.

Funayama, Shin'ichi. 1935. *Gendai yuibutsu ron no tetsugaku teki igi* (The philosophical significance of contemporary materialism). Tokyo: Sobunkaku.

———. 1959. *Meiji tetsugaku shi kenkyū* (Research on the history of philosophy in the Meiji era). Kyoto: Minerva Shobo.

———. 1965. *Taisho tetsugaku shi kenkyū* (Research on the history of philosophy in the Taisho era). Kyoto: Horitsu Bunka Sha.

———. 1968. *Showa yuibutsu ron shi* (History of Materialism). 2 vols. Tokyo: Fukumura Shuppan.

Furukawa, Yasu. 1989. *Kagaku no shakai shi* (A social history of science). Tokyo: Nansosha.

Fushimi, Kōji et al. 1979. *Bi no kikagaku* (Geometry of beauty). Tokyo: Chuokoron-sha.

Gibbons, Michael and Björn Wittrock, eds. 1985. *Science as a Commodity: Threats to the Open Community of Scholars*. Harlow, UK: Longman.

Gibbons, Michael et al. eds. 1994. *The New Production of Knowledge: The Dynamics of Science and Research in Contemporary Societies*. London: Sage.

Gillispie, Charles Coulston. 1966. *The Edge of Objectivity: An Essay in the History of Scientific Ideas*. Princeton, NJ: Princeton University Press.

Gotō, Kunio. 1969. *Kagakushi gaku nyūmon* (Introduction to the study of history of science). Kyoto: Horitsu Bunka Sha.

Gotō, Kunio, and Takehiko Takabayashi. 1957. *Kōgaku shi* (History of optics). Tokyo: Oyama Shoten.

Gotō, Masatoshi. 1999. *Yuizō ron* (Organ-ism). Tokyo: Fujinsha.

Gotō, Sueo. 1946. *Kagaku to bungaku* (Science and literature). Tokyo: Hokuryukan.

Gunji, Pegiō Yukio. 2002. *Seisei suru seimei* (Life that generates). Yokohama: Tetsugakushobo.

———. 2004. *Gensei keisan to sonzairon teki kansoku* (Protocomputing and ontological measurement). Tokyo: University of Tokyo Press.

Gutting, Gary. 1989. *Michel Foucault's Archaeology of Scientific Reason*. Cambridge: Cambridge University Press.

Habu, Kazuko. 2010. *Edo jidai, kampōyaku no rekishi* (The history of herbal medicine in the Edo era). Osaka: Seibundo Shuppan.

Hanada, Keisuke, ed. 1960. *Kagakuron* (Science thoery). Kōza—Konnichi no tetsugaku (Lectures: Modern day philosophy), vol. 3. Tokyo: San-Ichi Publishing.

Hanson, N. R. 1958. *Patterns of Discovery*. Cambridge: Cambridge University Press.

Hara, Mitsuo. 1946. *Shizen benshō hō no kenkyū* (Study on the natural dialectic method). Kyoto: Taigado.

———. 1948. *Kagaku to minshu shugi* (Science and democracy). Tokyo: San-Ichi Publishing.

———. 1953. *Kagaku nyūmon* (Introduction to chemistry). Tokyo: Iwanami Shoten.

———. 1954. *Kagaku o kizuita hitobito* (The people who built chemistry). Tokyo: Chuokoron-sha.

———. 1960. *Yuibutsushi kan no genri* (The principles of the historical views on materialism). Tokyo: Aoki Shoten.

Hasegawa, Toshikazu, and Mariko Hasegawa. 2000. *Shinka to ningen kōdō* (Evolution and human behavior). Tokyo: University of Tokyo Press.

Hashida, Kunihiko. 1939. *Gyō to shite no kagaku* (Science as asceticism). Tokyo: Iwanami Shoten.

Hashimoto, Keizo et al. 1981. *Shizenkan no hensen* (The transition of the view of nature). Tokyo: Gakujutsu Tosho Shuppan-sha.

Hattori, Toshirō. 1971. *Muromachi Azuchi Momoyama jidai igaku shi no kenkyū* (Studies on medical history from the Muromachi to the Azuchi-Momoyama Period). Tokyo: Yoshikawa Kobunkan.

————. 1978. *Edo jidai igaku shi no kenkyū* (A study on the history of medicine in the Edo Period). Tokyo: Yoshikawa Kobunkan.

Hayasaka, Toshio. 1989. *Oto no rekishi* (The history of sound). Tokyo: Tokyo Joho Tsushin Gakkai (The Institute of Electronics, Information and Communication Engineers); Tokyo: Corona Publishing.

Hayashi, Takashi (Kigi, Takatarō). 1936. *Jinsei no ahō* (Life's fool). Tokyo: Chusekisha.

————. 1941. *Kagaku e no shisaku* (Contemplation on science). Tokyo: Unebi Shobo.

————. 1951. *Kagaku gairon* (Introduction to science). Tokyo: Nakayama Shoten.

Hayashi, Tatsuo, and Osamu Kuno. 1974. *Shisō no doramaturugī* (Dramaturgy of thought). Tokyo: Heibonsha.

Hayashi, Tomohiro. 2003. *Raipunittsu* (Leibniz). Tokyo: University of Tokyo Press.

Hirai, Hiro. 2005. *Le concept de semence dans les théories de la matière à la Renaissance* (The concept of seeds in the theory of materials during Renaissance). Turnhout: Brepols.

————, ed. 2010. *Mikurokosumosu* (Microcosmos), the first series. Chofu: Getsuyosha.

Hirakawa, Hideyuki. 2010. *Kagaku wa dare no mono ka* (Who does science belong to?). Tokyo: NHK Publishing.

Hiramoto, Atsushi. 2010. *Senzen nihon no erekutoronikusu* (Electronics in prewar Japan). Kyoto: Minerva Shobo.

Hirata, Morizō. 1975. *Kirin no madara* (The spots on giraffes). Tokyo: Chuokoron-sha; Tokyo: Hayakawa Publishing, 2003.

Hirata, Yutaka. 1979. *Kagaku no kōkogaku* (The archaeology of science). Tokyo: Chuokoron-sha.

Hiromatsu, Wataru. 1973. *Kagaku no kiki to ninshiki ron* (The crisis of science and epistemology). Tokyo: Kinokuniya Company.

Hiromatsu, Wataru, and Makoto Katsumori. 1986. *Sōtaisei riron no tetsugaku* (A philosophy of relativism). Tokyo: Keiso Shobo.

Hirose, Hideo. 1965. *Koperunikusu* (Copernicus). Tokyo: Maki Shoten.

Hiroshige, Tetsu. 1960. *Sengo nihon no kagaku undō* (Scientific trends in postwar Japan). Tokyo: Chuokoron-sha.

————. 1965. *Kagaku to rekishi* (Science and history). Tokyo: Misuzu Shobo.

————. 1973. *Kagaku no shakai shi* (A social history of science). Tokyo: Chuokoron-sha.

————. 1979. *Kindai kagaku saikō* (Rethinking modern science). Tokyo: Asahi Shimbunsha; Tokyo: Chikumashobo, 2008.

————. 1980. *Sōtairon no keisei* (The creation of the theory of relativity), edited by Shigeko Nishio. Tokyo: Misuzu Shobo.

————. 1981. *Genshi kōzōron shi* (History of the theory of the structure of the atom), edited by Shigeko Nishio. Tokyo: Misuzu Shobo.

Honda, Hisao. 2010. *Katachi no seibutsugaku* (The biology of shape). Tokyo: NHK Publishing.

Honda, Shūrō. 1955. *Kagaku shisō shi gaisetsu* (Outline of the history of scientific thought). Tokyo: Asakura Publishing.

————. 1955. *Shizen kagaku shisō shi* (The history of thought on natural science). Tokyo: Sobunsha.

Hooykaas, R. et al. 1974. *The 'Conflict Thesis' and Cosmology*. Science and Belief: From Copernicus to Darwin, units 1–3. Milton Keynes: Open University Press.

Hoshino, Yoshirō, ed. 1971. *Kagaku gijutsu no shisō* (Thoughts of science and technology) in *Sengo nihon shisō taikei* (Series on postwar Japanese thought). Tokyo: Chikumashobo.

————, ed. 1975. *Sensō to gijutsu* (War and technology). Kyoto: Yukonsha.

————. 1948. *Gijutsu ron nōto* (Notes on technology theory). Tokyo: Shinzenbisha.

————. 1969. *Gijutsu kakushin no kompon mondai* (The fundamental problems of technological innovation), 2nd edition. Tokyo: Keiso Shobo.

————. 1972. *Han kōgai no ronri* (The logic of antipollution). Tokyo: Keiso Shobo.

————. 1993. *Gijutsu to seiji* (Technology and politics). Tokyo: Nippon Hyoron Sha.

Ienaga, Saburō. 1974. *Tanabe Hajime no shisō shi teki kenkyū* (A historical study on Hajime Tanabe's thought). Tokyo: Hosei University Press.

Iida, Ken'ichi. 1989. *Kagaku to gijutsu* (Science and technology). Nihon kindai shisō taikei (Series on Japanese modern thought), vol. 14. Tokyo: Iwanami Shoten.

Iida, Takashi, ed. 2007. *Tetsugaku no rekishi* (History of philosophy), vol. 11. Tokyo: Chuokoron Shinsha.

Ijiri, Shōji. 1977. *Shimpan kagaku ron* (Science studies: A new edition). Tokyo: Otsuki Shoten.

————. 1981–83. *Ijiri Shōji senshū* (Selected works of Shōji Ijiri). 10 vols. Tokyo: Otsuki Shoten.

Ikeda, Kiyohiko. 1988. *Kōzōshugi seibutsugaku to wa nanika* (What is structuralist biology?). Tokyo: Kaimeisha.

————. 1989. *Kōzōshugi to shinka ron* (Structuralism and evolution). Tokyo: Kaimeisha.

————. 1990. *Kōzōshugi kagaku ron no bōken (Adventures of structuralist scientific theory)*. Tokyo: Mainichi Newspapers.

————. 1992. *Bunrui to iu shisō* (The thought of classification). Tokyo: Shinchosha.

————. 1998. *Tadashiku ikiru to wa dō iu koto ka* (What does it mean to live properly?). Tokyo: Shinchosha.

————. 2002. *Seimei no keishiki* (The form of life). Yokohama: Tetsugakushobo.

————. 2011. *'Shinka ron' o kakikaeru* (Rewriting 'the theory of evolution'). Tokyo: Shinchosha.

Ikegami, Takashi. 2007. *Ugoki ga seimei o tsukuru* (Movement creates life). Tokyo: Seidosha.

Ikeuchi, Satoru. 1992. *Gendai uchūron o yomu* (Reading the modern cosmology). Sapporo: Hokkaido University Tosho Kankokai.

————. 2001a. *Kagaku wa ima dō natte iru no?* (What has become of science?). Tokyo: Shobunsha.

————. 2001b. *Tenmongaku to bungaku no aida* (Between astronomy and literature). Tokyo: Kosaido Publishing.

————. 2005. *Terada Torahiko to gendai* (Torahiko Terada and the modern times). Tokyo: Misuzu Shobo.

————. 2011. *Kansokuteki uchū ron e no shōtai* (Invitation to observational cosmology). Tokyo: Nikkei Business Publications.

Imada, Takechiyo. 1949. *Kagaku gairon* (Introduction to science). Tokyo: Seki Shoin.

Imai, Ryūkichi. 1968. *Kagaku to kokka* (Science and nation). Tokyo: Chuokoron-sha.

Inoue, Kiyotsune. 1968. *Igaku shi gaisetsu* (An introduction to the history of medicine). Enlarged and revised edition, Tokyo: Uchida Rokakuho Shinsha, 1971.

———. 1984. *Igaku shi gaisetsu* (An introduction to the history of medicine), 3rd enlarged and revised edition. Tokyo: Uchida Rokakuho Shinsha.

Inoue, Shōshichi, and Michio Kobayashi, eds. 1988. *Shizen kan no tenkai to keijijōgaku* (Evolution of the view of nature and metaphysics). Tokyo: Kinokuniya Company.

Inoue, Takeshi, ed. 1964. *Kagaku no shisō* (Scientific thought) 1&2. Gendai Nihon shisō taikei (Series on contemporary Japanese thought), vols. 25 and 26. Tokyo: Chikumashobo.

Irie, Jūkichi. 2010. *Dāuin to shinka shisō* (Charles Darwin and evolutionary thought). Kyoto: Showado.

Ishii, Atsushi. 1981. *Seishin igaku shippei shi* (The history of psychiatric disease). Tokyo: Kongo Shuppan.

Ishii, Etsurō. 1931. *Kagaku gairon* (Introduction to science). Tokyo: Koseikaku Shoten.

Ishii, Tomoyuki. 1937. *Kagaku seisaku ron* (Theory on science policy). Tokyo: Jichosha.

———. 1947. *Seibutsu gaku to yuibutsu benshō hō* (Biology and dialectical materialism). Tokyo: Shoko Shoin.

———. 1948. *Atarashii seimei ron no tame ni* (For a new theory of life). Tokyo: Doyusha.

Ishiwara, Jun. 1924. *Gendai no shizen kagaku* (Modern natural science). Tokyo: Iwanami Shoten.

———. 1925. *Kagaku no kompon mondai* (The fundamental problems of science). Tokyo: Kogakukai.

———. 1933. *Butsurigaku shi gaikan* (Overview of the history of physics). Tokyo: Iwanami Shoten.

———. 1938a. *Kagaku to shisō* (Science and thought). Tokyo: Kawade Shobo.

———. 1938b. *Shizen kagaku-teki sekai zō* (Image of the world of natural science). Tokyo: Iwanami Shoten.

Iso, Naomichi. 1993. *Kagaku shisō shi nyūmon* (Introduction to the history of scientific thought). Tokyo: Tokyo Kyogakusha.

Itakura, Kiyonobu. 1968. *Nihon rika kyōiku shi* (History of science education in Japan). Tokyo: Dai-ichi Hoki Shuppan.

———. 1969. *Kagaku to hōhō* (Science and methodology). Tokyo: Kisetusha.

———. 1971a. *Kagaku to kasetsu* (Science and hypotheses). Tokyo: Kisetusha.

———. 1971b. *Kagaku to shakai* (Science and society). Tokyo: Kisetusha.

———. 1973. *Kagaku no keisei to ronri* (Formation of science and theory). Tokyo: Kisetusha.

———. 1988. *Mohō no jidai* (The period of imitation). Upper and lower volumes. Tokyo: Kisetusha.

Itō, Shuntarō. 1976. *Bunmei ni okeru kagaku* (Science in civilizations). Tokyo: Keiso Shobo.

———. 1978. *Kindai kagaku no genryū* (Source of modern science). Tokyo: Chuokoron-sha

———. 1981. *Kagaku to genjitsu* (Science and reality). Tokyo: Chuokoron-sha.

———. 2008–10. *Itō Shuntarō chosaku shū* (The collected works of Shuntarō Itō). 12 vols. Kashiwa: Reitaku University Press.

Itō, Shuntarō et al., eds. 1980–89. *Kagaku no meicho* (Fine books on science). 20 vols. + separate volume. Tokyo: Asahi Shimbunsha.

Itō, Shuntarō, and Yōichiro Murakami, eds. 1989a. *Shakai kara yomu kagaku shi* (The history of science read from society). Tokyo: Baifukan.

—————, eds. 1989b. *Nihon kagakushi no shatei* (The range of Japanese science history). Tokyo: Baifukan.

Itō, Shuntarō, Kōkichi Hara, and Tamotsu Murata. 1975. *Sūgaku shi* (History of mathematics). Tokyo: Chikumashobo.

Itō, Shuntarō, Tetsu Hiroshige, and Yōichiro Murakami. 2002. *Shisōshi no naka no kagaku* (Science in the history of thought), newly rev. ed. Tokyo: Heibonsha.

Itō, Tokunosuke. 1931. *Gendai shizen kagaku mondai* (The problems of modern natural science). Tetsugaku kōza (Lectures on philosophy), vol. 7. Tokyo: Seibundo.

Iwasaki, Chikatsugu. 1971. *Nihon Marukusu shugi tetsugaku shi josetsu* (Introduction to the Japanese history of Marxist philosophy). Tokyo: Mirai-sha Publishers.

Iwatsuki, Toranosuke and Ichirō Watanabe. 1945. *Nihon kagaku dō* (The Japanese way of science). Tokyo: Meguro Shoten.

Kajihara, Hiroki. 1994. *Igaku shi gaikan* (Introduction to the history of medicine). Tokyo: Roppo Shuppansha.

Kakehashi, Akihide. 1934. *Busshitsu no tetsugaku-teki gainen* (The philosophical concept of substances). Kyoto: Seikei Shoin.

—————. 1949. *Sengo seishin no tankyū* (In search of postwar spirit). Tokyo: Rironsha.

Kamatani, Chikayoshi. 1989. *Nihon kindai kagaku kōgyō no seiritsu* (*The establishment of Japanese modern chemical industry*). Tokyo: Asakura Publishing.

Kanamori, Osamu. 1994. *Furansu kagaku ninshiki ron no keifu* (The genealogy of French epistemology of science). Tokyo: Keiso Shobo.

—————. 2000a. *Saiensu wōzu* (Science wars). Tokyo: University of Tokyo Press.

—————. 2003. *Fu no seimeiron* (Archaeology of negative knowledge). Tokyo: Keiso Shobo.

—————. 2004a. *Shizen shugi no rinkai* (Naturalism and its discontents). Tokyo: Keiso Shobo.

—————. 2004b. *Kagakuteki shikō no kōkogaku* (An archeology of scientific thought). Kyoto: Jimbun Shoin.

—————, ed. 2008. *Episutemorojī no genzai* (The present situation of epistemology). Tokyo: Keio University Press.

—————. 2009. *Nichijō sekai to keiken kagaku* (*Daily life and experience science*). Vol. 3 of *Terada Torahiko zenshū* (The complete works of Torahiko Terada), *Monthly report 3, 1-5*. Tokyo: Iwanami Shoten.

—————. 2010a. *"Seiseiji" no tetsugaku* (The philosophy of biopolitics). Kyoto: Minerva Shobo.

Kanamori, Osamu, and Hideto Nakajima, eds. 2004. *Kagaku ron no genzai* (The present situation of science studies). Tokyo: Keiso Shobo.

Kanamori, Osamu, and Hiroyuki Iyama. 2000b. *Gendai kagaku ron* (Modern scientific theory). Tokyo: Shin-yo-sha.

—————, ed. 2010b. *Kagaku shisō shi* (History of scientific thought). Tokyo: Keiso Shobo.

Kaneko, Kunihiko. 2006. *Life: An Introduction to Complex Systems Biology*. Berlin: Springer.

Kaneko, Tsutomu. 1981. *Ainshutain shokku* (The Einstein shock). 2 vols. Tokyo: Kawade Shobo Shinsha.

—————. 1986. *Shikō jikken to wa nanika* (What is a thought experiment?). Tokyo: Kodansha.

—————. 2005. *Edo jinbutsu kagaku shi* (History of scientists of the Edo Period). Tokyo: Chuokoron Shinsha.

Kasahara, Kenkichi, and Mitsuo Sugiura, eds. 1998. *Nijusseiki no sūgaku* (Mathematics in the 20th century). Tokyo: Nippon Hyoron Sha.

Kashiwagi, Hajime (Sonogami, Shizuo). 1949. *Yuibutsu ron keisei no kagaku shi teki haikei* (Chemical historical background to the formation of the materialist thesis). Kyoto: Hakuto Shokan.

————, ed. 1984. *Kagaku shi nyūmon* (Introduction to the history of science). Tokyo: Uchida Rokakuho.

Katō, Fumiharu. 2007. *Sūgaku suru seishin* (The spirit to do mathematics). Tokyo: Chuokoron Shinsha.

————. 2009. *Monogatari: Sūgaku no rekishi* (A narrative account: the history of mathematics). Tokyo: Chuokoron Shinsha.

Katō, Hisatake and Juichi Matsuyama, eds. 1999. *Kagaku gijutsu no yukue* (The future of science and technology). Kyoto: Minerva Shobo.

Kawade, Yoshimi. 2006. *Seibutsu kigō ron* (Biosemiotics). Kyoto: Kyoto University Press.

Kawagoe, Osamu, and Akihito Suzuki, eds. 2008. *Bunbetsu sareru seimei* (Classifying human life). Tokyo: Hosei University Press.

Kawahara, Hideki. 2010. *Chōsen sūgaku shi* (History of mathematics in Korea). Tokyo: University of Tokyo Press.

Kawakami, Shin'ichi. 1995. *Shima shima gaku* (A study of stripes). Tokyo: University of Tokyo Press.

Kawakami, Takeshi. 1965. *Gendai Nihon iryō shi* (Modern history of medicine in Japan). Tokyo: Keiso Shobo.

————. 1982. *Gendai Nihon byōnin shi* (A modern history of illness in Japan). Tokyo: Keiso Shobo.

Kawakami, Takeshi, and Fumiko Kosaka. 1992. *Sengo iryō shi josetsu* (Introduction to the history of postwar medicine). Tokyo: Keiso Shobo.

Kawakami, Tamejirō. 1931. *Shika igaku shi* (The history of dental medicine). Tokyo: Kanehara Shoten; Tokyo: Kagaku Shoin, 1988.

Kawakami, Tetsutarō, and Yoshimi Takeuchi. 1979. *Kindai no chōkoku* (Overcoming modernity). Tokyo: Fuzambo.

Kawakita, Yoshio. 1964. *Kansen ron* (On infection). Tokyo: Iwanami Shoten.

————. 1967. *Pasutūru* (Pasteur). Tokyo: Iwanami Shoten.

————. 1977. *Kindai igaku no shiteki kiban* (The historical basis of modern medicine). Upper and lower volumes. Tokyo: Iwanami Shoten.

————. 1982. *Igaku gairon* (An introduction to medicine). Tokyo: Shinko Trading, Publication Department of Medical Books.

Kawakita, Yoshio, and Chikara Sasaki. 1992. *Igaku shi to sūgaku shi no taiwa* (Conversation between the history of medicine and the history of mathematics). Tokyo: Chuokoron-sha.

Kawamoto, Hideo. 1995. *Ōtopoiēshisu* (Autopoiesis). Tokyo: Seidosha.

————. 2000a. *Ōtopoiēshisu no kakuchō* (Extension of autopoiesis). Tokyo: Seidosha.

————. 2000b. *Ōtopoiēshisu 2001* (Autopoiesis). Tokyo: Shin-yo-sha.

————. 2002. *Metamorufōze* (Metamorphose). Tokyo: Seidosha.

————. 2006. *Shisutemu genshōgaku* (Phenomenology of systems). Tokyo: Shin-yo-sha.

————. 2007. *Tetsugaku, nō o yusaburu* (Philosophy shakes up the brain). Tokyo: Nikkei Business Publications.

Kida, Gen, and Kazuo Kenmi. 2010. *Seishin no tetsugaku, nikutai no tetsugaku* (Philosophy of the mind, philophy of the body). Tokyo: Kodansha.

Kihara, Hiroji. 1982. *Seimei to busshitsu* (Life and matter). Hiratsuka: Tokai University Press.

Kihatara, Tarō. 1979. *Bunshi to uchū* (Molecules and the universe). Tokyo: Iwanami Shoten.

Kihira, Tadayoshi. 1937. *Nihon seishin to shizen kagaku* (The Japanese spirit and natural science). Tokyo: Nihon Shuppan Bunka Kyokai.

————. 1938. *Chi to gyō* (*Knowledge and action*). Tokyo: Koubundou.

Kimura, Bin. 1981. *Jiko, aida, jikan* (Self, space, time). Tokyo: Koubundou.

————. 1982. *Jikan to jiko* (Time and the the self). Tokyo: Chuokoron-sha.

————. 2001. *Kimura Bin chosakushū* (The collected works of Bin Kimura). 8 vols. Tokyo: Koubundou.

Kimura, Daiji, and Kōichi Kitanishi, eds. 2010. *Morisumi no seitai shi* (The life of people living in forests). Kyoto: Kyoto University Press.

Kimura, Shigemitsu, ed. 2010. *Nihon nōgyōshi* (History of agriculture in Japan). Tokyo: Yoshikawa Kobunkan.

Kimura, Yōjirō. 1981. *Shīboruto to Nihon no shokubutsu* (Siebold and Japanese plants). Tokyo: Kowa Shuppan.

————. 1983. *Nachurarisuto no keifu* (The genealogy of naturalists). Tokyo: Chuokoron-sha.

————. 1987. *Seibutsugaku shi ronshū* (A collection of theses on the history of biology). Tokyo: Yasaka Shobo.

Kito, Shūichi, and Mayumi Fukunaga, eds. 2009. *Kankyō rinrigaku* (Environmental Ethics). Tokyo: University of Tokyo Press.

Kobayashi, Hideo. 1952. *Chishitsugaku shi* (A history of geology). Kyoto: Minshushugi Kagakusha Kyokai Chigaku Dantai Kenkyu Bukai (Association for the Geological Collaboration of the Democratic Scientists Association).

Kobayashi, Michio. 1996. *Dekaruto no shizen tetsugaku* (Descartes' natural philosophy). Tokyo: Iwanami Shoten.

Kobayashi, Tadashi. 2005. *Dare ga kagaku gijutsu ni tsuite kangaeru no ka* (Who thinks about science and technology?). Nagoya: The University of Nagoya Press.

————. 2007. *Toransu saiensu no jidai* (The age of trans-science). Tokyo: NTT Publishing.

Kobori, Akira. 1956. *Sūgaku shi* (History of mathematics). Tokyo: Asakura Publishing.

————, ed. 1957. *Jūhasseiki no shizen kagaku* (Natural science in the 18th century). Tokyo: Kouseisha Kouseikaku.

Koizumi, Makoto et al., eds. 1938. *Ningen no tetsugaku teki kōsatsu* (Philosophical observations of humans). Tokyo: Risosha.

Komatsu, Yoshihiko. 1996. *Shi wa kyōmei suru* (Death resonates). Tokyo: Keiso Shobo.

————. 2004. *Nōshi/zōki ishoku no hontō no hanashi* (Honest talk about brain death and organ transplants). Kyoto: PHP Institute.

Komatsu, Yoshihiko, and Chiaki Kagawa, eds. 2010. *Metabaioeshikkusu no kōchiku* (The building of metabioethics). Tokyo: NTT Publishing.

Kondō, Yōitsu. 1946. *Kikagaku shisō shi* (The history of geometric thought). Vol. 1 of *Kondō Yōitsu sūgaku shi chosakushū* (The collected works of Yōitsu Kondō on the history of mathematics). Tokyo: Ito Shoten; Tokyo: Nippon Hyoron Sha, 1994.

————. 1947. *Sūgaku shisō shi josetsu* (An Introduction to the history of mathematical thought). Vol. 2 of *Kondō Yōitsu sūgaku shi chosakushū* (The collected works of Yōitsu Kondō on the history of mathematics). Tokyo: San-Ichi Publishing; Tokyo: Nippon Hyoron Sha, 1994.

————. 1948. *Kindai sūgaku shi ron* (On the modern history of mathematics). Tokyo: Hakuto Shokan.

————. 1952. *Shotō sūgaku no rekishi* (History of elemental mathematics). Tokyo: Iwasaki Shoten.

————. 1959b. *Dekaruto no shizen zō* (Descartes's image of nature). Vol. 4 of *Kondō Yōitsu sūgaku shi chosakushū* (The collected works of Yōitsu Kondō on the history of mathematics). Tokyo: Iwanami Shoten; Tokyo: Nippon Hyoron Sha, 1994.

————. 1977. *Sūgaku no tanjō* (The birth of mathematics). Kyoto: Gendai-Sugakusha.

————. 1994. *Kondō Yōitsu sūgaku shi chosakushū* (The collected works of Yōitsu Kondō on the history of mathematics), edited by Chikara Sasaki. 5 vols. Tokyo: Nippon Hyoron Sha.

Kondō, Yōitsu, and Kaichirō Fujiwara. 1959a. *Kagaku shisō shi* (History of scientific thought). Tokyo: Aoki Shoten.

Konishi, Eiichi. 1923. *Kagaku shisō shi: Kagaku hen* (History of scientific thought: Chemistry) Tokyo: Shinkosha.

Konno, Takeo. 1935. *Sūgaku ron* (On mathematics). Tokyo: Mikasa Shobo.

————. 1948. *Kagaku shisō shi* (History of scientific thought). Tokyo: Purebusu-sha.

Kōra, Takehisa. 1988. *Kōra Takehisa chosakushū* (The collected works of Takehisa Kōra). Vol. 3, *Shiteki seishin igaku shi* (A personal history of psychiatric medicine). Tokyo: Hakuyosha.

Koyama, Keiichi. 1937. *Sūri tetsugaku* (Mathematical philosophy). Tokyo: Monasu.

————. 1946. *Sūgaku no tetsugaku* (The philosophy of mathematics). Tokyo: Musashino Shuppansha.

Koyanagi, Kimiyo. 1992. *Pasukaru: Chokkan kara dantei made* (Pascal: From instinct to assertion). Nagoya: The University of Nagoya Press.

Koyré, Alexandre. 1957. *From the Closed World to the Infinite Universe*. Baltimore, Maryland: The Johns Hopkins University Press.

Kozai, Yoshishige. 1937. *Gendai tetsugaku* (Contemporary philosophy). Tokyo: Mikasa Shobo.

Kubo, Masaji. 1949–50. *Kagaku shi* (A history of chemistry). 2 vols. Tokyo: Hakusuisha.

Kuhn, Thomas S. 1957. *The Copernican Revolution: Planetary Astronomy in the Development of Western Thought*, Cambridge: Harvard University Press.

————. 1962. *The Structure of Scientific Revolutions*. Chicago: University of Chicago Press.

Kuki, Shūzō. 1935. *Gūzen sei no mondai* (The problem of contingency). Tokyo: Iwanami Shoten.

Kurahashi, Shigefumi. 1983. *Kagaku shakaigaku* (Science sociology). Kyoto: Koyo Shobo.

Kusakabe, Shirōta. 1919. *Butsurigaku hanron* (Introduction to physics), rev. ed. Upper and lower volumes. Tokyo: Shokabo.

————. 1925. *Butsurigaku taikan* (Outlines of modern physics), rev. ed. Tokyo: Shokabo.

Kuwaki, Ayao. 1922. *Butsuri gaku to ninshiki* (Physics and epistemology). Tokyo: Kaizosha.

————. 1944. *Kagaku shi kō* (Reflections on the history of science). Tokyo: Kawade Shobo.

Kuwaki, Gen'yoku. 1925. *Kagaku ni okeru tetsugaku teki hōhō* (Philosophical methods in science). Tokyo: Iwanami Shoten.

Latour, Bruno. 1987. *Science in Action: How to Follow Scientists and Engineers through Society.* Cambridge, Massachusetts: Harvard University Press.

Mabuchi, Kōichi. 1999. *Nihon no kindai gijutsu ha kōshite umareta* (How modern technology was born in Japan). Machida: Tamagawa University Press.

Maeda, Takakazu. 1944. *Nihon kagaku ron josetsu* (Introduction to debates on a Japanese science). Tokyo: Ikuei Shuppan.

Maruyama, Kei. 2002. *Seimei to wa nanika* (What is Life?), new edition. Tokyo: Tokyo Kyogakusha.

Matsui, Takafumi. 1989. *Wareware wa doko e iku no ka?* (Where are we going?). Tokyo: Tokuma Shoten.

————. 1995. *Chikyū rinri e* (Towards a global ethics). Tokyo: Iwanami Shoten.

————. 2003. *Uchū jin to shite no ikikata* (How to live as aliens). Tokyo: Iwanami Shoten.

————. 2009. *Uchūshi* (Cosmography). Tokyo: Iwanami Shoten.

Matsumae, Shigeyoshi. 1941. *Tōa gijutsu taisei ron* (On an East Asian technology system). Tokyo: Kagakushugi Kogyosha.

————. 1943. *Senji seisan ron* (A theory of production during wartime). Tokyo: Obunsha.

Matsumoto, Miwao. 2009. *Tekunosaiensu risuku to shakaigaku* (The social risks of technoscience). Tokyo: University of Tokyo Press.

Matsumoto, Shunkichi, ed. 2010. *Shinka wa naze tetsugaku no mondai ni narunoka* (Why does evolution matter to philosophy?). Tokyo: Keiso Shobo.

Matsuno, Yoshimatsu. 1943. *Kagaku shisō shi* (History of thought on chemistry). Tokyo: Sanseido.

Matsuyama, Juichi. 1997. *Nyūton to Kanto* (Newton and Kant). Kyoto: Koyo Shobo.

Miki, Kiyoshi. 1939. *Kōsō ryoku no ronri* (The logic of design power), no. 1. Tokyo: Iwanami Shoten. Vol. 8 of *Miki Kiyoshi zenshū* (The complete works of Kiyoshi Miki). Tokyo: Iwanami Shoten, 1967.

————. 1942. *Gijutsu tetsugaku* (Philosophy of technology). Tokyo: Iwanami Shoten. Vol. 7 of *Miki Kiyoshi zenshū* (The complete works of Kiyoshi Miki). Tokyo: Iwanami Shoten, 1967.

Miki, Sakae. 1955. *Chōsen igakushi oyobi shippei shi* (The history of medicine and diseases in Korea). Osaka: Miki Sakae; Tokyo: Ishiyaku Shuppan, 1972.

Miki, Shigeo. 1982. *Naizō no hataraki to kodomo no kokoro* (The functions of organs and the heart of a child). Newly bound enlarged edition, Tokyo: Tsukiji Shokan Publishing, 1995.

————. 1983. *Taiji no sekai* (The embryonic world). Tokyo: Chuokoron-sha.

————. 1989. *Seimei keitai no shizen shi* (A natural history of life forms). Tokyo: Ubusuna Shoin.

Mita, Hiroo. 1948. *Sūgaku shi no hōhōron: sūgaku no tetsugaku no tame ni* (Methodology of the history of mathematics: for the sake of mathematical philosophy). Tokyo: San-Ichi Publishing.

————. 1973. *Yama no shisō shi* (The history of thought on mountains). Tokyo: Iwanami Shoten.

Miyagawa, Yūichirō. 1986. *Shizen kagaku gairon* (Introduction to natural science), 2nd edition. Tokyo: Morikita Publishing.

Miyake, Gōichi. 1940. *Gaku no keisei to shizen-teki sekai* (The formation of scholarship and the natural world). Tokyo: Koubundou; Tokyo: Misuzu Shobo, 1973.

————. 1947. *Sūri tetsugaku shisō shi* (The history of thought on mathematics and philosophy). Tokyo: Koubundou.

Miyake, Nakako. 2003. *Sōzō to kyōsei* (Creation and symbiosis). Tokyo: Nansosha.

Miyamoto, Takenosuke. 1940. *Gendai gijutsu no kadai* (The challenges of modern technology). Tokyo: Iwanami Shoten.

————. 1941. *Kagaku no dōin* (Mobilization of science). Tokyo: Kaizosha.

Mizuno, Tadafumi. 1967. *Taiiku shisō shi josetsu* (Introduction to the history of gymnastic thought). Tokyo: Sekai Shyoin.

Mogi, Ken'ichirō. 2004. *Nō to kasō* (The brain and imagination). Tokyo: Shinchosha.

————. 2010. *Seimei to gūyūsei* (A life and contingency). Tokyo: Shinchosha.

Morioka, Masahiro. 2001. *Seimeigaku ni nani ga dekiru ka* (What can life studies do?). Tokyo: Keiso Shobo.

————. 2003. *Mutsū bunmei ron* (Painless civilization). Tokyo: Transview.

Murakami, Shūji. 1943. *Mizu no seikatsu kagaku* (Daily life science of water). Tokyo: Kashiwa Shoin.

Murakami, Yōichirō. 1968. *Nihon kindai kagaku no ayumi* (The advancement of Japanese modern science). Tokyo: Sanseido.

————. 1971. *Seiō kindai kagaku* (Modern science in the West). Tokyo: Shin-yo-sha.

————. 1974. *Kindai kagaku o koete* (Beyond modern science). Tokyo: Nihon Keizai Shimbunsha.

————. 1976. *Kindai kagaku to seizoku kakumei* (Modern science and the revolution of the sacred and the profane). New edition, Tokyo: Shin-yo-sha, 2002.

————. 1979a. *Atarashii kagaku ron* (The new theory of science). Tokyo: Kodansha.

————. 1979b. *Kagaku to nichijōsei no bunmyaku* (The context of science and the quotidian). Tokyo: Kaimeisha.

————, ed. 1979–82. *Chi no kakumei shi* (A history of revolutions in knowledge). 7 vols (only 5 volumes have been published). Tokyo: Asakura Publishing.

————. 1980a. *Nihonjin to kindai kagaku* (The Japanese and modern science). Tokyo: Shin-yo-sha.

————. 1980b. *Kagaku no dainamikkusu* (The dynamics of science). Tokyo: Saiensu-sha.

————. 1982. *Kagaku shi no gyaku enkinhō* (The inverted perspective of the history of science). Tokyo: Chuokoron-sha.

————. 1983. *Rekishi to shite no kagaku* (Science in a historical context). Tokyo: Chikumashobo.

————. 1994a. *Bunmei no naka no kagaku* (Science within civilization). Tokyo: Seidosha.

————. 1994b. *Kagakusha to wa nanika* (What is a scientist?). Tokyo: Shinchosha.

————. 1998. *Anzen gaku* (Safety science). Tokyo: Seidosha.

————. 2006. *Kōgaku no rekishi to gijutsu no rinri* (History of engineering and the ethics of technology). Tokyo: Iwanami Shoten.

Murata, Jun'ichi. 2006a. *Gijutsu no rinrigaku* (An ethical study of technology). Tokyo: Maruzen.

————, ed. 2006b. *Kyōsei no tame no gijutsu tetsugaku* (A philosophy of technology for coexistence). Tokyo: Mirai-sha Publishers.

————. 2009. *Gijutsu no tetsugaku* (A philosophy of technology). Tokyo: Iwanami Shoten.

Murata, Tamotsu. 1981. *Nihon no sūgaku seiyō no sūgaku* (Mathematics in Japan, mathematics in Western countries). Tokyo: Chuokoron-sha.

Nagai, Hiroshi. 1955. *Kindai kagaku tetsugaku no keisei* (The formation of modern philosophy of science). Tokyo: Sobunsha.

—. 1961. *Sūri no sonzai ron teki kiso* (The ontological basis of mathematics). Tokyo: Sobunsha.

—. 1963. *Gendai shizen tetsugaku no kenkyū* (A study on contemporary natural philosophy). Tokyo: Sobunsha.

—. 1966. *Kagaku gairon* (Introduction to science). Tokyo: Sobunsha.

—. 1973. *Seimei ron no tetsugaku teki kiso* (The philosophical basis of the theory on life). Tokyo: Iwanami Shoten.

Nagai, Hisomu. 1908, 1922. *Igaku to tetsugaku* (Medicine and philosophy). Tokyo: Tohodo; revised edition, Tokyo: Rakuyodo.

—. 1913. *Seimei ron* (An essay on life). Tokyo: Rakuyodo.

—. 1916. *Seibutsu gaku to tetsugaku to no sakai* (Between biology and philosophy). Tokyo: Rakuyodo.

—. 1929. *Arisutoterēsu yori Nyūton made* (From Aristotle to Newton). Tokyo: Shunjusha.

Nagano, Kei. 1975. *Seibutsugaku no kishu tachi* (The leading figures of biology). Tokyo: Asahi Shimbunsha.

—. 1993. *Hen'yō suru seibutsugaku* (Transforming biology). Tokyo: Seidosha.

Nagata, Hiroshi. 1935. *Gendai yuibutsu ron* (Contemporary debates on materialism). Tokyo: Mikasa Shobo.

—. 1936. *Nihon yuibutsu ron shi* (History of Japanese debates on materialism). Tokyo: Hakuyosha.

Nakagawa, Yonezō. 1964. *Igaku no bemmei* (A Justification of medicine). Tokyo: Seishin Shobo.

—. 1975. *Iryō teki ninshiki no tankyū* (An exploration into medical epistemology), augmented and renamed edition. Tokyo: Iryo Tosho Shuppansha.

—. 1976. *Kenkō no shisō* (The ideology of health). Tokyo: Ushio Publishing.

—. 1977. *I no rinri* (Medical ethics). Machida: Tamagawa University Press.

—. 1983. *Igaku tono tsukiaikata* (Human relationships with medical science). Kyoto: Jimbun Shoin.

—. 1996. *Igaku no fukakujitsusei* (The uncertainties of medicine). Tokyo: Nippon Hyoron Sha.

Nakai, Hisao. 1999. *Seiō seishin igaku haikei shi* (The historical background of Western psychiatric medicine). Tokyo: Misuzu Shobo.

Nakamura, Keiko. 1989. *Seimei kagaku to ningen* (Life science and human beings). Tokyo: NHK Publishing.

—. 1991. *Seimei kagaku kara seimei shi e* (From life science to biohistory). Tokyo: Shogakukan.

—. 1993. *Jiko sōshutsu suru seimei* (Self-creating life). Yokohama: Tetsugakushobo.

Nakamura, Kōshiro. 1980. *Kinsei sūgaku no rekishi* (History of modern mathematics). Tokyo: Nippon Hyoron Sha.

Nakamura, Teiri. 1970. *Seibutsugaku to shakai* (Biology and society). Tokyo: Misuzu Shobo.

—. 1976. *Kiki ni tatsu kagakusha* (Scientists on the edge of danger). Tokyo: Kawade Shobo Shinsha.

————. 1983. *Seibutsugaku no rekishi* (A history of biology), newly bound edition. Tokyo: Kawade Shobo Shinsha.

————. 2004. *Kindai seibutsugaku shi ronshū* (A collection of essays on the history of modern biology). Tokyo: Misuzu Shobo.

Nakane, Michiyo. 2010. *ε-δ rompō to sono keisei* (Epsilonics in nineteenth-century analysis: what makes mathematical analysis rigorous?). Tokyo: Kyoritsu Shuppan.

Nakanishi, Kei. 1989. *Shīboruto zengo* (Before and after Siebold). Nagasaki: Nagasaki Bunken-sha.

Nakaya, Ukichirō. 1938a. *Yuki* (Snow). Tokyo: Iwanami Shoten. Vol. 2 of *Nakaya Ukichirō shū* (The collected works of Ukichirō Nakaya). Tokyo: Iwanami Shoten, 2000.

————. 1938b. *Fuyu no hana* (Winter flowers). Tokyo: Iwanami Shoten.

————. 1940. *Nihon no kagaku—Hyōron shū* (Essays on science in Japan). Osaka: Sogensha.

————. 1956. *Kagaku to jinsei* (Science and life). Tokyo: Kawade Shobo.

————. 1958. *Kagaku no hōhō* (The ways of science). Tokyo: Iwanami Shoten. Vol. 7 of *Nakaya Ukichirō shū* (The collected works of Ukichirō Nakaya). Tokyo: Iwanami Shoten, 2001.

————. 2000–01. *Nakaya Ukichirō shū* (The collected works of Ukichirō Nakaya). 8 vols. Tokyo: Iwanami Shoten.

Nakayama, Shigeru. 1964. *Senseijutsu* (Astrology). Tokyo: Kinokuniya Company.

————. 1984a. *Ten no kagaku shi* (The history of science of the heavens). Tokyo: Asahi Shimbunsha.

————. 1984b. *Shimin no tame no kagaku ron* (On science for citizens). Tokyo: Shakai Hyoron Sha.

————. 1995. *Kagaku gijutsu no sengo shi* (The postwar history of science and technology). Tokyo: Iwanami Shoten.

Nakayama, Shigeru et al, eds. 1995–99. *Tsūshi 'Nihon no kagaku gijutsu'* (A historical overview of Japanese science and technology). 5 vols. + separate volume. Tokyo: Gakuyo Shobo.

Nakazawa, Shin'ichi. 2001. *Firosofia Yaponika* (Philosophy Japonica). Tokyo: Shueisha.

Nihon Butsuri Gakkai, ed. 1978. *Nihon no butsurigaku shi* (History of physics in Japan). Upper and lower volumes. Hiratsuka: Tokai University Press.

Nihon Kagakushi Gakkai, ed. 1963–72. *Nihon kagaku gijutsu shi taikei* (Series on the history of science and technology in Japan). 25 vols. + editorial policy + separate volume. Tokyo: Dai-ichi Hoki Shuppan.

————, ed. 1968. *Nihon kagaku gijutsushi taikei* (Series on the history of science and technology in Japan). Vol. 6, *Shisō* (Ideology). Tokyo: Dai-ichi Hoki Shuppan.

Niizuma, Akio. 2010. *Shinka ron no jidai* (The era of the evolution theory). Tokyo: Misuzu Shobo.

Ninomiya, Rikuo. 1983. *Shirarezaru Hipokuratesu* (The unknown Hippocrates). Tokyo: Shinohara Shuppan.

Nishigaki, Tōru. 1991. *Dejitaru narushisu* (Digital narcissus). Tokyo: Iwanami Shoten.

————. 2001. *IT kakumei* (IT revolution). Tokyo: Iwanami Shoten.

————. 2005. *Jōhōgaku teki tenkai* (Informatic turn). Tokyo: Shunjusha.

————. 2008. *Saibā petto/Uebu seimei jōhōron* (Cyber pet: Life information in the web). Tokyo: Chikura Shobo.

Nishio, Shigeko. 1993. *Gendai butsurigaku no chichi: Nīrusu Bōa* (The father of modern physics:

Niels Bohr). Tokyo: Chuokoron-sha

Noe, Keiichi. 1993a. *Kagaku no kaishaku gaku* (A hermeneutics of science). Tokyo: Shin-yo-sha; augmented edition, Tokyo: Chikumashobo, 2007.

——. 1993b. *Mukonkyo kara no shuppatsu* (Starting without a foundation). Tokyo: Keiso Shobo.

——. 1996. *Monogatari no tetsugaku* (The philosophy of stories). Tokyo: Iwanami Shoten.

——. 1998. *Kuun* (Kuhn). Tokyo: Kodansha.

Noguchi, Michizō. 1996. *Gensho seimeitai to shiteno ningen* (Humans as original life forms). Tokyo: Iwanami Shoten.

Ogawa, Mariko. 2001. *Feminizumu to kagaku/gijutsu* (Feminism and science/technology). Tokyo: Iwanami Shoten.

Ogawa, Seishū. 1943. *Seiyō igaku shi* (A history of Western medicine). Tokyo: Nisshin Shoin; Definitive edition, Tokyo: Shinrisha, 1947.

Ogawa, Tōru. 1983. *Katachi no butsuri gaku* (The physics of shape). Tokyo: Kaimeisha.

——. 2002. *Katachi tanken tai* (An expedition of shape). Tokyo: Iwanami Shoten.

Ogura, Kinnosuke. 1924. *Sūgaku kyōiku no kompon mondai* (Fundamental problems in mathematics education). Tokyo: Tamagawa University Press.

——. 1932b. *Sūgaku kyōiku shi* (History of mathematics education). Tokyo: Iwanami Shoten.

——. 1935–48. *Sūgaku shi kenkyū* (Research on the history of mathematics), vols. 1 and 2. Tokyo: Iwanami Shoten.

——. 1937. *Kagaku teki seishin to sūgaku kyōiku* (The scientific mind and mathematics education). Tokyo: Iwanami Shoten.

Ogura, Kinnosuke, and Nobutarō Nabeshima. 1957. *Gendai sūgaku kyōiku shi* (History of modern day mathematics education). Tokyo: Dainippon Tosho.

Ogura, Kinnosuke, and Kunio Oka. 1932a. *Shizen kagaku shi* (History of natural science). Tokyo: Chuokoron-sha.

Ogura, Kinnosuke, and Arata Osada. 1928. *Gendai sūgaku kyōiku no kaizō* (Reform of modern day mathematics education). Tokyo: Monasu.

Oka, Asajirō. 1904. *Shinka ron kōwa* (Discourse of the evolution theory). Tokyo: Kaiseikan.

——. 1926. *Saru no mure kara kyōwa koku made* (From a troop of monkeys to a republic). Tokyo: Kyoritsusha.

Oka, Kunio. 1930. *Shizen kagaku shi* (History of natural science). Tokyo: Shunjusha.

——. 1934. *Yuibutsu ron to shizen kagaku* (Materialism and natural science). Tokyo: Ohata Shoten.

——. 1936, 1948. *Kagaku shisō shi* (History of scientific thought) . Tokyo: Mikasa Shobo.

——. 1948–51. *Shizen kagakushi* (History of natural science). 7 vols. Tokyo: Hakuyosha.

——. 1950. *Kagaku teki jinseiron* (A scientific view of life). Tokyo: Bunrishoin.

——. 1957. *Kagaku to ningensei* (Science and humanity). Tokyo: San-Ichi Publishing.

——. 1996. *Atarashii gijutsu ron* (New theory on technology). Tokyo: Kobushi Shobo.

Okada, Minoru. 1984. *Furansu jinkō shisō no hatten* (Evolution of thought on French population). Tokyo: Chikurashobo.

Okada, Tokindo et al., eds. 1999. *Kagaku/gijutsu to ningen* (Science, technology and mankind). 11 vols. + separate volume. Tokyo: Iwanami Shoten.

Oki, Sayaka. 2011. *Kagaku akademī to "yūyō na kagaku"* (The science academy and "useful technology"). Nagoya: The University of Nagoya Press.

Ōkōchi, Masatoshi. 1941. *Seisan daiichi shugi* (A production-first policy). Tokyo: Kagakushugi Kogyosha.

———. 1942. *Kokubō keizai to kagaku* (The economics of national defence and science). Tokyo: Kagakushugi Kogyosha.

Ōkuma, Nobuyuki. 1941. *Kokka kagaku e no michi* (The path to state science). Tokyo: Tokyodo.

Okumura, Shōji. 1941. *Kōsaku kikai hattatsu shi* (History of the development of machine tools). Tokyo: Kagakushugi Kogyosha.

Omata, Waichirō. 2002. *Kindai seishin igaku no seiritsu* (The establishment of modern psychiatric medicine). Kyoto: Jimbun Shoin.

Omodaka, Hisayuki. 1957. *Tetsugaku to kagaku* (Technology and science). Tokyo: Houbunkan.

———. 1959. *Igaku gairon* (An Introduction to medical science). 3 vols. Osaka: Sogensha; Tokyo: Seishin Shobo, 1965.

———. 1981. *Igaku no tetsugaku* (Philosophy of medicine). Tokyo: Seishin Shobo.

Ōmori, Shōzō. 1976. *Mono to kokoro* (Objects and mind). Tokyo: University of Tokyo Press.

———. 1982. *Shin shikaku shinron* (A new theory on new vision). Tokyo: University of Tokyo Press.

———. 1992. *Jikan to jiga* (Time and self). Tokyo: Seidosha.

———. 1994. *Chi no kōchiku to sono jubaku* (The building of knowledge and its spell). Tokyo: Chikumashobo.

Ōmori, Shōzō et al., eds. 1985–86. *Shin Iwanami kōza: tetsugaku* (New Iwanami lecture series: Philosophy). Tokyo: Iwanami Shoten.

Ōmori, Shōzō, and Shuntarō Ito, eds. 1981. *Kagaku to tetsugaku no kaimen* (The interface between science and philosophy). Tokyo: Asahi Shimbunsha.

Ōno, Makoto, and Mariko Ogawa, eds. 1991. *Kagaku shi no sekai* (The world of science history). Tokyo: Maruzen.

Ōsawa, Masachi. 2010. *Ryōshi no shakai tetsugaku* (The social philophy of quantum mechanics). Tokyo: Kodansha.

Osborn, Henry Fairfield. 1894. *From the Greeks to Darwin: An Outline of the Development of the Evolution Idea*. New York: Macmillan.

Ōya, Shin'ichi. 1974. *Nihon kagaku shi sampo* (A stroll down the history of science in Japan). Tokyo: Chuokoron-sha.

Prokof'ev, V. 1952. *Великиерусские мыслители в ʹборъъе против идеализма и религии* (History of scientific thought in Soviet Union). Moscow: Молодая гвардия (Young guard).

Russell, Colin Archibald, ed. 1974. *The 'Conflict Thesis' and Cosmology. Science and Belief: From Copernicus to Darwin*, units 1–3. Milton Keynes: Open University Press.

Saigusa, Hiroto. 1934. *Nihon ni okeru tetsugaku teki kannen ron no hattatsu shi* (The history of the development of philosophical idealism in Japan). Tokyo: Bunpodo Shoten.

———. 1935a. *Benshōhō dansou* (Commentaries on dialictics). Tokyo: Chuokoron-sha.

——— (Tohiro, Kazō). 1935b. *Kindai nihon tetsugaku shi* (Modern history of philosophy in Japan). Tokyo: Nauka-sha.

———. 1937. *Nihon no shisō bunka* (The culture of Japanese thought). Tokyo: Daiichi Shobo.

———, ed. 1942–49. *Nihon kagaku koten zensho* (A compendium of Japanese classic works on science). 15 vols. Tokyo: Asahi Shimbunsha.

─────. 1940–43. *Gijutsuka hyōden* (A critical biography of engineers). Parts 1 and 2. Tokyo: Kagakushugi Kogyosha.

─────. 1940. *Gijutsu shi* (History of technology). Tokyo: Toyo Keizai.

─────. 1941a. *Gijutsu no shisō* (Technological thinking). Tokyo: Daiichi Shobo.

─────. 1941b. *Miura Baien no tetsugaku* (The philosophy of Baien Miura). Tokyo: Daiichi Shobo.

─────. 1951. *Gijutsu no tetsugaku* (A philosophy of technology). Tokyo: Iwanami Shoten.

Saigusa, Hiroto, and Ikutarō Shimizu. 1956. *Nihon tetsugaku shisō zensho* (A compendium of Japanese philosophical thought). Vol. 6, *Kagaku/shizen hen* (Science/nature). Tokyo: Heibonsha.

Saitō, Ken. 1997. *Yūkuriddo 'genron' no seiritsu* (The formation of Euclid's 'elements'). Tokyo: University of Tokyo Press.

Sakai, Shizu. 1982. *Nihon no iryō shi* (Japanese history of medicine). Tokyo: Tokyo Shoseki.

Sakamoto, Kenzō. 1975. *Kikai no genshōgaku* (A phenomenology of the machine). Tokyo: Iwanami Shoten.

─────. 1978. *Gendai kagaku o dō toraeruka* (How to perceive modern science). Tokyo: Kodansha.

─────. 1982. *'Wakeru' koto 'wakaru' koto* ('Separating' and 'understanding'). Tokyo: Kodansha.

─────. 1984. *Kagaku shisō shi* (The history of scientific thought). Tokyo: Iwanami Shoten.

─────. 1987. *Sentan gijutsu no yukue* (The future of advanced technology). Tokyo: Iwanami Shoten.

Sakano, Tōru. 2005. *Teikoku nihon to jinrui gakusha* (Imperial Japan and anthropologists). Tokyo: Keiso Shobo.

Sakata, Shōichi. 1947. *Butsurigaku to hōhō* (Physics and method). Tokyo: Hakuto Shokan.

Sakurai, Kunitomo. 1990. *Tenmongaku shi* (A history of astronomy). Tokyo: Asakura Publishing.

─────. 2010. *Nyūtorino ronsō wa ikanishite kaiketsu shitaka* (From the solar neutrino problems to the ultimate structure of matter). Tokyo: Kodansha.

Sakuta, Shōichi. 1934. *Kokumin kagaku no seiritsu* (The establishment of national science). Tokyo: Kokumin Seishin Bunka Kenkyujo (National Spiritual Cultural Research Institute).

Sarton, George. 1931. *Introduction to the History of Science*. Washington, D. C.: Carnegie Institution of Washington.

─────. 1931. *The History of Science and the New Humanism*. New York: H. Holt and Company.

Sasaki, Chikara. 1985. *Kagaku kakumei no rekishi kōzō* (Historical structure of the scientific revolution). Upper and lower volumes. Tokyo: Iwanami Shoten.

─────. 1992. *Kindai gakumon rinen no tanjō* (The birth of modern academic ideals). Tokyo: Iwanami Shoten.

─────. 1997a. *Gakumon ron* (On Learning). Tokyo: University of Tokyo Press.

─────. 1997b. *Marukusu shugi kagaku ron* (On Marxist science). Tokyo: Misuzu Shobo.

─────. 2000. *Kagaku gijutsu to gendai seiji* (Science, technology and modern politics). Tokyo: Chikumashobo.

─────. 2001. *Nijusseiki sūgaku shisō* (Mathematical thought in the twentieth century). Tokyo: Misuzu Shobo.

————. 2003. *Descartes's Mathematical Thought*. Boston Studies in the Philosophy and History of Science, vol. 237. Dordrecht: Springer.

————. 2010. *Sūgaku shi* (A history of mathematics). Tokyo: Iwanami Shoten.

Satō, Fumitaka. 2001. *Kagakusha no shōrai* (The future of scientists). Tokyo: Iwanami Shoten.

————. 2011. *Shokugyō to shiteno kagaku* (Science as a profession). Tokyo: Iwanami Shoten.

Satō, Jun'ichi et al., eds. 2010. *Sentan iryō no shakaigaku* (The sociology of advanced medicine). Kyoto: Sekaishisosha.

Satō, Katsuhiko. 1993. *Saishin uchū sōseiki* (The newest cosmic genesis). Tokyo: Tokuma Shoten.

————. 2008. *Uchūron nyūmon* (Introduction to cosmology). Tokyo: Iwanami Shoten.

————. 2010. *Infurēshon uchūron* (Cosmic inflation theory). Tokyo: Kodansha.

Satō, Ken'ichi. 2005. *Kinsei Nihon sūgaku shi* (A history of mathematics in early-modern Japan). Tokyo: University of Tokyo Press.

Satō, Nobue. 1932. *Shizen no ninshiki ni okeru genri* (The principles of perception of nature). Tokyo: Tetto Shoin.

————. 1937. *Kagaku no hōhō ni tsuite* (On methods of science). Tokyo: Nippon Hyoron Sha.

Shibata, Shingo, 1971. *Kagaku-gijutsu kakumei no riron* (Theory on science and technology revolution). Tokyo: Aoki Shoten.

————, ed. 1988. *Inochi o mamoru hōhō* (How to protect life). Tokyo: Banseisha.

————, ed. 1990. *Seibutsu saigai (baio hazadō) o fusegu hōhō* (How to prevent biological hazards). Tokyo: Banseisha.

Shibata, Shingo, Tadashi Suzuki, and Shōji Sofue, eds. 1991. *'Yuibutsu ron zensho' to gendai* ('A compendium on materialism' and the modern times). Tokyo: Kyuzansha.

Shibatani, Atsuhiro. 1960. *Seibutsugaku no kakumei* (The revolution in biology). Revised edition, Tokyo: Misuzu Shobo, 1970.

————. 1973. *Han kagaku ron* (An essay on antiscience). Tokyo: Misuzu Shobo.

————. 1977. *Anata ni totte kagaku to wa nanika* (What does science mean to you?). Tokyo: Misuzu Shobo.

————. 1989. *Han sabetsuron* (An essay on anti-discrimination). Tokyo: Akashi Shoten.

————. 1996. *Wareware ni totte kakumei to wa nanika* (What does revolution means to us?). Tokyo: Asahi Shimbunsha.

————. 1999. *Kōzō shugi seibutsugaku* (Structuralist biology). Tokyo: University of Tokyo Press.

Shiga, Kōji. 2007. *Sū to ryō no deai* (Encounter between numbers and volume). Tokyo: Kinokuniya Company.

Shimao, Nagayasu, ed. 1978. *Kagaku no rekishi* (History of science). Osaka: Sogensha.

————. 1967. *Kagaku shisō shi* (History of scientific thought). Onomichi: Keibunsha.

————. 1969. *Kagaku, gijutsu, shakai* (Science, technology, society). Onomichi: Keibunsha.

————. 1979. *Nyūton* (Newton). Tokyo: Iwanami Shoten.

————. 1995. *Chūgoku kagaku shi* (The history of Chinese chemistry). Tokyo: Asakura Publishing.

————. 2002. *Jimbutsu kagaku shi* (A biographical history of scientists). Tokyo: Asakura Publishing.

Shimomura, Toratarō. 1939. *Shizen tetsugaku* (Natural philosophy). Tokyo: Koubundou.

————. 1941. *Kagaku shi no tetsugaku* (A philosophy of the history of science). Tokyo: Koubundou. Vol. 1 of *Shimomura Toratarō chosakushū* (The collected works of Toratarō Shimomura). Tokyo: Misuzu Shobo, 1988.

————. 1944. *Mugen ron no keisei to kōzō* (The formation and structure of the theory of infinity). Tokyo: Koubundou.

————. 1988–99. *Shimomura Toratarō chosakushū* (The collected works of Toratarō Shimomura). 13 vols. Tokyo: Misuzu Shobo.

Shimosaka, Ei et al., eds. 1987–91. *Kagaku minaoshi sōsho* (Reevaluation of science series). 4 vols. Tokyo: Bokutakusha.

Shinmura, Taku. 1989. *Shi to yamai to kango no shakai shi* (The social history of death, disease and nursing). Tokyo: Hosei University Press.

————. 1991. *Oi to mitori no shakaishi* (The social history of aging and nursing). Tokyo: Hosei University Press.

————. 2006. *Kenkō no shakai shi* (The social history of health). Tokyo: Hosei University Press.

Shiraishi, Sadeo. 1948. *Sūgaku no tetsugaku* (The philosophy of mathematics). Tokyo: Hikari No Shobo.

————. 1951. *Sū to renzoku no tetsugaku* (The philosophy of numbers and continuity). Tokyo: Kyoritsu Shuppan.

Shiroyama, Hideaki, eds. *Kagaku gijutsu gabanansu* (Governance of science and technology). Tokyo: Toshindo.

Soda, Hajime. 1989. *Zusetsu Nihon iryō bunka shi* (An illustrated history of Japanese medical culture). Kyoto: Shibunkaku Shuppan.

Sogawa, Harue, and Seigo Matsuoka. 1979. *Kagaku teki yukai o megutte* (On scientific amusement). Tokyo: Kousakusha.

Suetsuna, Joichi. 1944. *Sūgaku to sūgakushi* (Mathematics and its history). Tokyo: Koubundou.

————. 1947. *Sūri to ronri* (Mathematical principles and logic). Tokyo: Koubundou.

Suetsuna, Joichi et al. 1950. *Kagaku to wa nanika* (What is science?). Tokyo: Koubundou.

Sugai, Jun'ichi. 1931. *Tetsugaku to shizen kagaku tono kōshō* (Negotiation between philosophy and natural science). In vol. 10 of *Iwanami kōza tetsugaku* (Iwanami lecture series of philosophy). Tokyo: Iwanami Shoten.

————. 1941. *Kagaku no kokoro* (The heart of science). Tokyo: Chuokoron-sha.

————. 1942. *Kagaku bunka no kichō* (The foundation of scientific culture). Tokyo: Nippon Hyoron Sha.

————. 1944. *Kagaku ni tsuchikau* (Cultivating science). Tokyo: Tennensha.

————. 1947. *Kagaku no michi to seishin* (The way of science and the sprit). Tokyo: Shimizu Shobo.

Sugawara, Takashi. 1957. *Rikigaku shi* (History of mechanics). Tokyo: Oyama Shoten.

Sugi, Yasusaburō. 1943. *Kagaku no furusato* (The hometown of science). Tokyo: Unebi Shobo.

————. 1944. *Kagaku to gakudō* (Science and academism). Tokyo: Meguro Shoten.

————. 1949. *Kagaku no shukumei* (The fate of science). Osaka: Hakugei Shobo.

Sugimoto, Isao, ed. 1967. *Kagaku shi* (History of science). Taikei nihonshi sōsho (Series on Japanese history), vol. 19. Tokyo: Yamakawa Shuppansha.

Suzuki, Akihito. 2006. *Madness at Home.* Berkeley: University of California Press.

Suzuki, Sadami, ed. 1995. *Taisho seimei shugi to gendai* (Taisho vitalism and the modern times). Tokyo: Kawade Shobo Shinsha.

————. 2007. *Seimeikan no tankyū* (Research on views of life). Tokyo: Sakuhinsha.

Suzuki, Zenji. 1983. *Nihon no yūseigaku* (Eugenics in Japan). Tokyo: Sankyo Shuppan.

Synge, J. L. et al. 1961. *Sekai kyōyō zenshū* (The collection of cultures of the world), vol. 29, trans. Saburō Ichii et al. Tokyo: Heibonsha.

Tada, Tomio. 1993. *Meneki no imiron* (The semantics of immunity). Tokyo: Seidosha.

————. 1997. *Seimei no imiron* (The semantics of life). Tokyo: Shinchosha.

Taguchi, Kikue. 2010. *Kindai kyōiku reimeiki ni okeru kenkō kyōiku no kenkyū* (A study on health education at the dawn of modern education). Tokyo: Kazamashobo.

Taguchi, Ryūzaburō. 1943. *Oto to ongaku* (Sound and music). Kyoto: Jimbun Shoin.

————. 1952. *Iro to oto* (Color and sound). Tokyo: Sanseido Shuppan.

Taguchi, Ryūzaburō, and Osamu Tsukakoshi. 1949. *Oto no bunka shi* (A cultural history of sound). Tokyo: Seibundo Shinkosha.

Taguchi, Yoshihiro. 1995. *Sunadokei no nanafushigi* (The seven wonders of the sandglass). Tokyo: Chuokoron-sha.

Takabayashi, Takehiko. 1948. *Netsugaku shi* (History of thermology). Kyoto: Nihon Kagaku Sha; 2nd edition, Tokyo: Kaimeisha, 1999.

————. 1977. *Ryōshi ron no hattten shi* (History of quantum theory). Tokyo: Chuokoron-sha.

Takada, Seiji. 1988. *Kagaku hōhōron josetsu* (Introduction to scientific methodology). Tokyo: Asakura Publishing.

Takagi, Jinzaburō. 1981. *Purutoniumu no kyōfu* (The terror of plutonium). Tokyo: Iwanami Shoten.

————. 1982. *Waga uchi naru ekorojī* (My inner ecology). Tokyo: Nosan Gyoson Bunka Kyokai (Rural Culture Association).

————. 1999. *Shimin kagakusha to shite ikiru* (Living as a citizen scientist). Tokyo: Iwanami Shoten.

————. 2000. *Toritachi no mau toki* (When birds dance). Tokyo: Kousakusha.

————. 2001–04. *Takagi Jinzaburō chosakushū* (The collected works of Jinzaburō Takagi). 12 vols. Tokyo: Nanatsumori Shokan.

Takagi, Teiji. 1928. *Sūgaku zatsudan* (Talks on mathematics). Tokyo: Kyoritsusha.

————. 1942. *Kinsei sūgaku shidan* (Discourse on the history of early modern mathematics). Tokyo: Kawade Shobo.

————. 1949. *Sūgaku no jiyū sei* (Freedom of mathematics). Tokyo: Kangaekata Kenkyusha.

Takagi, Teiji et al. 1936. *Ippan teki kyōyō to shiteno sūgaku ni tsuite* (Mathematics as general education). Tokyo: Iwanami Shoten.

Takahashi, Ken'ichi. 2006. *Garireo no meikyū* (Galileo's labyrinth). Tokyo: Kyoritsu Shuppan.

Takahashi, Ken'ichi et al. 1990. *Jiritsu suru kagakushi gaku* (The establishment of history of science). Tokyo: Hokuju Shuppan.

Takahashi, Kōichi. 1997. *Uchū, busshitsu, seimei* (Cosmos, matter, life). Kyoto: Yoshioka Shoten.

Takebe, Hiraki, and Takeshi Kawai. 1980. *Kagaku shisō shi* (History of scientific thought), newly rev. ed. Tokyo: Nansosha.

Taketani, Mitsuo. 1946. *Benshōhō no shomondai* (Various problems in the dialectic method). Tokyo: Rigakusha. Vol. 1 of *Taketani Mitsuo chosaku shū* (Collected works of Mitsuo Taketani).

Tokyo: Keiso Shobo, 1968.

————. 1950a. *Kagaku to gijutsu* (Science and technology). Tokyo: Rironsha. Vol. 4 of *Taketani Mitsuo chosaku shū* (Collected works of Mitsuo Taketani). Tokyo: Keiso Shobo, 1969.

————, ed. 1950b. *Genshiryoku* (Atomic energy). Tokyo: Mainichi Newspapers. Vol. 2 of *Taketani Mitsuo chosaku shū* (Collected works of Mitsuo Taketani). Tokyo: Keiso Shobo, 1968.

————. 1953a. *Sensō to kagaku* (War and science). Tokyo: Rironsha. Vol. 3 of *Taketani Mitsuo chosaku shū* (Collected works of Mitsuo Taketani). Tokyo: Keiso Shobo, 1968.

————. 1953b. *Minagoroshi sensō to shite no gendai sen* (Modern warfare as total annihilation). Tokyo: Mainichi Newspapers. Vol. 3 of *Taketani Mitsuo chosaku shū* (Collected works of Mitsuo Taketani). Tokyo: Keiso Shobo, 1968.

————, ed. 1960. *Gendai kagaku to kagaku ron* (Modern science and science theory). Shizen kagaku gairon (Introduction to natural science), vol. 2. Tokyo: Keiso Shobo.

————. 1975. *Shimin no ronri to kagaku* (Logic of civilians and science). Tokyo: Chikumashobo.

————. 1976. *Anzensei to kōgai* (Safety and pollution). Tokyo: Keiso Shobo.

————. 1982. *Kagakusha no shakai teki sekinin* (The soial responsibilities of scientists). Tokyo: Keiso Shobo.

————. 1996. *Kagaku nyūmon* (Introduction to science), enlarged edition. Tokyo: Keiso Shobo.

Taketani, Mitsuo, and Masayuki Nagasaki. 1993. *The Formation and Logic of Quantum Mechanics*. Singapore: World Scientific.

Takeuchi, Hitoshi. 1969. *Butsurigaku no rekishi* (History of physics). Tokyo: Idemitsu Shoten.

Takeuchi, Yoshito. 1993. *Kagaku shi* (History of chemistry). Tokyo: Hoso Daigaku Kyoiku Shinkokai (Foundation for the Promotion of the Open University of Japan).

Takeuchi, Yoshito, and Keiichi Yamada. 1992. *Kagaku no oitachi* (The rise of chemistry). Tokyo: Dainippon Tosho.

Takeuchi, Yoshito, and Kōshiro Yoshioka. 1973. *Kagaku no rekishi* (A history of chemistry). Tokyo: Idemitsu Shoten

Takizawa, Toshiyuki. 2003. *Yōjō ron no shisō* (The thought of discussions about nourishing life). Yokohama: Seori-shobo.

Tamamushi, Bun'ichi. 1967. *Kagaku to kyōyō* (Science and culture). Tokyo: Minshu Kyoiku Kyokai (Institute for Democratic Education).

————. 1970. *Kagaku, kyōiku, zuisō* (Science, education, random thoughts). Tokyo: Iwanami Shoten.

Tamura, Matsuhei, ed. 1980. *Girishia no kagaku* (Science in Greece). Sekai no meicho (Great books of the world), vol. 9. Tokyo: Chuokoron-sha.

Tanabe, Hajime. 1915. *Saikin no shizen kagaku* (Recent trends in natural science). Tokyo: Iwanami Shoten.

————. 1918. *Kagaku gairon* (Introduction to science). Tokyo: Iwanami Shoten.

————. 1925. *Sūri tetsugaku kenkyū* (Study of mathematical principles). Tokyo: Iwanami Shoten.

————. 1954. *Sūri no rekishi shugi tenkai* (Development of the historicism of mathematics). Tokyo: Chikumashobo.

————. 1955a. *Riron butsurigaku shinhōhōron teisetsu* (Proposal of a new methodology of theoretical physics). Tokyo: Chikumashobo.

————. 1955b. *Sōtaisei riron no benshōhō* (Dialectics of the theory of relativity). Tokyo: Chikumashobo.

Tanabe, Shintarō. 1960. *Gijutsu ron* (Technology theory). Tokyo: Aoki Shoten.

Tanaka, Hajime. 1973. *Shizen no tetsugaku* (Philosophy of nature). 2 vols. Tokyo: Shin Nihon Shuppansha.

Tanaka, Minoru. 1954. *Kindai kagaku shi* (A history of modern chemistry). Tokyo: Chukyo Shuppan.

Tateishi, Yūji. 2011. *Kankyō mondai no kagaku shakaigaku* (Environmental issues and the autonomy of science). Kyoto: Sekaishisosha.

Tateno, Yukio. 1973. *Hōshasen igaku shi* (The history of radiology). Tokyo: Iwanami Shoten.

Tatsukawa, Shōji. 1984. *Yamai to ningen no bunka shi* (The cultural history of disease and mankind). Tokyo: Shinchosha.

————. 1989. *Yamai no ningen shi* (A human history of disease). Tokyo: Chikumashobo.

————. 1995. *Kami no te hito no te: Gyakkō no igakushi* (Hands of God, hands of man: Medical history in the backlight). Kyoto: Jimbun Shoin.

Terada, Torahiko. 1996–99. *Terada Torahiko zenshū* (The complete works of Torahiko Terada). 30 vols. Tokyo: Iwanami Shoten.

Terajima, Masashi. 1937. *Nihon kagaku hattatsu shi* (History of the development of science in Japan). Onomichi: Keibunsha.

Toda, Morikazu. 2002a. *Omocha to kompeitō* (Toys and *kompeitō* sugar candies). Tokyo: Iwanami Shoten.

————. 2002b. *Butsuri to sōzō* (Physics and creation). Tokyo: Iwanami Shoten.

Tominari, Kimahei. 1939. *Nihon kagakushi yō* (The essence of the history of science in Japan). Tokyo: Koubundou.

————. 1941. *Gendai Nihon kagaku shi* (Modern history of science in Japan). Tokyo: Mikasa Shobo.

————. 1948. *Kagaku gairon* (Introduction to science). Tokyo: Mikasa Shobo.

Tomonaga, Sin-Itiro. 1949a. *Ryōshi rikigaku, teiseiban* (Quantum-mechanical, revised edition). Tokyo: Tozai Shuppansha.

————. 1949b. *Ryōshi rikigaku teki sekai zō* (Quantum-mechanical world image). Tokyo: Koubundou.

————. 1962. *Quantum mechanics.* New York: Interscience Publishers.

————. 1965. *Kagami no naka no sekai*(The world within a mirror). Tokyo: Misuzu Shobo.

————. 1979. *Butsurigaku to wa nandarōka* (What is physics?). 2 vols. Tokyo: Iwanami Shoten.

————. 2001–02. *Tomonaga Sin-Itiro chosakushū* (The collected works of Sin-Itiro Tomonaga), newly bound edition. 15 vols. Tokyo: Misuzu Shobo.

Tomooka, Nobusuke. 1941–42. *Seibutsugaku shi* (History of biology). 2 vols. Tokyo: Sengabo.

Tosaka, Jun. 1929. *Kagaku hōhō ron* (On scientific methodology). Tokyo: Iwanami Shoten. Vol. 1 of *Tosaka Jun zenshū* (The complete works of Jun Tosaka). Tokyo: Keiso Shobo, 1966.

————. 1933. *Gijutsu no tetsugaku* (A philosophy of technology). Tokyo: Jichosha. Vol. 1 of *Tosaka Jun zenshū* (The complete works of Jun Tosaka). Tokyo: Keiso Shobo, 1966.

————. 1935. *Kagakuron* (On science). Tokyo: Mikasa Shobo. Vol. 1 of *Tosaka Jun zenshū*

(The complete works of Jun Tosaka). Tokyo: Keiso Shobo, 1966.

Tosaka, Jun, and Tatsuzō Yamagishi. 1937. *Ninshiki ron* (Epistemology). Tokyo: Mikasa Shobo.

Tsuchiya, Takao. 1942. *Nihon kokubō kokka kensetsu no shiteki kōsatsu* (Historical observation on defense state building of Japan). Tokyo: Kagakushugi Kogyosha.

Tsuji, Tetsuo. 1973. *Nihon no kagaku shiso* (Scientific thought in Japan). Tokyo: Chuokoron-sha.

————, ed. 1995. *Nihon no butsuri gakusha* (Japanese physicists). Hiratsuka: Tokai University Press.

————. 2011. *Butsurigaku shi e no michi* (The way of the history of physics). Tokyo: Kobushi Shobo.

Tsukuba, Hisaharu. 1961. *Nihonjin no shisō—Nōhon shugi no sekai* (The philosophy of Japanese people—The world of physiocracy). Tokyo: San-Ichi Publishing.

Uchii, Sōshichi. 2006. *Kūkan no nazo, jikan no nazo* (Mysteries of space, mysteries of time). Tokyo: Chuokoron Shinsha.

Uda, Michitaka. 1939. *Umi* (The sea). Augmented version, Tokyo: Iwanami Shoten, 1953.

————. 1943. *Nankai hokumei* (The south seas and north oceans). Tokyo: Oyama Shoten.

————. 1950. *Terada Torahiko to no taiwa* (Conversations with Torahiko Terada). Tokyo: Koubundou.

Uda, Michitaka, and Zen'ichi Yasui. 1949. *Umi to seikatsu* (The sea and life). Tokyo: Meguro Shoten.

Ui, Jun. 2006. *Shinsōban gappon kōgai genron* (Newly bound edition, bound volume: The elementals of pollution). Tokyo: Akishobo.

Umesao, Tadao. 1989–94. *Umesao Tadao chosakushū* (The collected works of Tadao Umesao). 22 vols. + separate volume. Tokyo: Chuokoron-sha.

Uramoto, Masasaburō. 1941. *Seirigaku teki sekai zō* (Physiological world image). Tokyo: Risosha.

Usher, Abbott Payson. 1929. *A History of Mechanical Inventions*. New York: McGraw-Hill.

Watanabe, Itaru. 1974. *Raifu saiensu to ningen* (Life science and man). Tokyo: Nihon Keizai Shimbunsha.

————. 1976. *Ningen no shūen* (The end of man). Tokyo: Asahi Shimbunsha.

————. 1979. *Atarashii ningen kan to seimei kagaku* (The life sciences and a new view of man). Tokyo: Kodansha.

————. 1990. *Busshitsu bunmei kara seimei bunmei e* (From material civilization to civilization of life). Tokyo: Dobunshoin.

Watanabe, Masao. 1963. *Bunka shi ni okeru kindai kagaku* (Science in the history of modern culture). Tokyo: Mirai-sha Publishers.

————, ed. 1974. *Amerika bungaku ni okeru kagaku shisō* (Scientific thought in American literature). Tokyo: Kenkyusha.

————, ed. 1983. *Igirisu bungaku ni okeru kagaku shisō* (Scientific thought in British literature). Tokyo: Kenkyusha.

————. 1987. *Kagakusha to kirisuto kyō* (Scientists and christianity). Tokyo: Kodansha.

————. 1990. *The Japanese and Western Science*, trans. Otto Theodor Benfey. Philadelphia: University of Pennsylvania Press.

————. 1991. *Bunka to shite no kindai kagaku* (Modern science as culture). Tokyo: Maruzen.

————. 1992. *Kagaku no ayumi, kagaku to no deai* (The course of science, encounter with science). Tokyo: Baifukan.

Watanabe, Satoshi. 1948. *Jikan* (Time). Tokyo: Hakujitsu Shoin.

————. 1973. *Jikan no rekishi* (The history of time). Tokyo: Tokyo Tosho.

————. 1974. *Toki* (Time). Tokyo: Kawade Shobo Shinsha.

————. 1980. *Seimei to jiyū* (Life and freedom). Tokyo: Iwanami Shoten.

Watanabe, Toshio. 1983. *Kinsei nihon kagaku shi to Asada Gōryū* (History of science in early-modern Japan and Gōryū Asada). Tokyo: Yuzankaku.

————. 1986–87. *Kinsei nihon tenmongaku shi* (A history of astronomy in early-modern Japan). 2 vols. Tokyo: Kouseisha Kouseikaku.

Watanabe, Yoshifumi. 2010. *Jikan to dekigoto* (Time and happenings). Tokyo: Chuokoron-Shinsha.

Whitehead, A. N. 1925. *Science and the Modern World.* Cambridge: Cambridge University Press.

Yabuuchi, Kiyoshi. 1947. *Kinsei tenmongaku shi* (The early-modern history of astronomy). Tokyo: Kouseisha Kouseikaku.

————. 1949. *Chūgoku no tenmongaku* (Astronomy in China). Tokyo: Kouseisha Kouseikaku.

————. 1955. *Tenmongaku shi* (History of astrology). Tokyo: Asakura Publishing.

————. 1964. *Chūgoku kodai no kagaku* (Science in ancient China). Tokyo: Kadokawa Shoten.

————. 1969. *Chūgoku no tenmon rekihō* (Astronomical ephemeris in China). Enlarged and revised edition, Tokyo: Heibonsha, 1990.

————. 1970. *Chūgoku no kagaku bunmei* (Scientific civilization in China). Tokyo: Iwanami Shoten.

Yajima, Suketoshi. 1949. *Butsurigaku shi* (History of physics). Tokyo: Asakura Publishing.

————. 1950. *Makkusuueru* (Maxwell). Tokyo: Koubundou.

————. 1956. *Kagaku shisō shi nyūmon* (Introduction to the history of scientific thought). Tokyo: Shudosha.

Yamada, Keiji. 1978. *Shushi no shizengaku* (Zhu Xi's study of nature). Tokyo: Iwanami Shoten.

————. 1988. *Kuroi kotoba no kūkan* (The space of black words). Tokyo: Chuokoron-sha.

————. 1991. *Seisaku suru kōi to shite no gijutsu* (Technology as a means for creation). Tokyo: Asahi Shimbunsha.

————. 1999. *Chūgoku igaku no kigen* (The origin of Chinese medicine). Tokyo: Iwanami Shoten.

Yamada, Sakaji. 1996. *Ninshiki ron to gijutsu ron* (Epistemology and technology theory). Tokyo: Kobushi Shobo.

Yamaguchi, Tomiko, and Aiko Hibino, eds. 2009. *Hōga suru kagaku gijutsu* (Emerging technology). Kyoto: Kyoto University Press.

Yamamoto, Shun'ichi. 1982. *Nihon korera shi* (A history of cholera in Japan). Tokyo: University of Tokyo Press.

————. 1997. *Nihon rai shi* (A history of leprosy in Japan). Tokyo: University of Tokyo Press.

Yamamoto, Yoshitaka. 1981. *Jūryoku to rikigaku teki sekai* (Gravity and the mechanical world). Kyoto: Gendai-Sugakusha.

————. 1987. *Netsugaku shisō no shiteki tenkai* (The historical development of thermological thought). Kyoto: Gendai-Sugakusha.

————. 1997. *Koten rikigaku no keisei* (The formation of classical mechanics). Tokyo: Nippon

Hyoron Sha.

————. 2003. *Jiryoku to jūryoku no hakken* (The discovery of magnetic force and gravity). 3 vols. Tokyo: Misuzu Shobo.

————. 2007. *Jūrokuseiki bunka kakumei* (The sixteenth-century cultural revolution). 2 vols. Tokyo: Misuzu Shobo.

Yamanouchi, Takahiko, ed. 1970. *Gendai kagaku to ningen* (Modern science and human beings). Tokyo: Chuokoron-sha.

Yamaoka, Nozomu. 1968. *Kagaku shi den* (A tale of the history of chemistry), annotated edition. Tokyo: Uchida Rokakuho Shinsha.

————. 1971. *Kagaku shi sō* (A window on the history of chemistry). Tokyo: Uchida Rokakuho Shinsha.

————. 1976. *Kagaku shi hitsu* (Scribblings on the history of chemistry). Tokyo: Uchida Rokakuho Shinsha.

————. 1978. *Kagaku shi jin* (Dust from the history of chemistry). Tokyo: Uchida Rokakuho Shinsha.

Yamashita, Shinji, and Masato Fukushima, eds. 2005. *Gendai jinruigaku no purakushisu* (The praxis of modern anthropology). Tokyo: Yuhikaku Publishing.

Yano, Michio. 1986. *Mikkyō sensei jutsu* (Astrology of esoteric Buddhism). Tokyo: Tokyo Bijutsu.

————. 2004. *Hoshi uranai no bunka kōryū shi* (The history of cultural relations in astrology). Tokyo: Keiso Shobo.

Yano, Michio, Takanori Kusuba, and Takao Hayashi. 1997. *Indo sūgaku kenkyū* (A study on Indian mathematics). Tokyo: Kouseisha Kouseikaku.

Yasugi, Ryūichi. 1964. *Kagaku teki ningen no keisei* (Formation of scientific human beings). Tokyo: Meijitosho Shuppan.

Yokoyama, Toshiaki. 2003–11. *Nihon shinka shisō shi* (The history of the idea of revolution in Japan), vols. 1–3. Tokyo: Shinsuisha.

Yonemoto, Shōhei. 1985. *Baio eshikkusu* (Bioethics). Tokyo: Kodansha.

————. 1989. *Iden kanri shakai* (Genetically managed society). Tokyo: Koubundou.

————. 1994. *Chikyū kankyō mondai to wa nanika* (What is the environmental problem?). Tokyo: Iwanami Shoten.

————. 1998. *Chiseigaku no susume* (Introduction to the politics of knowledge). Tokyo: Chuokoron-sha.

————. 2006. *Baio poritikusu* (Biopolitics). Tokyo: Chuokoron Shinsha.

Yonemoto, Shōhei et al. 2000. *Yūseigaku to ningen shakai* (Eugenics and human society). Tokyo: Kodansha.

Yōrō, Takeshi. 1986. *Katachi o yomu* (Read the shape). Tokyo: Baifukan.

————. 1989. *Yuinōron* (Brainism). Tokyo: Seidosha.

————. 1997. *Rinshō tetsugaku* (Clinical philosophy). Yokohama: Tetsugakushobo.

————. 2005. *The Wall of Fools*, trans. Yoko Toyozaki and Stuart Varnam-Atkin. Tokyo: IBC Publishing.

Yoshida, Mitsukuni. 1955. *Nihon kagaku shi* (A history of science in Japan). Tokyo: Asakura Publishing.

————. 1961. *Nihon gijutsu shi kenkyū* (A study on the history of technology in Japan). Kyoto:

Gakugei Shuppansha.
————. 1963. *Renkin jutsu* (Alchemy). Tokyo: Chuokoron-sha.
————. 1985. *Mon'you no hakubutsu shi* (Natural history of patterns). Kyoto: Dohosha Shuppan.
Yoshida, Takeshi. 2000. *Kyosū no jōcho* (Square root of minus one: mathematics, physics and human mind: 'Imaginative in all directions'). Hiratsuka: Tokai University Press.
Yoshimoto, Hideyuki et al. 1995. *Kagaku to kokka to shūkyō* (Science and nation and religion). Tokyo: Heibonsha.
Yoshimura, Masaharu. 1999. *Seimei to wa nanika* (What is life?). Tokyo: Gendai Iryosha.
Yoshioka, Hitoshi. 1982. *Tekunotopia o koete* (Beyond technotopia). Revised edition, Tokyo: Shakai Hyoron Sha, 1985.
————. 1986. *Kagaku shakaigaku no kōsō* (Outline of a sociology of science). Tokyo: Libro Port.
————. 1987. *Kagaku kakumei no seijigaku* (A political study of scientific revolutions). Tokyo: Chuokoron-sha.
————. 1991. *Kagaku bunmei no bōsō katei* (Burnout of scientific civilization). Tokyo: Kaimeisha.
————. 1999. *Genshiryoku no shakai shi* (A social history of nuclear power). Tokyo: Asahi Shimbunsha.
Yoshioka, Shūichirō. 1938. *Sūgaku bunka shi* (Cultural history of mathematics). Tokyo: Kawade Shobo.
————. 1948. *Kagaku shisō shi* (History of scientific thought). Sekai tetsugaku kōza (Lectures on philosophies of the world), vol. 9. Tokyo: Hikari No Shobo.
————. 1952. *Nihon kagaku shisō shi gaisetsu* (Outline of the history of scientific thought in Japan). Tokyo: Shoko Shoin.
Yoshioka, Shūichirō et al. 1940–43. *Kagaku shi sōsho* (Series on the history of science). Tokyo: Sengabo.
Yuasa, Akira. 1952. *Seibutsugaku shi* (A history of biology). Tokyo: Koubundou.
Yuasa, Mitsutomo. 1961a. "Kagaku shi" (The history of science). In *Nihon gendai shi taikei* (Series on Japanese modern history). Tokyo: Toyo Keizai.
————. 1980–84. *Nihon no kagaku gijutsu 100 nen shi* (A hundred year history of science and technology in Japan). Upper and lower volumes. Tokyo: Chuokoron-sha.
Yuasa, Mitsutomo et al., eds. 1961b. *Kagaku kakumei* (Scientific revolution). Tokyo: Morikita Publishing.
Yuibutsu ron kenkyū kai. 1932–38. *Yuibutsu ron kenkyū* (Research on theories on materialism). 18 vols. + separate volume. Reprinted edition, Tokyo: Aoki Shoten, 1972–75.
————. 1972. *Yuibutsu ron kenkyū* (Research on theories on materialism), reprinted ed. vol. 1. Tokyo: Aoki Shoten.
————. 1973. *Yuibutsu ron kenkyū* (Research on theories on materialism), reprinted ed. vol. 2. Tokyo: Aoki Shoten.
Yukawa, Hideki. 1943. *Sonzai no rihō* (The law of existence). Tokyo: Iwanami Shoten.
————. 1946. *Me ni mienai mono* (The invisible). Tokyo: Kobunsha.
————. 1948a. *Kagaku to ningen sei* (Science and humanity). Tokyo: Kokuritsu Shoin.
————. 1948b. *Genshi to ningen* (Atom and human beings). Tokyo: Kobunsha.

————. 1961. *Gendai kagaku to ningen* (Modern science and human beings). Tokyo: Iwanami Shoten.

————. 1966. *Sōzō teki ningen* (The imaginative human). Tokyo: Chikumashobo.

————. 2007. *Yukawa Hideki chosaku shū* (The collected works of Hideki Yukawa). 10 vols. Tokyo: Iwanami Shoten.

Yukawa, Hideki, and Takeshi Inoue, eds. 1978–79. *Sekai no meicho* (Great books of the world). Vols. 79, 80, *Gendai no kagaku* (Modern science) 1, 2. Tokyo: Chuokoron-sha.

Yukawa, Hideki, and Tadao Umesao. 1967. *Ningen ni totte kagaku to wa nanika* (What does science mean to mankind?). Tokyo: Chuokoron-sha.

Zhou, Cheng. 2010. *Fukuzawa Yukichi to Chin Dokushū* (Fukuzawa Yukichi and Chen Duxiu). Tokyo: University of Tokyo Press.

Chapter 1

Asahi Graph. 1946. "Hatsuwarai shimpan iroha karuta (First laugh of the new year: Iroha Karuta, new edition)." January 1946: 12–15.

Asahi Shimbun. 1935. Tokyo morning edition, August 31: 11.

————. 1937a. Tokyo morning edition, March 5: 11, April 28: 4.

————. 1937b. Tokyo morning edition, July 16: 11.

————. 1938. Tokyo morning edition, June 15: 11.

————. 1939a. Tokyo morning edition, December 7: 5.

————. 1939b. "Sekai ichi no genshi jikkenshitsu RIKEN 'saikurotoron' toritsuke (RIKEN installs 'cyclotron,' world's largest atom laboratory)." Tokyo morning edition, February 24: 11.

————. 1941a. "Taigan no amerika (America as a spectator)." Tokyo morning edition, November 8: 5.

————. 1941b. "Beikoku no kagaku to gijutsu o tsuku shinkichōsha no zadankai 5 (Round table talk by recent returnees from abroad, no. 5: On science and technology of the US)." Tokyo evening edition, February 26: 3.

————. 1943. "Teki amerika no kagaku dōin jō (Mobilization of science in America, the enemy country: Part 1)." Tokyo morning edition, September 9: 1.

————.1944a. "Dempa kyokuchō kōtetsu (Director of the Radio Bureau recalled)." Tokyo morning edition, September 14: 1.

————. 1944b. "Genshi bakudan (The atomic bomb)." Tokyo morning edition, December 29: 2.

————. 1945. "Kagakusha shinshun no yume (Scientists: Dreams of the new year)." Tokyo morning edition, January 8: 2.

————. 1948. "Tensei jingo (column: The voice of heaven is the voice of people)." Tokyo morning edition, September 6: 1.

————. 1949a. "Yukawa hakase ni Nōberu shō Nihonjin de hatsu no eiyo (Dr. Yukawa receives the Noble prize, first time honor for Japanese)." Tokyo morning edition, November 4: 1.

————. 1949b. "Yukawa hakase jyushō ni kage no chikara Nagano hakase ga jyūninen mae ni suisen (Force behind Dr. Yukawa's Nobel prize: Dr. Nagaoka's recommendation 12 years ago)." Tokyo morning edition, November 10: 2.

Kagaku (Science). 1940a. "Dai saikurotoron no seisaku keikaku (Production plan of the large cyclotron)." 10 (3), March: 116.

————. 1940b. "Dai saikurotoron no seisaku (Production of the large cyclotron)." 10 (8), August: 311–312.

————. 1941. "Berkeley no shin saikurotoron (Berkeley's new cyclotron)," 11 (4), April: 188.

Kampō (Official gazette). 1944. "Dai hachijūyon kai teikoku gikai kizokuin giji sokkiroku dai-jūgo (Stenographic minutes of the 84th conference of the Japanese House of Peers)," extra edition, February 8: 137.

Mainichi Shimbun. 1944a. Osaka evening edition, January 7: 1.

————. 1944b. Osaka edition, October 16: 2.

————. "Mato (Target)." 1945. Osaka edition, January 2.

Shin Iwate Nippo. 1945. August 3: 2.

Yomiuri Hōchi. 1944a. "Teki ni otoranu kōkoku kanshō no kagaku jin (Scientists of Japan can compete with and beat those of the enemy)." Morning edition, August 26: 3.

————. 1944b. "Genshi bakudan shiyō (The use of atomic bombs)." Morning edition, December 29: 1.

————. 1945a. Morning edition, February 1: 1.

————. "Hatashite genshi bakudan ka: Yazaki rihaku ni kiku (Was it really an atomic bomb? Asking Dr. Yazaki)." 1945b. Morning edition, August 13: 2.

Yomiuri Shimbun. 1939. Evening edition February 18: 2.

————. 1940. Morning edition February 13: 7.

Kagaku chishiki (Scientific knowledge). 1936. "Nihon butsuri gakkai no ōgosho, Nagaoka Hantarō hakase (The mogul of the Japanese physics world, Dr. Hantarō Nagaoka)." 16 (1) : 66.

Aoyama, Tanemichi. 1908. "Kaikai no ji (Opening address) (by stenography)." *Gan Kenkyūkai kaihō* (Cancer Society newsletter), attached to *Gan* (Cancer) 2 (1), April 1908: 285–286.

Butsurigakushi Kenkyū Kankōkai, ed. 1969. *Genshi kōzō ron* (The theory of atomic constitution). Hiratsuka: Tokai University Press.

Churchill, Winston S. 1954. *Triumph and Tragedy.* The Second World War, Volume VI. London: Cassell.

Coben, Stanley. 1971. "The Scientific Establishment and the Transmission of Quantum Mechanics to the United States, 1919–32." *American Historical Review*, 76: 2, 442–466.

Ezawa, Hiroshi. 2006. "Yukawa, Tomonaga to Nihon no kiso butsurigaku (Yukawa, Tomonaga and basic physics in Japan)." *Nihon butsuri gakkaishi* (The physical society of Japan newsletter) 61 (12): 884–890.

————. 2007. "Kaisetsu (Commentary)." *Nishina Yoshio ōfuku shokan shū 3 Gendai butsurigaku no kaitaku dai saikurotoron, nigō kenkyū, sengo no saishuppatsu 1940–1951* (Correspondence of Yoshio Nishina 3: Development of modern physics: large cyclotron, Ni-Go Project, restarting afther the war 1940–1951). Tokyo: Misuzu Shobo.

————. 2010. "Genshi bakudan to iu kotoba no rekishi (The history of the word 'atomic bomb')." *Kagaku* (Science) 80 (11): 1128–1133.

Handō, Kazutoshi, Shūji Takeuchi, Masayasu Hosaka, and Ken'ichi Matsumoto. 2009. *Senryōka Nihon* (Japan under occupation). Tokyo: Chikumashobo.

Hanzawa, Sakuichirō. 1983. "Tomonaga sensei to no koto (Memories with Professor Tomonaga)." *Tomonaga Sin-Itiro chosakushū geppō* (The collected works of Sin-Itiro Tomonaga monthly report) 10: 1–4.

Hatano, Sadao. 1937. "Bōa kyōju kōenkai o moyooshite (Hosting a lecture by Professor Bohr)."

Kagaku chishiki (Scientific knowledge) 17 (7): 824–825.

Hatoyama, Haruko, ed. 1929. *Hatoyama no isshō* (The life of Kazuo Hatoyama). Privately published. Reprinted edition. Tokyo: Ozorasha, 1999).

Hatoyama, Michio. 1942. "Wagakoku genshikaku butsuri gakkai no sekimu (The responsibilities of our country's nuclear physics community)." *Kagaku gahō* (Scientific graphic) 31 (5), May: 18–22.

Heisenberg, Werner. 1930. *Die physikalischen Prinzipien der Quantentheorie* (The physical principles of quantum theory). Leipzig: S. Hirzel.

Iguchi, Haruo. 2010. "Shūsen: Mujōken kōfuku o meguru ronsō (The end of war: Debates regarding the unconditional surrender)." Chap. 13 in *Kaimei: Showa shi* (Interpretation: History of Showa), edited by Kiyotada Tsutsui, 237–258. Tokyo: Asahi Shimbun Publications.

Inoue, Nikichi. 1937. "Bōa kyōju ni kansha suru (Thanking Professor Bohr)." *Kagaku chishiki* (Scientific knowledge) 17 (7): 825.

Ishiwara, Jun. 1938. "Gakkai no dokujisei (The uniqueness of the world of academia)." *Asahi Shimbun*, Tokyo morning edition, November 18: 7.

Itakura, Kiyonobu. 1976. *Nagaoka Hantarō* (Hantarō Nagaoka). Tokyo: Asahi Shimbunsha.

Itakura, Kiyonobu, Tōsaku Kimura, and Eri Yagi. 1973. *Nagaoka Hantarō den* (The critical biography of Hantarō Nagaoka), supervised by Yoshio Fujioka. Tokyo: Asahi Shimbunsha.

Itō, Kenji. 2002. "Values of 'Pure Science': Nishina Yoshio's Wartime Discourse between Nationalism and Physics, 1940–1945." *Historical Studies in the Physical and Biological Sciences*, 33: 1, 61–86.

K.M. 1940. "Rōrensu ga kangaeru yonsen kyūhyaku ton no saikurotoron (The 4,900 ton cyclotron conceived by Lawrence)." *Kagaku gahō* (Scientific graphic) 29 (8): 129.

Kaburagi, Tokio, Tameichi Yasaki, and Rokurō Ōtake. 1941. "Zadankai beikoku no gakkai to gakufū (Round table talk on the world and culture of academia in the US)." *Kagaku gahō* (Scientific graphic) 30 (2): 49–60.

Katsuki, Atsushi. 1991. *Ryōshirikigaku no shokō no naka de: 'Butsurigaku Rinkōkai' soshikisha no hitori Suzuki Akira sensei ni kiku* (The dawn of quantum mechanics: Talking with Mr. Akira Suzuki, a founding member of 'Butsurigaku Rinkōkai [Private Seminar on New Physics]'). Tokyo: Seirinsha.

———. 2007. *Sone Take: Wasurerareta jikken butsuri gakusha* (A forgotten experimental physicist, Take Sone). Tokyo: Sekibundo.

Kimura, Motoharu. 1990. *Kaku to tomoni gojū nen* (50 years with nuclear weapons). Tokyo: Tsukiji Shokan Publishing.

Koizumi, Kenkichirō. 1975. "The Emergence of Japan's First Physicists: 1868–1900." *Historical Studies in the Physical Sciences*, 6: 3–108.

Konuma, Michiji. 2006. "Yukawa, Tomonaga no heiwa undō (The peace movement of Yukawa and Tomonaga)." *Nihon butsuri gakkaishi* (The physical society of Japan newsletter) 61 (12): 912–917.

Koshiba, Masatoshi. 2003. "Watashi no rirekisho 7 (My resume 7)." *Nihon Keizai Shimbun*, February 7.

Kumagusu, Minakata. 1911. Letters to Kunio Yanagita (October 17, 1911). In *Yanagita Kunio Minakata Kumagusu ōfuku shokanshū* (Letters between Kunio Yanagita and Kumagusu Minakata), edited by Iikura Shōhei, 156–171. Tokyo: Heibonsha, 1976.

Mori, Arinori. 1889. *Gakka oyobi kyōjuhō sōan* (Drafts of lectures and teaching methods). Vol. 2 of *Shinshū Mori Arinori zenshū* (New edition: The complete works of Arinori Mori), supervised by Toshiaki Ōkubo and edited by Hachirō Kaminuma and Takaaki Inuzuka, 170–173. Tokyo: Bunsendo, 1998 (The drafts written in 1889).

————. Year unknown. *Gakusei yōryō* (The main points of educational administration). Vol. 2 of *Shinshū Mori Arinori zenshū* (New edition: The complete works of Arinori Mori), 163–168 (memo from unknown year).

Nagaoka, Hantarō. 1911. "Nagaoka hakase no Niuton matsuri ni yosetaru shojō (Dr. Nagaoka's letter for the Newton Festival)." *Tokyo Butsuri Gakkō zasshi* (Tokyo School of Physics magazine) 20 (232): 132–134.

————. 1912. "Ōshu butsurigaku jikkenjō junranki (A tour of physics laboratories in Europe)." *Tokyo Butsuri Gakkō zasshi* (Tokyo School of Physics magazine) 21: 79–83

————. 1937. "Sōgō kenkyū no hitsuyō (The need for integrated research)." *Gakujutsu shinkō* (Promotion of science) 3: 6–8.

————. 1944. "Genshikaku bunretsu o heiki ni riyō suru hihan (Critistm for using nuclear fission for weapons)." *Gunji to gijutsu* (Military and technology), December: 1–6.

————. 1947. "Kyoka gyōretsu (Torchlight procession)." *Bungeishunjū* 7 (August): 2–5.

————. 1949. "Genshikaku tankyū no omoide (Memories of searching for atomic nucleus)." *Kagaku Asahi* 10 (1) (whole number 103): 22–25.

————. 1951. "Yukawa hakase no jushō o shukusu (Celebrating Dr. Yukawa's receiving of the Nobel Prize)." *Genshiryoku jidai no akebono* (The dawn of the nuclear power era), 176–182. Tokyo: Asahi Shimbunsha.

Nakane, Ryōhei, Yūichirō Nishina, Kōjirō Nishina, Yūji Yazaki, and Hiroshi Ezawa, eds. 2006a. *Nishina Yoshio ōfuku shokan shū 1—Gendai butsurigaku no kaitaku: Kopenhāgen jidai to Rikagaku Kenkyūjo, shoki 1919–1935* (Correspondence of Yoshio Nishina 1: Development of modern physics—The Copenhagen period and Rikagaku Kenkyūjo (Institute of Physical and Chemical Research), early period 1919–1935). Tokyo: Misuzu Shobo.

————, eds. 2006b. *Nishina Yoshio ōfuku shokan shū 2—Gendai butsurigaku no kaitaku uchūsen, shō saikurotoron, chūkanshi 1936–1939* (Correspondence of Yoshio Nishina 2 Development of modern physics: Cosmic rays, small cyclotron, mesons 1936–1939). Tokyo: Misuzu Shobo.

————, eds. 2007. *Nishina Yoshio ōfuku shokan shū 3—Gendai butsurigaku no kaitaku dai saikurotoron, nigō kenkyū, sengo no saishuppatsu 1940–1951* (Correspondence of Yoshio Nishina 3 Development of modern physics: large cyclotron, Ni-Go Project, restarting afther the war 1940–1951). Tokyo: Misuzu Shobo.

Nakao, Maika. 2008. *Nihon ni okeru "genbaku" kan: Senzen kara genbaku toka made* (How the Japanese view the "atomic bomb": From prewar to the bombings). Unpublished.

————. 2009. "The Image of the Atomic Bomb in Japan before Hiroshima." *Historia Scientiarum*, 19: 2, 119–131.

Natsume, Sōseki. 1901. Letters to Torahiko Terada (September 12, 1901). In vol. 14 of *Sōseki Zenshu* (The complete works of Sōseki), 188. Tokyo: Iwanami Shoten, 1966.

————. 1908. *Shojosaku tsuikai dan* (A recollection of the maiden work). Vol. 16 of *Sōseki zenshū* (The complete works of Sōseki), 603–607. Tokyo: Iwanami Shoten, 1967 (First appeared in 1908).

Nihon Tenmon Gakkai Hyakunenshi Hensan Iinkai, ed. 2008. *Nihon no tenmongaku no hyaku-nen* (One hundred years of astronomy in Japan). Tokyo: Kouseisha Kouseikaku.

Nishina, Yoshio. 1932. "Chogen (Preface)," to the lectures by Heisenberg and Dirac published as "Ryōshiron shomondai (Various problem of the quantum theory)," translated by Yoshio Nishina. *Zaidan hōjin keimeikai kiyō* (Annals of Keimeikai Foundation), vol. 11: 3–4.

————. 1940a. "1939 nen Nōberu butsurigakushō jyushōsha Rōrensu (The 1939 winner of the Nobel Prize in Physics, Lawrence)." *Kagaku chishiki* (Scientific knowledge) 20 (1): 110–114.

————. 1940b. "Amerika no kagaku (Science in the US)." *Riso* (Ideals), 14th year 6th volume: 655–666.

————. 1941a. "Kyōi no uchūsen (4): Nanseibun to kōseibun (The amazing cosmic rays (4): Soft and hard components)." *Asahi Shimbun*, Tokyo morning edition, June 18: 3.

————. 1941b. "Kaiko to tenbō (In retropect and looking forward)." *Kagaku* (Science) 11 (4): 182–183.

————. 1942. "Daitōa no saiken to junsui kagaku (Rebuilding of the Great East and pure science)." *Kagaku* (Science) 12 (3): 1.

————. 1943. "Sekaiteki no hakken: Uchūsen no naka ni 'chūkanshi' (A world-class discov-ery: 'Mesons' found in cosmic rays)." *Asahi Shimbun*, Tokyo morning edition, April 30: 4.

————. 1952. *Nishina Yoshio hakase ikōshu genshiryoku to watashi* (The posthumous collec-tion of Dr. Yoshio Nishina: Atomic power and I), enlarged and revised edition. Tokyo: Gaku-fu Shinsho.

Nomura, Kodō. 1959. "Tōjō Hidenori to Tanakadate Hakase (Hidenori Tōjō and Dr. Tanaka-date)." *Kodō hyakuwa* (A hundered essays by Kodō), 90–92. Tokyo: Chuko Bunko, 1981 (Original text published in 1959).

Okamoto, Takuji. 2000. "Nihonjin to nōberu butsurigaku shō (The Japanese and the Nobel Prize in Physics): 1901–1949." *Nihon butsuri gakkaishi* (The physical society of Japan newsletter) 55 (7): 525–530.

————. 2002. "Senzenki nihon no igakkai to nōberu seirigaku/igaku shō: Suisen kōdō no bunseki o chūshin ni (The world of medicine in prewar Japan and the Nobel Prize in Physiol-ogy or Medicine: Focusing on the analysis of recommendation activities)." *Tetsugaku/kagaku shi ronsō* (Essays on the history of philosophy and science) (4): 21–57.

————. 2003. "Senzenki no nihon no kagaku to nōberu shō: nōberu shō senkō shiryō kara (Chemistry in prewar Japan and the Nobel Prize: From documents of Nobel Prize selection)." *Gendai kagaku* (Chemistry today) (382): 61–64.

————. 2006a. "Ainshutain ga kuru: Taisho 11 nen, Doi Uzumi Rigakushi no kōkotsu to fuan (Einstein will come: Uzumi Doi and his anti-relativity theory in 1922)." *Kagaku gijutsu shi* (The Japanese journal for the history of science and technology) (9): 67–85.

————. 2006b. "Yukawa Hideki to Tomonaga Sin-Itiro: Kōryū no kiseki (Hideki Yukawa and Sin-Itiro Tomonaga: The history of their relationship)." *Nihon butsuri gakkaishi* (The physical society of Japan newsletter) 61 (12): 905–911.

————. 2007. "Kenkyūsha no jinkaku (Personality of researchers)." *Misuzu* (550), June: 19–21.

Okamoto, Takuji, Masahiro Ōsako, Kazuyoshi Suzuki, and Dana A. Freiburger. 2006. "Nagaoka Hantarō no shin shiryō ni tsuite (The new addition to the Hantarō Nagaoka papers)." *Bulletin of the National Science Museum, Series E* (Physical Sciences & Engineering) 29: 7–13.

Poincaré, Jules-Henri. 1905. *La valeur de la science* (The value of science). Paris: E. Flammarion.

Sagane, Ryōkichi. 1939. "Saikin no kōsokudo ryūshi hassei sōchi no jōsei ni tsuite (On recent trends of high-speed particle generators)." *Kagaku* (Science) 9 (12): 441–445.

————. 1941. *Genshikaku jikken sōchi* (The device for nuclear experiment). Tokyo: Iwanami Shoten.

————. 1947. *Kō enerugī ryūshi (oyobi ryōshi) hassei sōchi* (High energy particle [and quantum] generators). Vol. 1 of *Ryōshi butsurigaku no shimpo* (The evolution of quantum physics), 3rd edition, supervised by Yoshio Nishina, 107–142. Tokyo: Kyoritsu Shuppan (1st edition published in 1944).

Sakamoto, Takao, Ikuhiko Hata, Kazutoshi Handō, and Masayasu Hosaka. 2000. *Showa shi no ronten* (The issues of Showa history). Tokyo: Bunshun Shinsho.

Sako, Kiyoji. 1888. *Shō chūgaku yō butsurigaku mondō sanbyakudai* (Three hundred physics problems for elementary and junior high school students). Tokyo: Eisai Shinshisha.

Satō, Fumitaka, ed. 2008. *Shinpen: Soryūshi no sekai o hiraku—Yukawa, Tomonaga kara Nambu, Kobayashi, Maskawa e* (New edition: Exploring the world of elementary particles: from Yukawa, Tomonaga to Nambu, Kobayashi, and Maskawa). Kyoto: Kyoto University Press.

Scientific Advisory Group. 1947. "Reorganization of Science and Technology in Japan: Report of the Scientific Advisory Group to the National Academy of Sciences, United States of America, Tokyo, Japan, August 28, 1947"

Sone, Hiroshi, Mitsuharu Yūda, Nobuyo Higashi, and Haruki Senō. 2005. "Nihon no tennen bitamin A sangyō kaitaku no rekishi (A historical aspect of exploitation of natural vitamin A industry in Japan)." *Bitamin* (Vitamins) 79 (2), February: 97–112.

Suzuki, Tamon. 2006. "Showa nijūnen hachigatsu tōka no gozen kaigi: genbaku tōka to soren sansen no seijiteki eikyō no bunseki (The Imperial Conference of August 10, 1945: Analysis of the political implications of the atomic bombings and Soviet Union's participation in the war)." *Nihon seiji kenkyū* (Japanese political science research) 3 (1): 66–89.

Tajima, Eizō. 1995. *Aru genshi butsurigakusha no shōgai* (The life of a nuclear physicist). Tokyo: Shinjinbutsu Oraisha.

Taketani, Mitsuo. 1951. *Soryūshiron gurūpu no keisei: watashi no me de mita* (Formation of the elementary particle theory group: through my own eyes). In *Soryūshi no tankyū* (Exploring elementary particles), by Hideki Yukawa, Shōichi Sakata, and Taketani, Mitsuo, 81–240, 1965. Tokyo: Keiso Shobo. (First appeared in *Shinri no ba ni tachite* (Standing where the truth lies) by Hideki Yukawa, Shōichi Sakata, and Taketani, Mitsuo. Tokyo: Mainichi Newspapers, 1951).

————. 1958. "Genshiryoku to kagakusha: Nihon no kagakusha no ugoki (Atomic power and scientists: The movements of Japanese scientists)." In *Taketani Mitsuo chosaku shū 2: Genshiryoku to kagakusha* (Collected works of Mitsuo Taketani 2: Atomic power and scientists), 339–470, 1968). Tokyo: Keiso Shobo. (Original text published in 1958).

Tanakadate, Aikitu. 1915. "Kōkūki kōwa sueshō (Last chapter of talks on airplanes)." *Kuzu no ne* (Arrowroot). Tokyo: Nippon-no-Rōmazi-Sya, 126–128, 1938. (Speech at the Japanese House of Peers in 1915).

————. 1936. "(Zadankai) Tanakadate Hakase o kakonde (Round table talk with Dr. Tanakadate)." *Kagaku pen* (Science pen), first issue: 22–42.

——. 1944. "Senretsu dansō (A fragmentary thought on battle lines)." *Asahi Shimbun*, Tokyo morning edition, March 12: 2.

Terada, Torahiko. 1933. "Hopyōyō no kōri no wareru oto (The sounds of ice breaking in the Arctic Ocean)." Vol. 4 of *Terada Torahiko zuihitsushū* (A collection of essays by Torahiko Terada), edited by Toyotaka Komiya, 8–12. Tokyo: Iwanami Shoten, 1948 (First appeared in 1933).

——. 1935. "Gakkai keisatsu (Academy police)." *Kaki no tane* (Persimmon seed), 247–249. Tokyo: Iwanami Shoten, 1996.

The Committee for Yukawa Hall Archival Library, ed. 1982. "YHAL Resources Hideki Yukawa (I)." *Soryūshiron kenkyū* (Elementary particle theory research) 65: 239–269.

Tomonaga, Sin-Itiro. 1956. "Jūnen no hitorigoto (Soliloquy of a decade)." *Tomonaga Sin-Itiro chosakushū 1 Chōjū giga* (The collected works of Sin-Itiro Tomonaga 1: Scrolls of frolicking birds and animals), 100–103. Tokyo: Misuzu Shobo, 1981. (First appeared in *Shizen* (Nature), 1956 May issue).

Tomonaga, Sin-Itiro, Masa Takeuchi, Fumio Yamazaki, Chihiro Ishii, Minoru Oda, Hiroo Kumagai, Asao Sugimoto, and Yōichi Fujimoto. 1961. "Zadan: Nishina sensei to kakubutsurigaku no hatten: Nishina Yoshio sensei no jusshūnen o mukaete (Round table talk: Professor Nishina and the development of nuclear physics: Commemorating the tenth anniversary of Professor Yoshio Nishina)." *Tomonaga Sin-Itiro chosakushū 6 Hirakareta kenkyūjo to shidōsha tachi* (The collected works of Sin-Itiro Tomonaga 6: Open laboratories and their leaders), 94–151. Tokyo: Misuzu Shobo, 1982. (First appeared in *Shizen* [Nature], 1956 February and March issues).

Tomonaga, Sin-Itiro, and Hidehiko Tamaki, eds. 1952. *Nishina Yoshio: Denki to kaisō* (Yoshiko Nishina: Biography and recollection). Tokyo: Misuzu Shobo.

Tsuboi, Chūji. 1946. "Iwayuru kagaku shinkō ni tsuite (On the so-called promotion of science)." *Sekai* (World), January: 70–74.

Watanabe, Satoshi. 1946. "Wakai kagakusha e (To young scientists)." *Sekai* (World), June: 86–93.

Yamanaka, Hisashi. 2001. *Shinbun wa sensō o bika seyo* (Newspapers should glorify wars). Tokyo: Shogakukan.

Yamazaki, Masakatsu. 2010. "Riken no senji kaku kenkyū ni taisuru zerudouicchi hariton ronbun no eikyō (The influence of the Zel'dovich-Khariton paper on Riken's wartime nuclear research)." *Nihon Kagakushi Gakkai dai 57 kai nenkai/sōkai kenkyū happyō kōen yōshi shū* (The History of Science Society of Japan 57th annual/general meeting presentation abstract), 91.

Yazaki, Tameichi. 1937. "Kenkyūjo gaikan: Rikagaku kenkyūjo genshikaku jikkenshitsu (Introducing laboratories: Rikagaku Kenkyūjo [Institute of Physical and Chemical Research] Atomic Nucleus Laboratory)." *Kagaku* (Science) 7 (7): 292–295.

——. 1940. "Rōrensu wa jinkō uchūsen made kangaete iru (Lawrence is considering as far as man-made cosmic rays)." *Kagaku gahō* (Scientific graphic) 29 (5), backside of insert.

Yomiuri Shimbunsha. 1988. *Shōwa shi no tennō: Genbaku tōka* (The Emperor in the history of Showa: The atomic bombings). Tokyo: Kadokawa Bunko.

Yoshihara, Kenji. 2010. "Hiroshima genbaku no hōshanō o hakatta hitobito (A memory of the chemists who measured the radio-activity produced by the Hiroshima atomic bomb)." *Kaga-*

kushi kenkyū (The Journal of the Japanese Society for the History of Chemistry) 37: 193–195.

Yukawa, Hideo. 1944a. "Kagaku kōgyō jōshiki tokuhon: Kayaku (Basic knowledge of chemical engineering: Gunpowder)." *Gakusei no kagaku* (Science for students) 30 (4): 41–44.

————. 1944b. "Mokei hikōki tokuhon 2 (Model airplanes 2)." *Kodomo no kagaku* (Science for children) 7 (3): 235–237.

————. 1951. "Shirukukazein ko ni okeru buna/mizume no henshinzai to setchakuryoku (Sapwood and heartwood of beech/Japanese cherry birch trees and their adhesive strength in silk casein glue)." *Mokuzai kogyō* (Lumber industry) 6 (2): 89.

Chapter 2

Association of Young Researchers of Biochemistry. 2009. *Hikaru kurage ga nōberu shō o totta riyū: Keikō tampakushitsu GFP no hakken monogatari* (The reasons why the luminous jellyfish won a Nobel Prize: The story behind the discovery of the green fluorescent protein), supervised by Shōichi Ishiura. Tokyo: Nippon Hyoron Sha.

Baird, Davis. 2004. *Thing Knowledge: A Philosophy of Scientific Instruments.* Berkeley, Calif.: University of California Press.

Bertard, Gabriel. 1894. "Sur le latex de l'arbre à laque (On latex of the lacquer tree)." Compt. rend. 118: 1215–1218.

Dōke, Tatsumasa. 1979. *Nippon no kagaku no yoake* (Dawn of Japanese science). Tokyo: Iwanami Shoten.

EPTA Editorial Office, ed. 2006. "Tokushū: Taiwan kikō (Feature article: Travelling Taiwan)." *EPTA* (26). Tokyo: Kishohin Kagaku Kaiho Kenkyujo.

Fischer, Emil, and Carl Harries. 1902. "Über Vacuumdistillation (On vacuum distillation)." *Ber. Dtsch. Chem. Ges.* (Reports of the German Chemical Society) 35: 2158–2163.

Hachijū-nenshi Hensan Iinkai, ed. 2003. *Hachijū-nenshi* (The eighty years of history). Tokyo: Takasago International Corporation.

Harries, Carl. 1904. "Über die Wirkungsweise des Ozons bei der Oxydation. Ein Beitrag zur Chemie des Sauerstoffs (The operation of ozone in oxidation. A contribution to the chemistry of oxygen)." *Ber. Dtsch. Chem. Ges.* (Reports of the German Chemical Society) 37: 839–841.

————. 1905. "Über die Einwirkung des Ozons auf organische Verbindungen (The action of ozone on organic compounds)." *Liebigs Annalen der Chemie* 343 (2–3): 311–344.

Huang, Zhao Tang. 1985. *Taiwan sōtokufu* (Taiwan Governor-General Office). Tokyo: Kyoiku-sha.

Itō, Kiyoshi. 1993. *Taiwan: Yonhyakunen no rekishi to tembō* (Taiwan: 400 years of history and future prospects). Tokyo: Chuokoron-sha.

Kaji, Masanori. 1997. *Menderēefu no shūkiritsu hakken* (Mendeleev's discovery of the periodic law of the chemical elements: the scientific and social context of his discovery). Sapporo: Hokkaido University Tosho Kankokai.

————. 2008. "NOZOE, TETSUO." In *New Dictionary of Scienctific Biography*, edited by Noretta Koertge, vol. 5, 287–293. Detroit, New York et al.: Charles Scribner's Sons.

————. 2008. "Taiwan jidai no Nozoe Tetsuo to hinokichiōru: Tennenbutsu kagaku toshiteno yūki kagaku (Tetsuo Nozoe in Taiwan and hinokitiol: Organic chemistry as natural chemistry)." *Gakujutsu no dōkō* (Science trend) 13 (7): 82–88.

309

Kanamori, Osamu, ed. 2010. *Kagaku shisō shi* (History of scientific thought). Tokyo: Keiso Shobo.

Kawamoto Yūji, and Kazumasa Nakatani. 1971. *Kawamoto Kōmin den* (Biography of Kōmin Kawamoto). Tokyo: Kyoritsu Shuppan.

Kikuchi, Yoshiyuki. 2000. "Redefining academic chemistry: Jōji Sakurai and the introduction of physical chemistry into Meiji Japan." *Historia Scientiarum* 9: 215–256.

————. 2004. "Sakurai Jōji to igirisujin kagakusha konekushon (Jōji Sakurai and his connections with British chemists)." *Kagakushi kenkyū* (The journal of the Japanese society for the history of chemistry) 31: 239–267.

————. 2006. "The English model of chemical education in Meiji Japan: Transfer and acculturation," Ph.D. diss., The Open University.

Kim, Dong-Won. 2007. *Yoshio Nishina: Father of Modern Physics in Japan*. New York & London: Taylor & Francis.

Knight, David. 1992. *Ideas in Chemistry: A History of the Science*. London: The Athlone Press.

Kojima, Kōta, ed. 2002. *Tokyo-to no chimei* (The place names of Tokyo Prefecture). Nihon rekishi chimei takei (Series on historical place names of Japan), vol. 13. Tokyo: Heibonsha (Searched on Japan Knowledge website. https://japanknowledge. com/contents/rekishi/index. html).

Kubota, Takashi. 2005. *Nihon no yūki kagaku no kaitaku sha: Majima Rikō* (The pioneer of Japanese organic chemistry: Rikō Majima), published by Ichirō Kubota, produced by Tokyo Kagaku Dojin.

Majima Rikō. 1945a. "'Kenkyū jitsurei hen' no kankō ni tsuite (On the publication of 'Reseach example volume')." *Kagaku jikkengaku* (Study on chemical experiments), part 2, vol. 13, Research example volume 1, 1–2. Tokyo: Kawade Shobo.

————. 1945b. "Urushi shuseibun kenkyū no kaiko" (Reminiscence of the main components of Japanese lacquer)." *Kagaku jikkengaku* (Study on chemical experiments), part 2, vol. 13, Research example volume 1, 577–619. Tokyo: Kawade Shobo. (Republished in *Posthumous collection*, 1970: 63–102. Citations in this chapter are from the republication).

————. 1954. "Waga shōgai no kaiko (Reflection of my life)." *Kagaku no ryōiki* (Field of chemistry), 8 (1): 1–11, (3): 137–146. (Republished in *Posthumous collection*, 1970: 7–49. Citations in this chapter are from the republication).

Majima Rikō Sensei Ikōshu Kankō Iinkai, ed. 1970. *Majima Rikō sensei: Ikō to tsuioku* (Professor Rikō Majima: Posthumous manuscripts and recollections). Tokyo: Tokyo Kagaku Dojin. (Referred to as [Posthumous collection, 1970] in the text).

Matsuda, Gonroku. 2001. *Urushi no hanashi* (Stories of Japanese lacquer). Iwanami Bunko. Tokyo: Iwanami Shoten. (First published in November 1964 as a book in the Iwanami Shinsho series).

Miyama, Kisaburō. 1907. "Urushi jiru shuseibun oyobi urushi jiru hin'i kenteihō kenkyū hōkoku (Research report of the main components and evaluation method of Japanese lacquer sap)." *Kōgyō-kagaku zasshi* (The journal of chemical industry) 10: 107–124.

Miyaura, Takashi. 2004. "Gunji engo jigyō ni okeru dōin/shigenka no kōsatsu: Nishitama-gun Osoki-mura no jirei o chūshin ni (A study on the mobilization and utilization in the backing of military personnel project: Focusing on the example of Osoki Village in Nishitama County)." *Seisaku kenkyū (Ritsumeikan Daigaku)* (Policy research [Ritsumeikan University]), 12

(1): 111–124.

Nozoe, Tetsuo. 1951. "Substitution products of tropolone and allied compounds." *Nature* 167: 1055–1057.

————. 1966. "Kagaku o kokorozashite 40 nen (Forty years of my devotion to chemistry)." *Nozoe Tetsuo kyōju ronbun mokuroku shū* (Catalogue of dissertations by Professor Tetsuo Nozoe), by Nozoe Tetsuo Kyōju Gotaikan Kinenkai. 1–46. (Written especially for the catalogue).

————. 1991. *Seventy Years in Organic Chemistry.* Washington, DC: American Chemical Society.

————. 1999. "Hinokiyu no kenkyū kara toroponioido no kagaku e (From Japanese cypress oil research to the chemistry of troponoid)." *Nozoe Tetsuo sensei kenkyū ronbun/chosaku mokuroku* 1926–1998 (Catalogue of dissertations and works by Professor Tetsuo Nozoe), by Nozoe Tetsuo Sensei Tsuitō Jigyōkai, 85–151. (First appeared as a seven part series in *Nyū furēbā* [New Flavour] magazine by Flavor Gijutsu Kenkyūkai, 1977–78).

Numata, Jirō. 1989. *Yōgaku* (Western learning). Tokyo: Yoshikawa Kobunkan.

Ōkubo, Toshiaki. 1997. *Nihon no daigaku* (Japanese universities). Machida: Tamagawa University Press (First edition, Osaka: Sogensha, 1943).

Rocke, Alan J. 1984. *Chemical Atomism in the Nineteenth Century: From Dalton to Cannizzaro.* Columbus: Ohio State University Press.

Sakudō, Yoshio, and Taketo Etō, eds. 1976. *Hokkaidō daigaku hyakunen shi* (A hundred year history of Hokkaidō University). Tokyo: Zaikai Hyoron Shinsha.

Segrè, Emilio. 1980. *From X-rays to Quarks: Modern Physicists and Their Discoveries.* San Francisco: W. H. Freeman.

Shiba, Tetsuo. 1987. "Majima Rikō nikki shō: Showa 5 nen–Showa 19 nen (Excerpts from the journal of Rikō Majima: from 1931–1944)." *Osaka Daigaku shi kiyō* (Bulletin of the history of Osaka University) 4: 72–122.

Shimomura, Osamu. 2008. "Discovery of Green Fluorescent Protein, GFP." *Nobel Lecture*, December 8, 2008. [http://nobelprize. org/nobel_prizes/chemistry/laureates/2008/shimomura_lecture.pdf]

Stöckhardt, Julius Adolph. 1846. *Die Schule der Chemie oder erster Unterricht in der Chemie, versinnlicht durch einfache Versuche. Zum Schulgebrauch und zur Selbstbelehrung, insbesondere für angehende Apotheker, Landwirte, Gewerbetreibende etc* (For the school of chemistry or the first chemistry lessons, sensualize by simple experiments. For school and self study especially for future pharmacists, farmers or retailers). Braunschweig: Friedrich Vieweg und Sohn.

Tokyo Teikoku Daigaku, ed. 1926. *Tokyo Teikoku Daigaku sotsugyōsei shimei roku* (Alumni list of Tokyo Imperial University). Tokyo: Tokyo Teikoku Daigaku. (Can be viewed on the Digital Library from the Meiji Era page of the National Diet Library website. http://kindai.ndl.go.jp/)

Tōhoku Daigaku Hyakunenshi Henshū Iinkai, ed. 2005. *Tōhoku Daigaku hyakunenshi go: Bukyokushi ni* (A hundred year history of Tōhoku University 5: Deparment history 2). Sendai: Tōhoku University Press.

————, ed. 2007. *Tōhoku Daigaku hyakunenshi ichi: Tsūshi ichi* (A hundred year history of Tōhoku University 5: History overview 1). Sendai: Tōhoku University Press.

Tokyo Daigaku Daigakuin Rigakukei Kenkyūka/Rigakubu Kagaku Kyōshitsu Zasshikai, eds.

2007. *Tokyo Daigaku Rigakubu Kagaku Kyōshitsu no ayumi* (History of the chemistry department of the college of science at Tokyo university). Tokyo: Kokusai Bunken Insatsusha. (Referred to as [Tokyo University Department of Chemistry, 2007] in the text).

Udagawa, Yōan. 1975. *Seimi kaisō: Fukkoku to gendaigo yaku/chū* (Seimi kaisō: Reprint and modern translation/annotation). Tokyo: Kodansha.

Umetani, Noboru. 1996. *Ogata Kōan to Tekijuku* (Kōan Ogata and Tekijuku). Suita, Osaka: Osaka University Press.

Wakabayashi, Masahiro. 2001. *Taiwan: Henyō shi chūcho suru aidentitī* (Taiwan and its changing and hesitating identity). Tokyo: Chikumashobo.

Willstätter, Richard, and Erwin W. Mayer. 1908a. "Über Reduktion mit Platin und Wasserstoff bei gewöhnlicher Temperatur I (About reduction with platinum and hydrogen at ordinary temperature I)." *Ber. Dtsch. Chem. Ges* (Reports of the German Chemical Society) 41: 1475–1480.

―――. 1908b. "Über Reduktion mit Platin und Wasserstoff. II. Über Dihydrocholesterin (About reduction with platinum and hydrogen at ordinary temperature II. About dihydrocholesterol)." *Ber. Dtsch. Chem. Ges.* (Reports of the German Chemical Society) 41: 2199–2203.

Chapter 3

Cho, Hon-yong. 1942. "漢方医学의危機를앞두고 (Future crisis of kampō critical commentary on kampō medicine)." *Kampō igaku no hihanteki kaisetsu* (Critical commentary on Chinese medicine), 132–133. Tokyo: Toyo Iyakusha.

Chōsen Nippō Shasetsu. 1930. "Minshū hoken no jūdai kekkan: Haibyō shibōsha no gekizō genjō (Serious defect in national health: Deaths from lung diseases surging)." *Chōsen Tsūshin*, May 26, 1930: 2.

Fukagawa, Shindō. 1934. *Kan'yō igaku ronsō shi: Seiji tōsō hen* (The history of controversy between Chinese and Western medicine). Tokyo: Kyūhan To Igakusha.

Hasegawa, Tai. 1893. *Kampōi keizoku ni tsuite* (On letting kampō practitioners survive). Privately published.

Kawaguchi. Toshikazu, "Yakusō no saibai to riyō ni tsuite (Culivation and utilization of kampō medicine)." *Keijō Shokō Kaigijo keizai geppō* (Keijō Chamber of Commerce monthly economic report), July: 27. Seoul: Keijō Chamber of Economics.

Keijō Teikoku Daigaku Sōritsu Gojūsshūnen Kinenshi Henshū Iinkai, ed. 1976. *Kompeki haruka ni: Keijō Teikoku Daigaku sōritsu gojūsshūnen kinenshi* (Deep blue in the distance: Keijō Imperial University 50th anniversary magazine). Seoul: Keijō Teikoku Daigaku Dōsōkai.

Kōseishō Imukyoku, ed. 1955. *Isei hachijūnen shi* (The eighty years' history of the medical law). Tokyo: Insatsukyoku Choyokyoku.

―――. 1976. *Isei hyakunen shi* (The hundred years' history of the medical law). 3 vols. Tokyo: Gyosei.

Kosoto, Hiroshi. 1999. *Kampō no rekishi: Chūgoku/nippon no dentō igaku* (The history of kampō: Traditional medicine in China and Japan). Tokyo: Taishukan Shoten.

Koyasu, Nobukuni. 2003. '*Ajia*' *wa dō katararete kitaka: Kindai Nihon no orientarizumu* (How Asia has been told: Modern Japan's Orientalism). Tokyo: Fujiwara Shoten.

Nakayama, Tadanao. 1926. "Kampō igaku fukkō ron (An essay on the renaissance of kampō medicine)." *Nihon oyobi nihonjin* (Japan and Japanese) 109, 1–73. Tokyo: Seikyosha.

―――. 1933. *Kampō igaku no shin kenkyū: kaitei fukyūban* (Revised popular edition: New research on kampō medicine). Tokyo: Hobunkan.

Nihon Kagakushi Gakkai, ed. 1967. *Nihon kagaku gijutsu shi taikei 24: Igaku 1* (Series on the history of science and technology in Japan 24: Medicine 1). Tokyo: Dai-ichi Hoki Shuppan.

Nihon Tōyō Igakkai Gakujutsu Kyōiku Iinkai, ed. 2002. *Nyūmon kampō igaku* (Introduction to kampō medicine). Tokyo: Nankodo.

Oberlander, Christian. 2004. "The Rise of Scientific Medicine in Japan: Beriberi the Driving Force in the Quest for Specific Causes and the Introduction of Bacteriology," (Special Issue) History of Medicine and Biology in East Asia. *Historia Scientiarum, Second Series: International Journal of the History of Science Society of Japan* 13 (3): 176–199.

Ogawa, Teizō, and Shizu Sakai, eds. 1980. *Matsumoto Jun jiden/ Nagayo Sensai jiden* (Autobiography of Jun Matsumoto/Autobiography of Sensai Nagayo). Tokyo: Heibonsha.

Ōtsuka, Yasuo. 1989. "Edo jidai igaku no shosō (Various aspects of medine in the Edo period)." In *Kōza kagaku shi 4: Nihon kagaku shi no shatei* (Lectures on scientific history 4: The range capacity of Japanese science), edited by Shuntarō Itō and Yōichirō Murakami, 357. Tokyo: Baifukan.

Ōtsuka, Yoshinori. 1939a. "Kagaku no senrei o hetaru kampōi o kyōsei seyo (Foster kampō practitioners who have undergone the baptism of science)." *Tōa igaku* (East Asian medicine) (1): 1.

―――. 1939b. "Chūgoku kampō ikai no genkyō to nikka teikei ni tsuite (2) (The present situation of the world of Chinese kampō and the coalition between Japan and China [2])." *Tōa igaku* (East Asian medicine) (2): 4.

―――. 1940. "Kampō igaku ni okeru wa to kō to no seishin (The ethos of harmony and attach in kampō medicine)." *Tōa igaku* (East Asian medicine) (18): 1.

―――. 1943a. "Showa no kampō ikai (The world of Showa kampō)." *Kampō to kan'yaku* (Kampō and kampō medicine) 10 (5): 1–4.

―――. 1943b. "Igaku ni arawaretaru Nihon (The emergence of Japan in the medical world)." *Kampō to kan'yaku* (Kampō and kampō medicine) 10 (5): 171–186.

―――. 1966. *Rinshō ōyō shōkanron kaisetsu* (Advanced medical practice: 'On Cold Damage'). Osaka: Sogensha.

―――. 1982. *Ōtsuka Yoshinori chosakushū (bessatsu) tōyō igakushi, nempu, sakuin* (The collected works of Yoshinori Ōtsuka (separate volume): History of Eastern medicine, chronological list, index). Tokyo: Shunyodo Shoten.

Ōtsuka, Yoshinori. 2001. *Shinsōban kampō igaku* (Newly bound edition: Kampō medicine). Osaka: Sogensha.

Shin, Chang-Geon. 1999. "Hadō ni kōsuru ōdo to shiteno igaku: 1930 nendai chōsen ni okeru tōzai igaku ronsō kara (Medicine as right against might: Focusing on the controversy over Eastern and Western medicine in the mid-1930s Korea)." *Shisō* (Ideology) (905): 65–92. Tokyo: Iwanami Shoten.

―――. 2005. "Cho Hon-yong no seijiteki igaku shisō (Political thought of medicine of Cho Hon-yong)." *Kankokushiron 42: Kankoku kingendai kagaku gijutsushi no tenkai* (The dicussion on Korean history 42: The development of Korean thought on modern science and technology), edited by Kokushi Hensan Iinkai: 115–152. (Dissertation written in Korean).

———. 2007. "Keijō teikoku daigaku ni okeru kan'yaku kenkyū no seiritsu (The establishment of the study on the kampō in Keijō Imperial University)." *Shakai to rekishi* (Society and history) 76: 105–139. (Dissertation written in Korean).

Sugihara, Tokuyuki. 1929. "Chōsen ninjin ni tsuite (1) (On ginseng [1])." *Bunkyō no Chōsen* (Educational Korea) (10): 28–36.

———. 1939a. "Kampō igaku no kagakuteki kentō (A scientific consideration of kampō medicine)." *Chōsen oyobi Manshū* (Korea and Manchuria) 374: 41–43.

———. 1939b. "Kampō igaku no kagakuteki kentō (sono ni) (A scientific consideration of kampō medicine [2])." *Chōsen oyobi Manshū* (Korea and Manchuria) 375: 34–37.

———. 1939c. "Chōsen ni okeru kampō igaku to shōkan ron (Kampō medicine and 'On Cold Damage' in Korea)." *Chōsen* (Korea) 292: 26–44.

———. 1940. "Kampō igaku sōnen ni tsuite (On scientific thought in kampō medicine)" *Tairiku bunka kenkyū* (Study on the continental culture), edited by Keijō Imperial University Continental Culture Research Committee, 389–423. Tokyo: Iwanami Shoten.

———. 1940. *Kampō shohōgaku* (A study of kampō prescription). Tokyo: Kanehara & Co.

———. 1950. *Kampō igaku: Shisō hen* (Kampō medicine: Ideology). Kyoto: Nagasue Shoten.

———. 1956. *Kampō igaku: Shōkanron hen* (Kampō medicine: 'On Cold Damage'). Kyoto: Nagasue Shoten.

Sugiyama, Jirō. 1984. "Meiji shoki ni kampō igaku wa naze hitei saretaka (Why kampō medicine was not accepted in early Meiji Period)." *Seibutsugakushi kenkyū* (Japanese journal of the history of biology) 43: 30–40.

———. 1987. "Kampō to seiyō igaku (Kampō medicine and Western medicine)." In *Kagaku minaoshi sōsho 1: Kagaku to hikagaku no aida—kagagu to taishū* (The series of scientific review: The boundary between science and the comparative study—science and the populace), edited by Ei Shimosaka, Jirō Sugiyama, and Kiyoshi Takada, 203–240. Tokyo, Bokutakusha.

Tatsuno, Kazuo. 1939. "Kampō to shimpi shugi (Kampō and mysticism)." *Tōa igaku* (East Asian medicine) (11): 1.

———. 1940. "Manshū no tabi (Travel in Manchuria)." *Tōa igaku* (East Asian medicine) (19): 7.

Umihara, Ryō. 2007. *Kindai iryō no shakaishi chishiki, gijutsu, jōhō* (Social history of modern medicine: Knowledge, techonology, information). Tokyo: Yoshikawa Kobunkan.

Wada, Keijūrō. 1910. *Kampō to yōhō* (Kampō medicine and Western medicine), privately published. In *Kampō igaku kenkyū: Wada Keijūrō ikōshu* (Kampō medicine research: The posthumous collection of Keijūrō Wada), edited by Masatsugu Wada. Yokosuka: Ido No Nippon Sha, 1979.

———. 1974. *Zōho: Ikai no tettsui* (The iron hammer of the medical world: Augmented edition). Tokyo: Chugoku Kampō.

Yakazu, Dōmei. 1939. "Tōa igaku kyōkai hakkai shiki kaikai no ji (Opening speech of the inaugural ceremony of the Association of East Asian Medicine)." *Tōa igaku* (East Asian medicine) (1): 3.

———. 1940a. "Kampō no gainen to gendai teki shimei (The concepts of kampō of its contemporary missions)." *Tōa igaku* (East Asian medicine) (20): 2–3.

———. 1940b. "Nihon iji shinpo sha no shasetsu o kentō shi manshūkoku oyobi chūgoku no kan'i mondai ni oyobu (3) (Consideration of the editorial of Japanese Medical Journal Extended to the problems of Manchuria and China [3])." *Tōa igaku* (East Asian medicine) (20): 6–7.

————. 1979. *Zōho kaitei: Meiji 110 nen kampō igaku no hensen to shōrai - Kampō ryakushi nempyō* (Enlarged and revised edition: The 110th year of Meiji era, the history and future of kampō medicine: Brief chronology of kampō). Tokyo: Shunyodo Publishing.

Yamada, Terutane. 1996. "Nihon kampō igaku no denshō to keifu (Tradition and genealogy of Japanese kampō igaku)." *Nihon tōyō igaku zasshi* (Journal of Oriental medicine in Japan) 46 (4), 505–518. Tokyo: Nihon Toyo Igakkai.

Yasui, Hiromichi. 2007. "Nihon kampō shogakuha no nagare (Overview of various schools of Japanese kampō igaku)." *Nihon tōyō igaku zasshi* (Journal of Oriental medicine in Japan) 58 (2), 177–202. Tokyo: Nihon Toyo Igakkai.

Yumoto, Kyūshin. 1927. *Kōkan igaku* (Sino-Japanese medicine). Tokyo: Ryogen.

INDEXES

Name Index

A

Adams, Roger アダムズ, R.   165
Aichi, Keiichi 愛知敬一   128, 216
Aida, Gundayū 会田軍太夫   92
Akahori, Shirō 赤堀四郎   207, 227
Amano, Kiyoshi 天野清   43, 275
Anderson, Carl David アンダーソン, C. D.
    142, 143, 169
Ando, Shōeki 安藤昌益   14
Andreyev, Leonid アンドレーエフ, L.   14
Aoki, Seizō 青木靖三   43, 275
Aoki, Tamotsu 青木保   26, 275
Aomi, Jun'ichi 碧海純一   65, 275
Aoyama, Tanemichi 青山胤通   123, 302
Arakatsu, Bunsaku 荒勝文策   153
Araki, Toshima 荒木俊馬   95, 275
Aristotle アリストテレス   63
Asada, Gōryū 麻田剛立   10, 14
Asada, Sōhaku 浅田宗伯   250
Asada, Tsunesaburō 浅田常三郎   158
Asahina, Yasuhiko 朝比奈泰彦   228
Atkinson, Robert William アトキンソン, R. W.
    182, 188, 226
Ayusawa, Shintarō 鮎沢信太郎   95, 275

B

Bachelard, Gaston バシュラール, G.   225
Baeyer, Johann Friedrich Wilhelm Adolf
    von バイヤー, J. F. W. A. von   187
Baird, Davis ベアード, D.   224, 308
Barrès, Maurice バレス, M.   92, 275
Beethoven, Ludwig van ベートーベン, L. van
    127
Behring, Emil Adolf von ベーリング, E. A. von
    141
Bergson, Henri ベルクソン, H.   10, 49
Bernard, Claude ベルナール, C.   74
Bertrand, Gabriel ベルトラン, G.   188
Bethe, Hans Albrecht ベーテ, H. A.   138,
    167

Binswanger, Ludwig ビンスヴァンガー, L.
    51
Bismarck-Schonhausen, Otto Eduard
    Leopold von ビスマルク, O. E. L. von
    229
Bohr, Niels Henrik David ボーア, N. H. D.
    42, 129, 136, 137, 140, 143, 144, 148,
    161, 288, 302, 304
Born, Max ボルン, M.   129
Bolyai, Farkas ボヤイ, F. (ボヤイ, 父)   40
Bolyai, Janos ボヤイ, J. (ボヤイ, 子)   40
Bose, Jagadish Chandra ボース, J. C.   139,
    141
Boutroux, Emile ブトルー, E.   21
Bragg, William Henry ブラッグ, W. H.
    122, 169
Broglie, Louis Victor de ド・ブロイ, L.   151
Broglie, Louis-César-Victor-Maurice de
    ド・ブロイ, M.   151
Brouwer, Luitzen Egbertus Jan ブラウワー,
    L. E. J.   41
Brown, J. C. ブラウン, J. C.   8
Bunsen, Robert Wilhelm ブンゼン, R. W.
    46
Burckhardt, Jacob ブルクハルト, J.   22
Butterfield, Herbert バターフィールド, H.
    57, 275

C

Campbell, Norman Robert キャンベル, N.
    R.   122
Canguilhem, Georges カンギレム, G.   50,
    275
Carnap, Rudolf カルナップ, R.   67
Cassirer, Ernst カッシーラー, E.   40
Cavalieri, Bonaventura Francesco カヴァリ
    エリ, B. F.   95
Cavendish, Henry キャヴェンディッシュ, H.
    46
Chadwick, James チャドウィック, J.   142
Cho, Hon-yong 趙憲泳   311

Churchill, Winston チャーチル, W. 176, 302

Compton, Arthur Holly コンプトン, A. H. 169

Comte, Auguste コント, A. 30

Cook, James Wilfred クック, J. W. 205

Copernicus, Nicolaus コペルニクス, N. 10, 42, 57, 275, 278, 279, 289

Coster, Dirk コスター, D. 145

Cournot, Antoine Augustin クールノー, A. A. 21

Crowther, James Gerald クラウサー, J. G. 8, 89, 275

D

Dalton, John ドルトン, J. 179

Dannemann, Friedrich ダンネマン, F. 276

Darwin, Charles Galton ダーウィン, C. G. 168

Descartes, Rene デカルト, R. 41, 91

Dewar, Michael J. S. デュワー, M. J. S. 205

Dewar, Sir James デュワー, J. 193

Dirac, Paul Adrien Maurice ディラック, P. A. M. 129, 134, 135, 138, 167

Divers, Edward ダイヴァース, E. 185, 193, 227

Dodge, Joseph ドッジ, J. 44

Doi, Toshitsura 土井利位 32, 276

Doi, Uzumi 土井不曇 127, 128, 130, 132, 305

Driesch, Hans ドリーシュ, H. 78, 276

Duhem, Pierre デュエム, P. 12

E

Eddington, Sir Arthur Stanley エディントン, A. S. 14, 127

Einstein, Albert アインシュタイン, A. 127, 230

Emerson, Ralph Waldo エマーソン, R. W. 64

Enriques, Federigo エンリクェス, F. 8, 276

Erdmann, Johann Eduard エルトマン, J. E. 40

Erdtman, Holger エルドマン, H. 205, 231

Euclid (Eukleides) ユークリッド (エウクレイデス) 40, 73, 131, 291

Ezawa, Hiroshi 江沢洋 137, 144, 176, 302, 304

F

Farrington, Benjamin ファリントン, B. 8, 276

Fermi, Enrico フェルミ, E. 134, 168

Feyerabend, Paul Karl ファイヤアーベント, P. K. 60, 66

Fibiger, Johannes Andreas Grib フィビゲル, J. A. G. 141

Fischer, Hermann Emil フィッシャー, H. E. 187, 190, 192, 229, 308

Francis of Assisi アッシジのフランチェスコ 22

Friche, Vladimir Maksimovich フリーチェ, V. M. 15

Fujigaki, Yūko 藤垣裕子 82, 276

Fujikawa, Yū 富士川游 48

Fujimune, Kanji 藤宗寛治 42, 276

Fujinami, Shin'ichirō 藤波信一郎 15

Fujioka, Sakutarō 藤岡作太郎 93

Fujioka, Yoshio 藤岡由夫 34, 93, 276

Fujisawa, Ikunosuke 藤澤幾之輔 197

Fujisawa, Rikitarō 藤沢利喜太郎 39

Fujita, Motoharu 藤田元春 95, 276

Fujiwara, Kaichirō 藤原佳一郎 8

Fujiwara, Sakuhei 藤原咲平 93, 276

Fukagawa, Shindō 深川晨堂 265

Fukuda, Mahito 福田眞人 97, 276

Fukui, Ken'ichi 福井謙一 207, 232, 276

Fukushima, Masato 福島真人 100, 299

Fukuzawa, Yukichi 福沢諭吉 18

Funayama, Shin'ichi 舩山信一 89, 277

Furuhashi, Hironoshin 古橋広之進 168

Furukawa, Yasu 古川安 96, 277

Fushimi, Kōji 伏見康治 32, 277

G

Galilei, Galileo ガリレイ, G. (ガリレオ) 57, 126, 127

Gardner, Eugene ガードナー, E. 167

Gauss, Johann Carl Friedrich ガウス, J. C. F. 40
Gilbert, William ギルバート, W. 56
Goethe, Johann Wolfgang von ゲーテ, J. W. von 67
Gotō, Masatoshi 後藤仁敏 98, 277
Gunning, Jan Willem フニング, J. W. 226
Gutting, Gary ガッティング, G. 277

H

Haga, Tamemasa 垪和為昌 185, 190, 229
Handō, Kazutoshi 半藤一利 159, 302
Hanson, Norwood Russell ハンソン, N. R. 60
Hara, Mitsuo 原光雄 36, 37, 45, 180, 234, 277
Harries, Carl ハリエス, C. 191, 308
Harvey, William ハーヴェイ, W. 47
Hasegawa, Tai 長谷川泰 241, 243, 251, 265, 311
Hashida, Kunihiko 橋田邦彦 23, 24, 92, 277
Hatano, Sadao 波多野貞夫 143, 302
Hatoyama, Hideo 鳩山秀夫 108, 176
Hatoyama, Kazuo 鳩山和夫 108
Hatoyama, Michio 鳩山道夫 148, 150, 158, 303
Hattori, Toshirō 服部敏良 48, 278
Hawthorne, Nathaniel ホーソン, N. 64
Hayasaka, Toshio 早坂寿雄 94, 278
Hayashi, Takashi 林襄 34, 94, 278
Hayashi, Tatsuo 林達夫 14, 278
Hegel, Georg Wilhelm Friedrich ヘーゲル, G. W. F. 11, 18, 54
Heisenberg, Werner Karl ハイゼンベルク, W. K. 129, 134, 135, 136, 140, 142, 144, 161, 303
Hiraga, Yoshimi 平賀義美 （see Ishimatsu, Sadamu 石松決） 188
Hiraga, Yuzuru 平賀譲 112, 156
Hirai, Hiro 平井浩 87, 278
Hirakawa, Hideyuki 平川秀幸 82, 278
Hirata, Morizo 平田森三 32
Hirata, Yoshimasa 平田義正 206

Hiromatsu, Wataru 廣松渉 65, 278
Hirose, Hideo 広瀬秀雄 42, 278
Hiroshige, Tetsu 広重徹 43, 94, 278
Hoashi, Banri 帆足万理 30
Hobbes, Thomas ホッブス, T. 41
Hofmann, August Wilhelm von ホフマン, A. W. von 186
Honda, Kōtarō 本多光太郎 125, 141, 142, 156
Honda, Shūrō 本多修郎 8, 11, 278
Honda, Toshiaki 本多利明 14
Hori, Takeo 堀健夫 131
Horiuchi, Kyōko 堀内恭子 200
Horiuchi, Seiichi 堀内政一 200
Hoshino, Yoshirō 星野芳郎 37, 279
Husserl, Edmund フッサール, E. 41

I

Ichinomiya, Torao 一宮虎雄 143
Ienaga, Saburō 家永三郎 13, 279
Ijiri, Shōji 井尻正二 54, 98, 279
Ikeda, Kikunae 池田菊苗 109, 184, 186, 225
Ikeda, Kiyohiko 池田清彦 98, 279
Ikeuchi, Osamu 池内紀 72
Ikeuchi, Satoru 池内了 72, 279
Inō, Tadataka 伊能忠敬 114, 115
Inoue, Kiyotsune 井上清恒 48, 280
Inoue, Nikichi 井上仁吉 143
Inoue, Shūzō 井上修三 184
Inoue, Takeshi 井上健 151, 280
Ishiwara, Jun 石原純 93, 126-128, 130, 131, 144, 145, 280, 303
Ishii, Atsushi 石井厚 96, 280
Ishii, Tomoyuki 石井友幸 19, 280
Ishimatsu, Sadamu 石松決 (see Hiraga, Yoshimi 平賀義美) 188
Iso, Naomichi 磯直道 9, 280
Itakura, Kiyonobu 板倉聖宣 54, 280, 303
Itō, Junkichi 伊藤順吉 155
Itō, Shuntarō 伊東俊太郎 62, 265, 280, 281
Itō, Yōji 伊藤庸二 153

Iwatsuki, Toranosuke 岩付寅之助 92, 281

J

Joliot-Curie, Irène ジョリオ・キュリー, I. 142
Joliot-Curie, Jean Frédéric ジョリオ・キュリー, J. F. 142
Jordan, Pascual ヨルダン, P. 129

K

Kaburagi, Tokio 鏑木外岐雄 303
Kafuku, Kinzō 加福均三 199, 230
Kainosho, Masayasu 甲斐荘正泰 231
Kainoshō, Tadaka 甲斐荘楠香 231
Kakehashi, Akihide 梯明秀 90, 281
Kamatani, Chikayoshi 鎌谷親善 46, 281
Kanamori, Osamu 金森修 viii, 9, 100, 225, 264, 273, 281, 309
Kaneko, Kunihiko 金子邦彦 281
Kaneko, Tsutomu 金子務 96, 281
Kanō, Kōkichi 狩野亨吉 14, 111
Kant, Immanuel カント, I. 40, 66, 91, 95
Kashiwagi, Hajime 柏木肇 38, 282
Katayama, Masao 片山正夫 196
Katō, Fumiharu 加藤文元 42, 282
Katō, Gen'ichi 加藤元一 141
Katō, Hiroyuki 加藤弘之 18
Katsura, Shigehiro 桂重鴻 201
Kawade, Yoshimi 川出由巳 47, 282
Kawaguchi, Hiroshi 川口浩 15
Kawaguchi, Toshikazu 川口利一 266
Kawai, Takeshi 川井雄 8, 294
Kawakami, Shin'ichi 川上紳一 32, 282
Kawakami, Takeshi 川上武 48, 282
Kawakami, Tamejirō 川上為次郎 96, 282
Kawakami, Tetsutarō 河上徹太郎 282
Kawakita, Yoshio 川喜田愛郎 49, 51, 282
Kawamoto, Hideo 河本英夫 67, 282
Kawamoto, Kōmin 川本幸民 181, 226
Keimatsu, Shōzaemon 慶松勝左衛門 258
Kepler, Johannes ケプラー, J. 57, 63
Kigi, Takatarō 木々高太郎 94, 278
Kihara, Tarō 木原太郎 96
Kihira, Tadayoshi 紀平正美 24, 283

Kikuchi, Kan 菊池寛 141
Kikuchi, Seishi 菊池正士 133, 138, 139, 142, 149, 153
Kikuchi, Taiji 菊池泰二 137
Kimura, Bin 木村敏 49, 51, 283
Kimura, Chōkyū 木村長久 239, 250
Kimura, Hakushō 木村博昭 249, 250
Kimura, Hisashi 木村栄 105, 119, 141
Kimura, Masamichi 木村正路 132
Kimura, Yōjirō 木村陽二郎 46, 283
Kitao, Jirō 北尾次郎 39
Kitasato, Shibasaburō 北里柴三郎 39, 119, 141
Kiuchi, Masazō 木内政蔵 130
Klein, Oscar Benjamin クライン, O. B. 134, 137
Knott, Cargill Gilston ノット, C. G. 118
Kobayashi, Hideo 小林英夫 95, 283
Kobayashi, Makoto 小林誠 103
Kobayashi, Minoru 小林稔 137, 144
Kobayashi, Tadashi 小林傳司 82, 283
Komatsu, Yoshihiko 小松美彦 74, 283
Kondō, Heizaburō 近藤平三郎 228
Kondō, Yōitsu 近藤洋逸 8, 39, 283, 284
Konno, Takeo 今野武雄 8, 19, 284
Konoe, Fumimaro 近衛文麿 164
Kōra, Takehisa 高良武久 96, 284
Koshiba, Masatoshi 小柴昌俊 103, 170, 303
Kosoto, Hiroshi 小曽戸洋 265, 311
Kotō, Bunjirō 小藤文次郎 39, 185
Koyama, Keiichi 児山敬一 93, 284
Koyasu, Nobukuni 子安宣邦 263, 267, 312
Kozai, Yoshishige 古在由重 18, 34, 284
Kripke, Saul クリプキ, S. 67, 88
Kubo, Masaji 久保昌二 45, 284
Kubota, Bennosuke 久保田勉之助 228, 231
Kuhara, Mitsuru 久原躬弦 185, 233
Kuhn, Thomas クーン, T. 57, 284
Kujirai, Tsunetarō 鯨井恒太郎 137
Kuki, Shūzō 九鬼周造 21, 284

Kundt, August Adolf Eduard Eberhard ク
ント, A. A. E. E. 125
Kuno, Osamu 久野収 14
Kurahashi, Shigefumi 倉橋重史 96, 284
Kuroda, Eiko 黒田暎子 64
Kushibiki, Junjirō 櫛引純二郎 216, 220
Kuwaki, Ayao 桑木彧雄 27, 30, 126, 130, 284

L

Laporte, Otto ラポルテ, O. 134
Latour, Bruno ラトゥール, B. 100, 285
Lattes, César ラッテス, C. 167
Lavoisier, Antoine Laurent ラヴォワジエ, A. L. 181
Lawrence, Ernest Orlando ローレンス, E. O. 142, 145-148, 152, 161, 162
Leblanc, Nicolas ルブラン, N. 46
Leibniz, Gottfried Wilhelm ライプニッツ, G. W. 91
Leonardo da Vinci レオナルド・ダ・ヴィンチ 22
Lobachevsky, Nikolai Ivanovich ロバチェフスキー, N. I. 40
Locke, John ロック, J. 66
Lodge, Oliver Joseph ロッジ, O. J. 121
Lotze, Rudolf Hermann ロッツェ, R. H. 40
Lysenko, Trofim Denisovich ルイセンコ, T. D. 47, 100

M

Mach, Ernst マッハ, E. 12
Maeda, Takakazu 前田隆一 24, 92, 285
Majima, Minoru 眞島實 209, 210, 215, 216, 217
Majima, Rikō 眞島利行 181, 183, 184, 193, 196, 206, 208, 209, 211, 213, 217, 219, 221-223, 225, 226, 227, 231, 232, 270
Majima, Toshimitsu 眞島利三 209, 210, 213
Majima, Toshitami 眞島利民 183, 184
Majima, Toshizumi 眞島利往 183
Majima, Yukio 眞島行雄 226
Manase, Dōsan 曲直瀬道三 239

Marshak, Robert E. マルシャク, R. E. 167
Marx, Karl マルクス, K. 19
Masaoka, Shiki 正岡子規 96
Maskawa, Toshihide 益川敏英 103
Matsubara, Kōichi 松原行一 186, 190
Matsui, Naokichi 松井直吉 182
Matsui, Takafumi 松井孝典 71, 285
Matsumae, Shigeyoshi 松前重義 26, 285
Matsumoto, Miwao 松本三和夫 75, 285
Matsuoka, Seigō 松岡正剛 65
Matsuyama, Juichi 松山壽一 95, 285
Maxwell, James Clerk マックスウェル, J. C. 42
Melville, Herman メルヴィル, H. 64
Mendeleev, Dmitrii Ivanovich メンデレーエフ, D. I. 225
Mercer, Rosemary メルサー, R. 97
Merton, Robert マートン, R. 58
Michurin, Ivan Vladimirovich ミチューリン, I. V. 100
Miki, Kiyoshi 三木清 16, 20, 285
Miki, Sakae 三木榮 96, 285
Miki, Shigeo 三木成夫 71, 98, 285
Millikan, R.A. ミリカン, R. A. 113, 169
Minakata, Kumagusu 南方熊楠 110
Minobe, Tatsukichi 美濃部達吉 164
Mita, Hiroo 三田博雄 97, 285
Miura, Baien 三浦梅園 17, 53
Miyake, Gōichi 三宅剛一 91, 285
Miyama, Kisaburō 三山喜三郎 189, 228, 309
Miyamoto, Takenosuke 宮本武之輔 26, 286
Miyazaki, Michimasa 宮崎道正 224, 233
Miyazaki, Yasusada 宮崎安貞 10
Miyazawa, Kenji 宮沢賢治 96
Mizuno, Tadafumi 水野忠文 96, 286
Mizushima, San'ichiro 水島三一郎 155
Moleschott, Jacob モレスホット, J. 11
Mori, Arinori 森有礼 117, 176, 303
Mori, Dōhaku 森道伯 251
Mori, Ōgai (Rintarō) 森鷗外 (林太郎) 55
Morse, Edward Sylvester モース, E. S. 64
Mott, Nevill Francis モット, N. F. 168

Murakami, Shūji 村上秀二　25, 286
Murakami, Yōichirō 村上陽一郎　60, 68, 265, 286
Murata, Jun'ichi 村田純一　95, 286
Murata, Tamotsu 村田全　95, 287

N

Nagai, Hiroshi 永井博　22, 287
Nagai, Hisomu 永井潜　89, 287
Nagai, Nagayoshi 長井長義　186, 228
Nagano, Kei 長野敬　47, 287
Nagaoka, Hantarō 長岡半太郎　105, 106, 138, 141, 162, 175, 218, 234, 304
Nagata, Hiroshi 永田広志　17, 287
Nagayo, Sensai 長与専斎　242, 265
Nakae, Chōmin 中江兆民　18
Nakagawa, Yonezō 中川米造　49, 50, 51, 287
Nakai, Hisao 中井久夫　96, 287
Nakajima, Hideto 中島秀人　100, 281
Nakamura, Keiko 中村桂子　70, 287
Nakamura, Teiri 中村禎里　47, 287
Nakane, Genkei 中根元圭　14
Nakane, Ryōhei 中根良平　304
Nakao, Maika 中尾麻伊香　304
Nakaya, Ukichirō 中谷宇吉郎　32, 288
Nakayama, Shigeru 中山茂　58, 288
Nakayama, Tadanao 中山忠直　239, 240, 248, 250, 254, 266, 312
Nakazawa, Shin'ichi 中沢新一　13, 288
Nambu, Yōichirō 南部陽一郎　103
Natsume, Sōseki 夏目漱石　100, 109, 228, 304
Neddermeyer, Seth Henry ネッダーマイヤー, S. H.　143, 169
Needham, Joseph ニーダム, J.　53
Negishi, Eiichi 根岸英一　232
Neumann, John von ノイマン, J. von　41
Newton, Isaac ニュートン, I.　41, 43, 57, 63, 67, 95, 127
Nishi, Amane 西周　18
Nishida, Sotohiko 西田外彦　131, 132
Nishina, Yoshio 仁科芳雄　135, 136, 142, 175, 218, 233, 305

Nishio, Shigeko 西尾成子　43, 288
Nobel, Alfred Bernhard ノーベル, A. B.　169
Noe, Keiichi 野家啓一　65, 289
Noguchi, Hideyo 野口英世　156
Nomura, Kodō 野村胡堂　305
Noyori, Ryōji 野依良治　232
Nozoe, Jūichi 野副重一　196, 197
Nozoe, Tetsuo 野副鐵男　195-198, 203, 204, 230, 270, 310

O

Ochiai, Eiji 落合英二　228
Oda, Nobunaga 織田信長　48
Ogawa, Seishū 小川政修　48, 289
Ogawa, Teizō 小川鼎三　265, 312
Ogawa, Tōru 小川泰　32, 289
Ogura, Kinnosuke 小倉金之助　28, 289
Oka, Asajirō 丘浅次郎　64, 90, 289
Oka, Kunio 岡邦雄　8, 9, 14, 89, 289
Okamoto, Takuji 岡本拓司　88, 270, 305
Okanishi, Tameto 岡西為人　255
Ōkōchi, Masatoshi 大河内正敏　26, 149, 164, 289
Okuda, Kenzō 奥田謙蔵　247
Ōkuma, Nobuyuki 大熊信行　26, 290
Okuno, Masazō 奥野政蔵　220
Omata, Waichirō 小俣和一郎　96, 290
Omodaka, Hisayuki 澤瀉久敬　49, 290
Onnes, Heike Kamerlingh オネス, H. K.　125, 145
Ōmori, Shōzō 大森荘蔵　65, 68, 290
Onozuka, Kiheiji 小野塚喜平次　171
Oppenheimer, J. Robert オッペンハイマー, J. R.　143
Osborn, Henry Fairfield オズボーン（オスボーン）, H. F.　290
Ostwald, Friedrich Wilhelm オストワルト, F. W.　225
Ōtsuka, Yasuo 大塚恭男　247, 265, 312
Ōtsuka, Yoshinori 大塚敬節　238-240, 250-252, 264, 266, 312

P

Paneth, Friedrich Adolf パネト, F. A.　225
Partington, James Riddick パーティントン, J. R.　225
Pauling, Linus Carl ポーリング, L. C.　202, 206
Pavlov, Ivan Petrovich パヴロフ, I. P.　141
Peierls, Rudolf Ernst パイエルス, R. E.　138
Peirce, Charles Sanders パース, C. S.　63
Perkin, Jr., William Henry パーキンJr., W. H.　190
Planck, Max Karl Ernst Ludwig プランク, M. K. E. L.　12, 129
Plato プラトン　85, 91
Plekhanov, Georgij Valentinovich プレハーノフ, G. V.　15
Poe, Edgar Allan ポー, E. A.　64
Poincaré, Jules-Henri ポアンカレ, J.-H.　12, 30, 121, 306
Polanyi, Michael ポランニー, M.　225
Popper, Sir Karl Raimund ポパー, K. R.　62
Powell, Cecil Frank パウエル, C. F.　167-169
Prokofev, V. I. プロコフィエフ, V. I.　8, 290

Q

Quine, Willard van Orman クワイン, W. van O.　67, 88

R

Raman, Chandrasekhara Venkara ラマン, C. V.　140, 141
Ramsay, Sir William ラムジー, W.　231
Reichenbach, Hans ライヘンバッハ, H.　62
Rickert, Heinrich John リッケルト, H. J.　16
Riemann, Georg Friedrich Bernhard リーマン, G. F. B.　40
Robinson, Sir Robert ロビンソン, R.　231
Rocke, Alan J. ロック, A. J.　310
Rutherford, Ernest ラザフォード, E.　121, 172

S

Sagane, Ryōkichi 嵯峨根遼吉　138, 145, 146, 158, 306
Saigusa, Hiroto 三枝博音　16, 17, 290, 291
Saitō, Ken 斎藤憲　73, 291
Sakai, Shizu 酒井シヅ　48, 265, 291
Sakamoto, Kenzō 坂本賢三　5, 9, 291
Sakamoto, Takao 坂本多加雄　306
Sakano, Tōru 坂野徹　73, 291
Sakata, Shōichi 坂田昌一　137, 144, 151, 153, 167, 291
Sako, Kiyoji 迫喜代治　176, 306
Sakurai, Jōji 桜井錠二　39, 182, 185, 186, 190, 191, 227
Sakurai, Kunitomo 桜井邦朋　95, 291
Sakuta, Shōichi 作田荘一　24, 291
Sarton, George サートン, G.　291
Sasaki, Chikara 佐々木力　39, 40, 291
Satō, Katsuhiko 佐藤勝彦　99, 292
Satō, Ken'ichi 佐藤賢一　73, 292
Scerri, Eric R. シェリー, E. R.　225
Schein, Marcel シャイン, M.　168
Schott, George Adolphus ショット, G. A.　120, 121
Schrödinger, Ernest シュレーディンガー, E.　129
Schummer, Joachim シューマー, J.　225
Seki, Takakazu 関孝和　10, 14
Sekiguchi, Shigeki 関口蕃樹　232
Serber, Robert サーバー, R.　143
Seta, Yūichi 世田雄一　97
Shiba, Tetsuo 芝哲夫　232, 310
Shibata, Shingo 芝田進午　13, 292
Shibatani, Atsuhiro 柴谷篤弘　69, 292
Shiga, Kōji 志賀浩二　42, 292
Shimao, Nagayasu 島尾永康　8, 43, 46, 97, 234, 292
Shimazaki, Tōson 島崎藤村　141
Shimizu, Fujitarō 清水藤太郎　239
Shimomura, Osamu 下村脩　206, 207, 231, 232, 310

Shimomura, Toratarō 下村寅太郎　21, 34, 91, 293
Shimosaka, Ei 下坂英　68, 264, 265, 293
Shinkai, Mieko 新開美枝子　191, 229
Shinmura, Taku 新村拓　97, 293
Shinran 親鸞　20
Shirakawa, Hideki 白川英樹　232
Siegbahn, Karl Manne Georg シーグバーン, K. M. G.　157, 170, 171
Sōda, Hajime 宗田一　48
Sommerfeld, Arnold Johannes Wilhelm ゾンマーフェルト, A. J. W.　134
Sogawa, Harue 十川治江　65, 293
Sone, Hiroshi 曽根博　306
Sone, Take 曽禰武　135
Stark, Johannes シュタルク, J.　124
Stern, Otto シュテルン, O.　168
Stevenson, Edward C. スティーヴンソン, E. C.　143
Stöckhardt, J.A. シュテックハルト, J. A.　226, 310
Street, Jabez Curry ストリート, J. C.　143
Stueckelberg, Ernst Carl Gerlach ステュッケルベルク, E. C. G.　143, 144
Suetsuna, Jōichi 末綱恕一　28, 34
Sugai, Jun'ichi 菅井準一　27, 293
Sugasawa, Shigehiko 菅沢重彦　205, 231
Sugawara, Takeshi 菅原仰　43
Sugi, Yasusaburo 杉靖三郎　92
Sugihara, Tokuyuki 杉原徳行　240, 255, 256, 258, 264, 267
Sugimoto, Isao 杉本勲　58, 293
Suginome, Harusada 杉野目晴貞　230
Sugita, Gempaku 杉田玄白　181
Sugiura, Shigetake 杉浦重剛　180
Sugiura, Yoshikatsu 杉浦義勝　136
Sugiyama, Jirō 杉山滋郎　264, 265, 313
Sun Yat Sen 孫文　110
Suzuki, Akihito 鈴木晃仁　87, 294
Suzuki, Akira 鈴木章　232
Suzuki, Kantarō 鈴木貫太郎　33
Suzuki, Sadami 鈴木貞美　89, 294
Suzuki, Umetarō 鈴木梅太郎　125, 141
Suzuki, Yasuzō 鈴木安蔵　15

Suzuki, Zenji 鈴木善次　99, 294
Svedberg, Theodor "The" スヴェドベリ, T.　168

T

Tagore, Rabindranath タゴール, R.　140
Taguchi, Ryūzaburō 田口卯三郎　32, 94, 294
Taine, Hippolyte テーヌ, H.　15
Tajima, Eizō 田島英三　306
Takabayashi, Takehiko 高林武彦　43, 294
Takada, Seiji 高田誠二　94, 294
Takagi, Jinzaburō 高木仁三郎　76, 294
Takagi, Teiji 高木貞治　28, 34, 294
Takahashi, Katsumi 高橋克己　166
Takahashi, Ken'ichi 高橋憲一　73, 294
Takahashi, Korekiyo 高橋是清　184, 227
Takamine, Toshio 高嶺俊夫　130
Takasu, Rokurō 高須碌郎　233
Takebe, Hiraku 武部啓　8
Takebe, Kenkō 建部賢弘　10
Takeuchi, Hitoshi 竹内均　43, 295
Takeuchi, Masa 竹内柾　138, 143, 302
Takeuchi, Yoshito 竹内敬人　45, 295
Takeya, Mitsuo 武谷三男　20
Takizawa, Toshiyuki 瀧澤利行　96, 295
Tamaki, Hidehiko 玉木英彦　160
Tamaki, Kajūrō 玉城嘉十郎　131
Tamiya, Hiroshi 田宮博　34
Tamura, Matsuhei 田村松平　131, 132, 295
Tanabe, Hajime 田邊(田辺)元　12, 13, 20, 21, 40, 121, 295
Tanaka, Hajime 田中一　90, 296
Tanaka, Kōichi 田中耕一　232
Tanaka, Minoru 田中実　45, 296
Tanaka, Shōzō 田中正造　76
Tanakadate, Aikitu 田中舘愛橘　39, 107, 110, 119, 126, 155, 159, 172
Tanikawa, Yasutaka 谷川安孝　151
Tateno, Yukio 館野之男　96
Tatsukawa, Shōji 立川昭二　48, 296
Tatsuno, Kazuo 龍野一雄　238, 252, 256, 258, 264, 267, 313

Tejima, Seiichi 手島精一　228
Terada, Torahiko 寺田寅彦　31, 72, 110, 126, 128, 130, 296, 307
Thales of Miletus ターレス　89
Thibaud, Jean ティボー, J.　168
Thomson, Joseph John トムソン, J. J.　121, 176
Toda, Morikazu 戸田盛和　93, 296
Tokutomi, Sohō 徳富蘇峰　141
Tomonaga, Sin-Itirō 朝永振一郎　35, 296, 307
Tosaka, Jun 戸坂潤　16, 296
Toyama, Hiraku 遠山啓　54
Tsuboi, Chuji 坪井忠二　133
Tsuboi, Shōgorō 坪井正五郎　228
Tsuda, Kyōsuke 津田恭介　228
Tsuda, Mamichi 津田真道　18
Tsuji, Tetsuo 辻哲夫　97, 297
Tsukakoshi, Osamu 塚越修　94

U

Uchihashi, Katsuto 内橋克人　95
Uda, Michitaka 宇田道隆　93, 297
Udagawa, Yōan 宇田川榕菴　181, 311
Uhlenbeck, George Eugene ユーレンベック, G. E.　130
Ui, Jun 宇井純　76, 297
Uramoto, Seizaburō 浦本政三郎　24

V

Vico, Giambattista ヴィーコ, G.　41
Virchow, Rudolf Ludwig Karl ウィルヒョウ, R. L. K.　56
Vogt, Karl Christoph フォークト, K. C.　11

W

Wada, Keijūrō 和田啓十郎　239, 240, 243, 247–250, 254, 264, 265, 313
Wallach, Otto ワラッハ, O.　187
Watanabe, Ichirō 渡邊市郎　92
Watanabe, Itaru 渡辺格　69, 297
Watanabe, Masao 渡辺正雄　63, 297
Watanabe, Satoshi 渡邊慧　96, 165, 298, 307

Watanabe, Toshio 渡辺敏夫　95, 298
Wentzel, Gregor ヴェンツェル, G.　168
Werne, Alfred ウェルナー, A.　191
Weyl, Hermann ワイル, H.　41
William of Ockham オッカムのウィリアム　91
Williamson, Alexander W. ウィリアムソン, A. W.　182, 226
Willstätter, Richard ヴィルシュテッター, R.　192–194, 311
Wittgenstein, Ludwig ウィトゲンシュタイン, L.　41, 65, 66, 88

Y

Yabuuchi, Kiyoshi 藪内清　52, 298
Yagi, Hidetsugu 八木秀次　139
Yajima, Suketoshi 矢島祐利　8, 42, 43, 298
Yakazu, Dōmei 矢数道明　239, 240, 250, 251, 254, 258, 261, 266, 267, 313
Yakazu, Kaku 矢数格　250
Yamada, Keiji 山田慶児　53, 298
Yamada, Sakaji 山田坂仁　37, 298
Yamada, Terutane 山田光胤　239, 265, 266, 314
Yamagata, Bantō 山片幡桃　18
Yamagiwa, Katsusaburō 山極勝三郎　125, 141
Yamakawa, Kenjirō 山川健次郎　64
Yamamoto, Mineo 山本峰雄　158
Yamamoto, Shun'ichi 山本俊一　48, 298
Yamamoto, Yoshitaka 山本義隆　43, 45, 298
Yamanaka, Hisashi 山中恒　159, 307
Yamanouchi, Takahiko 山内恭彦　132, 299
Yamaoka, Nozomu 山岡望　45, 234, 299
Yamashita, Shinji 山下晋司　299
Yamawaki, Tōyō 山脇東洋　10
Yanagita, Kunio 柳田国男　67, 110
Yanagiya, Sorei 柳谷素霊　252
Yano, Michio 矢野道雄　53, 299
Yasui, Hiromichi 安井廣迪　239, 265, 314
Yasui, Zen'ichi 安井善一　93

Yazaki, Tameichi 矢崎為一　145, 147, 148, 153, 162, 307
Yokoyama, Taikan 横山大観　141
Yonemoto, Shōhei 米本昌平　78, 299
Yōrō, Takeshi 養老孟司　99, 299
Yoshida, Hikorokurō 吉田彦六郎　188
Yoshida, Mitsukuni 吉田光邦　52, 299
Yoshida, Takeshi 吉田武　42, 300
Yoshihara, Kenji 吉原賢二　159, 307
Yoshimasu, Tōdō 吉益東洞　243, 246
Yoshioka, Hitoshi 吉岡斉　59, 78, 79, 300
Yoshioka, Shūichirō 吉岡修一郎　8, 10, 300
Yuasa, Akira 湯浅明　46, 300
Yuasa, Mitsutomo 湯浅光朝　38, 57, 300
Yukawa, Hideki 湯川秀樹　35, 103, 131, 153, 156-158, 270, 300, 301
Yukawa, Hideo 湯川日出男　156, 159, 308
Yumoto, Kyūshin 湯本求真　239, 247, 250, 254, 265, 266, 314

Z

Zinin, Nikolai Nikolaevich ジーニン, N. N. 225

Subject Index

A

abduction アブダクション 63
academic science アカデミズム科学 59
academic urges 学問的誘惑 87
academy police 学界警察 127, 128
Academy Prize 学士院賞 142, 205
aequorin イクオリン 207
Agency of Science and Technology 技術院 26
agenda of logical positivism 科学の論理学 66
aliens 宇宙人 71, 285
all observation is always already theoretically-informed 観察の理論負荷性 66
analysis of Being (Daseinsanalysis) 現存在分析 51
Anatomische Tabellen, Kaitai shinsho (New book of anatomy)『解体新書』 181
anatomy 解剖学 242
Anglican Church イギリス国教会系 210–212, 232
anointment 抹油礼 211
anthroposphere 人間圏 71, 72
anti-relativity 反相対論 118, 127
apagoge アパゴーゲー 63
applied science 応用学 24, 25, 113, 117, 166
Arcadia アルカディア 72
arcane scientific fields 鵺的な学問 5
archeological gem 考古学的な宝蔵体 88
art of making elixirs 煉丹術 97
aspect perception アスペクト知覚 66
Association of East Asian Medicine 東亜医学協会 238, 239, 251, 258, 265, 266, 313
atomic bomb 原子爆弾 92, 152, 153, 155, 157, 159–164, 176, 301, 302, 304, 307, 308

atomic model 原子模型 119–122, 125, 154, 169, 171, 172, 176
atomic nuclei 原子核 103, 104, 153
atomic weights 原子量 179, 180, 225

B

Baden school バーデン学派 16
Bansho Shirabesho (the Institute for the Study of Barbarian Books) 蛮書調所 181
basic medicine 基礎医学 243, 244, 270
basic research 純粋研究 149
basic science 純粋科学 117, 149, 150, 156, 163, 165, 166, 172
battle of treatment between kampō and Western medicine 漢洋脚気相撲 244
battlefield surgeons 金創医 49
beriberi 脚気 55, 122, 265
bioethics 生命倫理学 50, 51, 74, 78, 283, 299
Bioethics Roundtable 生命倫理会議 74
biohistory 生命誌 70, 287
biological semiotics 生物記号論 47
biology research group in the biology section 生物学史研究会 47
biomemory 生命記憶 71
biosphere 生物圏 71
biotechnology バイオテクノロジー 47, 48, 74
black-body radiation 黒体輻射 43
Bose statistics ボース統計 139
buffer 緩衝装置 84

C

capitalist industry 資本主義工業 27
CAS (Chemical Abstracts Service) registration numbers CAS登録番号 225
catechol カテコール 189, 190, 192
causal treatment 原因療法 243, 244, 264

Central Research Institute of Taiwan's Governor-General 台湾総督府中央研究所 199

chemical atomic theory 化学的原子論 179, 181, 225

Chemistry Department in the College of Science at the Imperial University 帝国大学理科大学化学科 182

cholera コレラ 48, 49, 297

Christian キリスト教徒 48, 49, 116, 176, 196, 209–215, 222, 232, 265, 297, 312

Christianity キリスト教 49, 116, 209, 211–214, 232

Chūkanshi kondankai (meson roundtable) 中間子懇談会 151

Chunqiu (The spring and autumn annals) 『春秋』 107

citizen science 市民科学 77

Citizens' Nuclear Information Center 原子力資料情報室 77

classes in hypothetical experiments 仮説実験授業 55

classic foundation of modern chemistry 現代化学の古典的な基礎 180

classification of methods of discovery 発見法の類型学 63

clinical philosophy 臨床哲学 99

collapse of the faculty of liberal arts 教養部解体 80

colonial science 植民地科学 224

Committee on Physics 物理懇談会 153

Competitive View of Science 競争的科学観 114, 115, 118, 174

concept of scientific revolution 科学革命論 57, 58

conscious application theory 意識的適用説 20

consensus development conferences コンセンサス会議 82

contemporary response to the problems of science and technology 科学技術問題への同時代的対応 74

context-dependent notion of object recognition 物体認知の文脈依存性 61

controversies in technological theory 技術論論争 37

controversies of relativism 相対主義論争 57

coordinators of social issues 社会問題調整官 84

Copernicus of Japan 日本のコペルニクス 10

cosmic rays 宇宙線 138, 139, 143, 144, 146–148, 150–152, 154, 155, 158, 161, 167, 174, 176, 304, 305, 307

criticism of science 科学の批判的対象化 7, 16

cybernetics サイバネティクス 6

cyclotron サイクロトロン 33, 104, 129, 138, 139, 143, 145–149, 152, 154–156, 158, 161–168, 176, 301–304

cypridina luciferin ウミホタルルシフェリン 206

D

Daigaku Nankō 大学南校 109, 182

death 死 10, 18, 48, 69, 71, 74, 94, 97, 117, 172, 174, 185, 208–217, 220, 221, 227, 232, 234, 241, 283, 293

death of Majima's family members 眞島の肉親の死 209, 215

democratic science 民主主義科学 34, 94

Democratic Scientists Association (Minka) 民主主義科学者協会(民科) 33, 47, 75

Department of Science in the Cabinet Planning Board 企画院科学部 26

development of the dialectical method 弁証法的発展 9

discovery 発見 45, 62, 63, 89, 119, 125, 127, 129, 151, 152, 154, 155, 167, 169, 170, 200, 207, 213, 229, 231, 232, 244, 277, 299, 305, 308, 310

distant past 遠い過去 76, 85, 86

documentary records 資料的なもの 56

Dodge Line ドッジ・ライン 44

dogmatic theory of art 教条的芸術論 15

domain-specific nature of individual sciences 領域画定的な科学性   54
Dongui Bogam 東医宝鑑   262
dual cosmic forces, yin and yang 陰陽思想   53

E

East Asian medicine 東洋医学   238, 239, 240, 247, 250–253, 255, 258, 261, 263–267, 312–314
East Asian Medicine Movement 東亜医学運動   240, 250–253, 255, 258, 261, 263, 264
East-West comparative medicine theory 東西医学比較論   243
eco-socialism 環境社会主義   95
Einstein boom アインシュタインブーム   127
electronic theories in organic chemistry 有機電子論   224
elementals of pollution, the 公害原論   76, 297
elementary particle physics 素粒子物理学   103, 104, 170
elementary particles 素粒子   33, 44, 88, 104, 163, 167, 170, 270, 306
elements of the histories of scientific thought 科学思想史的なもの   55
emerging monism 立ち現われ一元論   65, 66
emperor's address regarding the backing of military personnel 軍人援護に関する勅語   222
enlightenment view of the history of scientific thought 啓蒙主義的科学思想史   7
entropy エントロピー   96
environmental problems 地球環境問題   72, 74
epistemological study of quantum theory 量子論の認識論的研究   43
epistemology 認識論   18, 30, 34–36, 50, 54, 65, 66, 73, 272 278, 281, 284, 287, 296, 298
ethics for engineers 技術者倫理   7

etiology 病原学   244
everyday world 日常的世界   61
evidence-based treatment 対証療法   254
existence of atoms and molecules 原子·分子の実在性   180

F

field theory 場の理論   151, 167, 168
First Advanced Middle School 第一高等中学校   184
First Higher School 第一高等学校   127, 184, 185, 187, 233
flathead harpoons 平頭銛   94
food safety issues 食品安全問題   74
foreign teachers お雇い外国人   116, 181
form of action 行為の形   20
formalism 形式主義   41
Formosan cypress ベニヒ   199
Foundation for Japanese Chemical Research 財団法人日本化学研究会   220
foundation of mathematics 数学基礎論   41
Fulaohua 福語   198

G

generic joining 類型的展開   85
genetically modified organisms 遺伝子組み換え生物   74
get involved in society 直接的な社会参加   86
get with the times 現代性   86
GHQ 連合国最高司令官総司令部   33, 231
Gosei school 後世派   245, 246, 250
Governor-General of Taiwan 台湾総督府   198, 200, 203
green fluorescent protein 緑色蛍光蛋白質   207, 232
Guidelines for Science and Technology under the New Structure 科学技術新体制確立要綱   26

H

Hansen's disease (leprosy) ハンセン病 49

Harries' vacuum distillation methods ハリエスの高度減圧蒸留法 194

Hartree approximation ハートリー近似 134

Hattori Hōkōkai Prize 服部報公会賞 144, 154

hinokichin ヒノキチン 199, 200, 203

hinokitiol ヒノキチオール 196, 201–205, 224, 231, 308

histoire de la science (a history of science as a whole) 綜合的科学思想史 30

histoire des sciences (history of particular sciences) 個別科学史 30

historical view of the dynamics of various civilizations 文明動態史観 62

historicity 歴史性 5, 7, 24, 40, 70, 85

histories of Chinese science 中国の科学史 52

histories of science focusing on research of documentary records 資料的な科学史 56

histories of scientific thought centered on biotechnology バイオテクノロジーの科学思想史 48

history of biology 生物学史 46–48, 283, 287, 296, 300, 313

history of eugenics 優生学史 99

history of mathematical thought 数学思想史 4, 39, 41

history of mathematics 数学史 10, 28, 39–42, 73, 95, 97, 282–285, 289, 292, 300

history of medical philosophy 医学思想史 89

history of medicine 医学史 48, 49, 51, 52, 96, 97, 265, 278, 280, 281, 282, 285, 291, 312

history of physics 物理学史 35, 42, 43, 45, 66, 97, 130, 280, 288, 295, 297, 298

history of science 科学史 3, 5, 7, 10, 11, 13, 21, 22, 27, 28, 30, 33, 35, 36, 38, 39, 42–44, 45, 52–58, 60–63, 65, 67, 68, 72–74, 76, 77, 80–88, 93, 95, 96, 98, 100, 173, 225, 265 275, 277, 278, 281, 282, 284, 286, 288, 290–294, 296, 298–300, 305, 307, 312

history of scientific thought 科学思想史 viii, 3–12, 16, 19–22, 28, 30, 33, 35, 38–42, 44–46, 49, 54, 56, 58, 64, 65, 67, 68, 71, 73–75, 77–79, 84–89, 92, 93, 96–98, 100, 179, 180, 183, 224, 225, 264, 269, 271, 272, 278, 280, 281, 284, 289–292, 294, 298, 300, 308

history of thought in physics 物理思想史 4, 88

history of vitalism 生気論史 78

history towards science 科学への歴史 22

Hokkaidō Imperial University 北海道帝国大学 183, 195, 217, 218, 230

holistic theories 全体論 19

how to determine atomic weights 原子量の決定法 180

hydrourushiol ヒドロウルシオール 194

hydrourushiol dimethyl ether ヒドロウルシオールジメチルエーテル 194

hyperfine structure 超微細構造 134

I

idea of converting Japan into one of the world's most science and technology creating countries 科学技術創造立国論 81

idea of paradigms パラダイム論 56

idealism 観念論 9, 11, 14, 15, 18, 23, 290

idiographic 個性記述的 16

immediate utility 直接的効用性 87

Imperial College of Engineering 工部大学校 107, 185, 227

Imperial radio decree at the end of the war 終戦の詔勅（書） 162

Imperial System 天皇制 221

incommensurability 不可共約性論 57, 60

independence 主体性 5, 40, 47, 61, 111, 123, 133

Indian histories of science インド科学史 53

induced cancer in rabbit ears 人工兎耳癌 125

inductive reasoning 帰納主義 10

industrial history 産業史 46

industry 産業連関 viii, 26, 27, 38, 46, 58, 65, 76, 92, 99, 104, 166, 174, 188, 197, 199, 203, 220, 231, 234, 270, 275, 281, 306, 308, 309

information society 情報社会 74

inorganic chemical industry 無機化学工業 46

Institute of Physical and Chemical Research (RIKEN) 理化学研究所 (理研) 26, 137, 218

intellectuals cooperated with the war effort 知識人の戦争協力 91

intermediate coupling 中間結合 151, 165

introduction of modern chemistry to Japan 日本における近代化学の導入 181

introduction to science 科学概論 44, 80

intuitionism 直観主義 41

investigators 担当調査官 81

issue of nuclear power plants 原発問題 74

issue of science and technology 科学技術問題 74

J

Japan Kampō Medicine Association 日本漢方医学会 239, 250

Japan Society for Oriental Medicine 日本東洋医学会 237

Japan Society for the Promotion of Science 日本学術振興会 44

Japan Wireless Telegraph Company 日本無線電信株式会社 145

Japanese Georges Canguilhem 日本のカンギレム 50

Japanese History of Science Society 日本科学史学会 27

Japanese lacquer trees ウルシ 188

Japanese science 日本的科学 23–25, 31, 39, 57, 58, 92, 103, 126, 154, 158, 175, 226, 265, 281, 285, 288, 308, 312

Japanese understanding of nature 日本人的自然観 52

Japanese works, such as The Kojiki: Records of Ancient Matters, Nihongi: Chronicles of Japan from the Earliest Times to AD 697 記紀歌謡 52

journal club 雑誌会 130, 187

justification 正当化 15, 50, 55, 62, 68, 85, 127

K

Kagaku Kenkyūsho 科学研究所 164

Kaiseijo 開成所 181, 226

kampō medicine 漢方医学 238–256, 258–267, 270, 311–314

Kampō Revival Movement 漢方医学復興運動 239, 242

kampō revivalist thought 漢方医学復興論 250

Kao Soap's Taiwan factory 花王石鹸台湾工場 202

Keijō Imperial University 京城帝国大学 197, 200, 240, 255–261, 264, 266, 311, 313

Kikagaku teki shizen kan (The Geometric view of nature) 幾何学的自然観 96

Kindai no chōkoku (Overcoming Modernity) 近代の超克 91

kinetic theory of gases 気体分子運動論 35

Kōgakuryō 工学寮 227

Kohō school 古方派 243, 245–247, 250

kompeitō candies 金平糖 93

Kousakusha 工作舎 64, 293, 294

Kyōryū school 共立学校 184, 227

Kyoto Imperial University 京都帝国大学 131, 132, 134, 136, 137, 144, 153, 165, 185, 226, 227, 231

Kyoto Normal Middle School 京都尋常中学 184

Kyoto Prefectural First Junior High School 京都府立第一中学校 184

L

laboratory instruments and equipment for analysis 実験器具・分析器具 224

laccol ラッコール 189

language game 言語ゲーム 41

life sciences 生命科学 49, 69, 70, 71, 78, 98, 297

literary prosopography 文献群のプロゾポグラフィ 3

literature 文献集団 87

logic of discovery 発見の論理 63

logic of species 種の論理 89

logicism 論理主義 41

loose chain of events 弛緩した連鎖 85

M

Majima Award 眞島賞 205

Majima's journal 眞島日記 209, 210, 214–219, 221, 228, 230, 233, 270

makyō, a Japanese magic mirror 魔鏡 64

Manchuria Medical College 満州医科大学 255

many-time theory 多時間理論 138, 165, 167

Marxism マルクス主義 9, 11–13, 16, 17, 20, 33, 66, 90

materialism 唯物論 9, 11, 13–19, 89, 90, 277, 280, 287, 289, 292, 300

Materialism Study Group (Yuiken) 唯物論研究会（唯研） 12, 13

materialist dialectical biology 唯物弁証法的生物学 19

math education 数学教育 29, 30

mathema マテーマタ 29

matrix mechanics 行列力学 129–131

mechanism of the machine 機械の機械性 5

medical care in Imperial Japan 帝国医療 239

medical philosophy 医学哲学 89, 237

Medicinal Plant Cultivation Movement 薬草栽培奨励運動 257

meson theory 中間子論 139, 159, 167, 168, 171

mesons 中間子 150, 151, 154, 158, 167, 304, 305

military medical services 軍陣医学 241

Minamata disease 水俣病 76

Mitsubishi Kagaku Institute of Life Sciences 三菱化学生命科学研究所 70, 78

Mitsubishi-Kasei Institute of Life Sciences 三菱化成生命科学研究所 98

Mitsui Hōonkai (Mitsui Foundation for the Return of Blessings) 三井報恩会 145

modern history of scientific thought in chemistry 近代化学思想史 224

modernization movement 現代化運動 83

molecular biology 分子生物学 47, 48, 69, 70

molecular weights 原子量・分子量概念 192, 225

monopoly capitalist system 独占資本主義体制 44

muon μ粒子 167–169

N

Nagaoka Hantarō den (The critical biography of Hantarō Nagaoka)『長岡半太郎伝』 175

narrative, descriptive conception of philosophy 物語の哲学 67

National Institute for the Humanities at Kyoto University 京都大学人文科学研究所 53

national policy for the development of science 国策科学 26, 92

national research institute of a science of daily life 生活科学研究所 26

national science 国民科学 24, 91, 291

National Spiritual Cultural Research
　Institute 国民精神文化研究所　26, 91, 92
nationalism ナショナリズム　23, 114, 303
natural dialectic method 自然弁証法　11,
　37, 38, 277
natural philosophy 自然哲学　21, 22, 71,
　91, 283, 287, 291
natural products 天然物　183, 187,
　194–196, 205–207, 220–224, 230, 231,
　237
natural products that were unique to
　Asia「東洋特産」の天然物　188
Nature of the Chemical Bond, The 『化学結
　合の本質』　201
Neo-Kantianism 新カント派　12, 88, 94
neo-Malthusian discussion ネオマルサス主義
　70
neoliberalism 新自由主義　95
neutrons 中性子　139, 148, 152, 157
new East Asian medicine 新東洋医学
　263
new philosophy of science 新科学哲学
　56, 60, 61, 65–68, 82, 98
Ni-Go Project 二号研究　152, 153, 160,
　161, 302, 304
Nihon Kagaku Sōran (Complete abstracts
　of Japanese chemical literature)『日本化
　学総覧』　216, 219, 220, 233
Nobel Prize ノーベル賞　35, 99, 103, 104,
　121, 125, 127, 136, 140–142, 145, 151,
　154, 159, 168–171, 174–176, 206, 207,
　231, 232, 301, 304, 305, 308, 310
nomothetic 法則定立的　16
non-Euclidean geometry 非ユークリッド幾何
　学　40, 131
nonbenzoid aromatic chemistry 非ベンゼン
　系芳香族　195
normal temperature and pressure
　catalytic reduction methods 常温常圧接
　触還元法　194
nuclear and elementary particle 原子核・素
　粒子　103, 104
nuclear force 核力　139, 143, 168
nuclear power industry 原子力事業　76

O

objective reflection 対象の客観的反映　37
observation is biased by theory 事実の理論
　負荷性　60
old quantum theory 初期量子論　43
Order of Cultural Merit 文化勲章　141,
　154, 205, 231
organ transplantation 臓器移植　74
oryzanin (vitamin B1—thiamine) オリザニ
　ン　125
Osaka Imperial University 大阪帝国大学
　137, 138, 155, 165, 183, 195, 200, 209,
　215, 217, 218, 221, 230
ozonolysis オゾン分解　191, 192, 194

P

paradigm パラダイム　57, 58, 60, 67–69
particle physics 素粒子論　35, 66, 103,
　104, 170
pathology 病理学　97, 244
Pauling ポーリング　201, 206
periodicity 時代概念　57
pessimistic ペシミズム　90, 124
pharmacognosy laboratory 生薬研究所
　257, 260, 261
philosophies of biotechnology バイオテクノ
　ロジーの生物哲学　48
philosophy of biology 生物哲学　19
philosophy of chemistry 化学哲学　37,
　225
philosophy of identity 同一性の哲学　98
philosophy of Ki 気の哲学　54
philosophy of life 生の哲学　18
philosophy of psychiatry 精神医学の哲学
　51
philosophy of science 科学哲学　3, 12, 34,
　56, 58, 60–62, 65–68, 82, 88, 89, 98,
　180, 287
philosophy of technology 技術哲学　7,
　16, 17, 20, 37, 95, 276, 285, 286, 291,
　296
photons 光子　139
physics essays 物理的エッセイ　31

physics for everyday life 日常生活寄りの物理学 31, 32

physiological anthropology 生理学的人間学 24

physiology 生理学 74, 92, 97, 141, 244, 245, 247-249

pion π中間子 167, 168

Planetary Books プラネタリー・ブックス 65

plate tectonics プレートテクトニクス 97

policies for demilitarization of scientific research 科学研究非軍事化政策 33

political nature of science 科学の政治性 76

political study of science 科学の政治化 69, 77-79, 88

popularity of science and engineering 理工科ブーム 44

positivism 実証主義 11, 66, 98, 99

postmodernism ポストモダニズム 41, 68

Private Seminar on New Physics 物理学輪講会 130-132, 138, 139, 303

Project F F号研究 153

proletarian art movement プロレタリア芸術運動 15

prosopography プロゾポグラフィ 3, 87, 88

protons 陽子 139

psychiatry 精神医学 51

psychosis 精神病 49

public 市民 21, 32, 33, 42, 59, 73, 76, 83, 84, 91, 92, 95, 99, 103, 120, 162-164, 185, 208, 221, 225, 227, 231

pure science 純正学 117

Q

quantum chemistry research 量子化学研究 224

quantum electrodynamics 量子電気力学 103, 104, 138, 167

quantum mechanics 量子力学 6, 21, 23, 35, 43, 66, 93, 103-105, 113, 116, 129-134, 136-139, 142, 173, 275, 290, 295, 296, 302, 303

quantum physics 量子物理学 42, 96, 113, 175, 306

quantum theory 量子論 43, 93, 124, 125, 129, 130, 131, 133, 136, 151

quantum theory of fields 場の量子論 151

quarter wavelength principle 四分の一波長原理 147

quasi-magical worldview 魔術的自然観 45

quasi-regularity 準・法則性 85

R

reaction of field 場の反作用 151, 165

recent past 近い過去 86

reciprocity principle 相補性原理 43

reducing learning to everyday life 生活単元学習 25

regular seminars on physics 物理学懇話会 130

regulation school 社会調整論 62

relationship between scientists and non-scientists 専門家・非専門家の関係 82

relativity boom 相対論ブーム 127

remaining challenges facing a history of thought in chemistry 日本化学思想史の課題 223

renormalization くりこみ 167

Republic of China 中華民国 202, 203

Research Institute for Theoretical Physics 理論物理学研究所 92

research on great research 大研究の研究 187

Research on Theories on Materialism (*Yuibutsu ron kenkyū*) 唯物論研究 13

resonance 共鳴概念 147, 201, 206, 264

revolution of the sacred/profane distinction 聖俗革命 60

Right Livelihood Award ライト・ライブリフッド賞 99

rosin acid ロジン酸 201, 231

Royal Institution 王立研究所 193

Russo-Japanese War 日露戦争 39, 108, 122, 123, 125, 126, 176

S

Saisei-Gakusha 済生学舎　241

science agora サイエンス・アゴラ　83

science and society 科学と社会　55, 76, 83

science and technology communications 科学技術コミュニケーション　82

Science and Technology Council 科学技術審議会　26

science and technology promotion 科学技術振興　28, 38

science as practice 行としての科学　24

science café サイエンス・カフェ　83

Science Council of Japan 日本学術会議　34, 45, 164

science education 理科教育　25, 36, 54, 55, 83, 280

science essays 科学随想的なもの　31

science for daily life 生活科学　26

science is culture 文化としての科学　35

science magazines 科学系雑誌　36

science of whales 鯨学　64

science service サービス科学　59

Science, Technology and Society (STS) STS　82

science theory 科学論　92, 295

science wars サイエンス・ウォーズ　58

scientific industry 科学主義工業　27, 92

scientific literacy 科学技術リテラシー　83

scientific revolution 科学革命　40, 45, 57, 58, 60, 67, 79, 284, 291, 300

scientific study of politics 科学政治学　75

scientific warfare 科学戦　23

scientific world 科学的世界　12, 28, 61, 63, 99, 173

scientifically hermeneutic program 科学の解釈学　66

second quantization 第二量子化　134

seiches セイシ　119

Seimi Kaisō (Introduction of Chemistry) 『舎密開宗』　181, 226

self-creating 自己創出　70

self-replicating 自己複製　70

Setchū school 折衷派　239, 250

Shanghai Science Institute 上海自然科学研究所　260

Shiji (Records of the Grand Historian of China)『史記』　107

Shinkō to Kagaku (Faith and Science) 信仰と科学　211

Shōkan ron (Treatise on Cold Damage Disorders, On Cold Damage) 傷寒論　239, 259

social participation in the present 現代性への社会参加　84

social utility 社会的効用性　80, 86, 87, 95

society that stresses alternative environmental resources 環境資源重視型の社会　95

sociology of science 科学社会学　3, 30, 58, 59, 61, 75, 79, 82, 88, 99, 100, 300

sociology of science and technology 科学技術社会学　79, 99

sociology of scientific knowledge (SSK) 科学知識の社会学 (SSK)　58, 82

Solvay Conference on Physics ソルヴェイ会議　144, 145

Sōtō Zen 曹洞禅　23

special relativity 特殊相対性理論　124, 127, 129, 134

state control of technology 技術の国家管理　27

stepping back from experience 経験離脱性　31

strategy of science and technology promotion 科学技術振興策　28

structural organic chemistry 有機構造論　225

structural understanding 様式概念　57, 58

structuralist biology 構造主義生物学　98, 279, 292

super-many-time theory 超多時間理論　138, 165, 167

Swiss Federal Institute of Technology スイス連邦工科学校　192, 230

symptomatic theory 病勢論　248, 249

symptomatic treatment 対症療法　55, 254, 255

synchrocyclotron シンクロサイクロトロン　167

systemized science 体制化科学　59

T

Taihoku Imperial University 台北帝国大学　197, 200, 201, 203, 230, 231

Taisho vitalism 大正生命主義　89

Taiwan 台湾　196–206, 224, 228, 230, 231, 270, 308, 311

Taiwan cypress 台湾ヒノキ　196, 198–201

Taiwanese 台湾語／台湾人　198

Takasago Chemical Corporation 高砂化学工業　201

Terada's physics 寺田物理学　31, 32

terpene テルペン　187, 191

terpinene テルピネン　191

tetrodotoxin テトロドトキシン　231

theories for promoting science and technology 科学技術振興論　23

theories of probability 確率論　21

theories of relativity 相対性理論　23, 66

theory of autopoiesis オートポイエーシス論　67

theory of formal discipline 形式陶冶説　29

theory of material discipline 実質陶冶説　29

theory of organic projection 器官投影説　17

theory of the fourth kingdom 第四王国論　17

theory regarding technology as a systematic means of labor 労働手段体系説　37

thesis of the independence or the isolation of science 科学の自律性・孤絶性テーゼ　61

three categories of phenomenology 三段階論　36

Tōhoku Imperial University 東北帝国大学　124, 183, 189, 191–198, 201, 208, 209, 217, 220, 222, 227, 229, 232, 234

Tokyo Kaisei Gakkō 東京開成学校　181, 182

Tokyo Kaisei Middle School 東京開成中学校　227

Tokyo School of Medicine 東京医学校　182, 219

Tokyo University of Engineering 東京工業大学　183, 195, 217, 233

228 Incident 二・二八事件　204

trachoma トラホーム　49

traditional Chinese medicine 伝統医学　39, 253

tradition of organic chemistry research 有機化学研究伝統　206

trips overseas 海外出張　219

tropolone トロポロン　205, 206, 309

Truman's statement トルーマン声明　160

tuberculosis 結核　17, 49, 97, 122, 190, 201, 276

two-meson theory 二中間子論　167, 168

U

University of Kiel キール大学　189, 191, 229

University of Tokyo 東京大学　27, 76, 96, 107, 109, 110, 172, 182, 185, 204, 205, 219, 227, 228, 233

urushic acid 漆酸　188, 189, 228

urushiol ウルシオール　188–195, 224, 228

urushiol dimethyl ether ウルシオールジメチルエーテル　190, 192, 194

US Scientific Advisory Group 米国学術顧問団　165

utility of the history of scientific thought 科学思想史の効用性　87

utopia ユートピア　72

V

vacuum pump 真空ポンプ　152, 162, 190

values of the higher school education system 旧制高校教養主義　128

Vargula hilgendorfii (the sea-firefly) ウミホタル　206

view of science as relativistic 相対主義的科
　学観　82
vitalism 生気論　19, 78, 89, 276, 293
vitamins ビタミン　55
vulgar materialism 俗流唯物論　11

W

wave mechanics 波動力学　129, 130
"we should love ordinary human beings"
　「愛すべき俗人」　70
welfare of the people 民衆の福祉　44, 94
Western medicine 西洋医学　48, 237, 238,
　240–255, 257, 260–265, 270, 289, 311–
　313
Western learning 洋学　115, 181, 226
Westernized kampō treatment 洋医的漢方
　療法　263

Y

Yin/Yang and the Five Elements 陰陽五行
　245, 246
Yuibutsu ron zensho (A compendium on
　materialism)『唯物論全書』　13
Yukawa particle 湯川粒子　147, 150, 154,
　158
Yukawa theory 湯川理論　144, 150–152,
　154, 161, 168, 170
yukon ユコン　144

Z

z-term Z項　119, 154

ABOUT THE AUTHORS

Osamu Kanamori, *the Editor*

Osamu KANAMORI was born in Sapporo in 1954. Having studied at the Graduate School of Humanities and Sociology, the University of Tokyo, he received a doctorate in philosophy from Pantheon-Sorbonne University (*Université Paris 1 Panthéon-Sorbonne*). He lectured at the University of Tsukuba and taught as associate professor at Tokyo University of Marine Science and Technology. Currently he is a professor at the Graduate School of Education of the University of Tokyo. He specializes in the studies of French philosophy, history of scientific thought, and bioethics.

Selected writings: *Bashurāru* (Gaston Bachelard), Tokyo, Kodansha, 1996; *Saiensu wōzu* (Science wars), Tokyo, University of Tokyo Press, 2000; *Kagaku teki shikō no kōkogaku* (Archeology of scientific thought), Kyoto, Jimbun Shoin, 2004; *'Seiseiji' no tetsugaku* (The philosophy of biopolitics), Kyoto, Minerva Shobo, 2010; *Gōremu no seimei ron* (Theory of life of golems), Tokyo, Heibonsha, 2010; *Dōbutsu ni tamashii wa arunoka* (Do animals have souls?), Tokyo, Chuokoron Shinsha, 2012; *Kagaku no kiki* (Crisis of science), Tokyo, Shueisha, 2015

Selected edited books: *Kagaku shisō shi* (History of scientific thought), Tokyo, Keiso Shobo Publishing, 2010; *Gōrisei no kōkogaku* (Archeology of rationality), Tokyo, University of Tokyo Press, 2012; *Episutemorojī* (Epistemology), Tokyo, Keio University Press, 2013.

* * *

Takuji Okamoto

Takuji OKAMOTO was born in Aichi Prefecture in 1967. He studied at the University of Tokyo, Graduate School of Science, where he obtained his doctorate of philosophy. He has been an assistant at Niigata University, Faculty of Humanities, and is currently an associate professor in the Graduate School of Arts and Sciences at the University of Tokyo. He specializes in the study of the history of science, the history of technology and the technology of advanced education.

Selected writings: *Hajimete no sūgaku* (Mathematics for Beginners) (co-authored) edited by Michiko Yajima and Sumio Wada, Tokyo, Beret Publishing, 2004; *Hajimete yomu butsurigaku no rekishi* (The history of physics for novice readers) (co-authored), Tokyo, Beret Publishing, 2007; *Kagaku to shakai: Senzenki nihon ni okeru kokka, gakumon, sensō no shosō* (Science and society: Aspects of nation, academism, and war in prewar Japan), Tokyo, Saiensu-sha, 2014.

Masanori Kaji

Masanori KAJI was born in Kanagawa Prefecture in 1956. He completed the doctoral course run by the Graduate School of Science and Engineering at the Tokyo Institute of Technology, where he received a doctorate of philosophy. He has been a special researcher at the Japan Society for the Promotion of Science, a student sponsored by the Soviet government, and an assistant professor at Tokyo Institute of Technology, teaching courses in the School of Engineering, Humanities and Social Science. He is currently a professor at Tokyo Institute of Technology in the Graduate School of Decision Science and Technology. He specializes in the history of science.

Selected writings: *Menderēefu no shūkiritsu hakken* (The discovery of the periodic law by

Mendelejev), Sapporo, Hokkaido University Press, 1997; *Menderēefu: Genso no shūkiritsu no hakken sha* (Mendelejev: The man who discovered the periodic law of the elements), Tokyo, Toyo Shoten, 2007.

Edited books: *Kagakushatte nanda?* (What are scientists?), Tokyo, Maruzen, 2007; *Kagaku gijutsu komyunikēshon nyūmon* (Introduction to scientific communication), Tokyo, Baifukan, 2009; *Early Responses to the Periodic System*, New York, Oxford University Press, 2015.

SHIN CHANG-GEON

SHIN Chang-Geon was born in Kanagawa Prefecture in 1964. He studied at the University of Tokyo in the Graduate School of Arts and Sciences, where he was awarded a Master's degree in Science. He is currently a professor at Tokyo University of Science in the Faculty of Engineering, Division I. He specializes in the history of science and medicine.

Selected writings: *Teikoku no shikaku/shikaku* (The visible and blind sides of the empire) (co-edited), Tokyo, Seikyusha, 2010; *Chōsen kindai kagaku gijutsu shi kenkyū* (Study on the history of modern science and history in Korea), Tokyo, Koseisha, 2010; *Kankokushi ron 42: Kankoku kin gendai kagaku gijutsu shi no tenkai* (Essays on Korean history 42: The development of the history of science and technology in modern and contemporary Korea [in the Korean language]) (co-authored), Gwacheon, National Institute of Korean History, 2005; Yoshihiko Komatsu, Kenji Doi (*eds.*), *Shūkyō to seimei rinri* (Religion and life ethics), Kyoto, Nakanishiya Publishing, 2005.

（英文版）昭和前期の科学思想史
Essays on the History of Scientific Thought in Modern Japan

2016年3月27日　　第1刷発行

編　者　金森　修
訳　者　クリストファー・カー、M. G. シェフタル
発行所　一般財団法人 出版文化産業振興財団
　　　　〒101-0051 東京都千代田区神田神保町 3-12-3
　　　　電話　03-5211-7282（代）
　　　　ホームページ　http://www.jpic.or.jp/
印刷・製本所　大日本印刷株式会社

©2011 by Osamu Kanamori
Printed in Japan
ISBN 978-4-916055-61-3